APPARATUS AND METHODS
OF OCEANOGRAPHY

APPARATUS AND METHODS OF OCEANOGRAPHY

PART ONE: CHEMICAL

H. BARNES

B.Sc., B.A., Ph.D., D.Sc., F.R.I.C.
The Marine Station, Millport, Scotland

Ruskin House

GEORGE ALLEN & UNWIN LTD
MUSEUM STREET LONDON

FIRST PUBLISHED 1959

*Printed in Great Britain
in 10 on 11 pt. Times Roman type
by Jarrold and Sons Ltd.
Norwich*

PREFACE

In 1947 the Executive Committee of the International Association of Physical Oceanography (IAPO) agreed to the suggestion by its President, the late Professor H. U. Sverdrup, to establish a committee for the Preparation of a Technical Handbook in Physical Oceanography. Five members of the committee were appointed and accepted the responsibility for the preparation of the following sections: A: Ship Facilities, B: Work at Sea, C: Processing at Sea, D: Processing Ashore, and E: Glossary.

In 1950 the manuscript of section D had been completed by E. C. LaFond: 'Processing Oceanographic Data'. It was circulated among interested members of the Association and issued in 1951 as Hydrographic Office Publication No. 614.

With the other sections very little happened and when, in 1954, the opportunity appeared to have a book on methods in oceanography prepared by Dr Barnes, the Executive Committee abandoned its original plan and immediately declared willing to render any possible assistance, 'believing that there is a definite need for a book of that kind and that it is a proper task for the IAPO to help towards producing it'.

It is a great satisfaction to know that Part I, on Chemical Methods, is now in print. It will meet a strong and increasing need and will be welcomed by anyone active in oceanographic research. The names of the author and of the specialists mentioned in the Introduction guarantee its high standard.

Bergen the 1st of January 1959
HÅKON MOSBY
Président: *Association internationale d'Océanographie physique*

CONTENTS

INTRODUCTION		11
ACKNOWLEDGEMENTS		13
1.	Colour Comparators and Photometric Analysis	15
2.	Errors and Precision	60
3.	The Calculation of Results: Calibration Curves	78
4.	Chlorinity	84
5.	The Potentiometric Determinations of pH	99
6.	Inorganic Nitrogen: Nitrate	113
7.	Inorganic Nitrogen: Nitrite	126
8.	Inorganic Nitrogen: Ammonia	129
9.	Organic Nitrogen in Sea Water and Plankton	142
10.	Inorganic Phosphorus: Phosphate	151
11.	Organic Phosphorus in Sea Water and Plankton	157
12.	Inorganic Silicon: Silicate	163
13.	Organic Carbon of Sea Water and Plankton	168
14.	Oxygen	178
15.	Alkalinity	200
16.	The Carbon Dioxide System in Sea Water	206
17.	The Conservative Elements: Micro-Methods	209
18.	Trace Metals	224
19.	Plankton Pigments	240
20.	Filtration	247
21.	The Physical and Chemical Examination of Sediments	250
APPENDIX		269
TABLES		273
INDEX		325

ILLUSTRATIONS

1. Passage of light through a cell containing a coloured solution _page_ 20
2. Spectral transmittancy curve for the iron-phenanthroline complex 23
3. Calibration curves for a filter photometer (iron-phenanthroline complex) 24
4. Transmittancy and absorbancy curves for solutions of potassium permanganate at three wave-lengths 25
5. Transmittancy/wave-length, transmittancy/frequency, and transmittancy/wave-number curves for solutions of potassium permanganate (linear scales) 26
6. Transmittancy/wave-length curves for solutions of potassium permanganate (semi-logarithmic scales) 27
7. Absorbancy/wave-length curves for solutions of potassium permanganate 28
8. Absorbancy/wave-length curves for solutions of potassium permanganate (linear scales) 29
9. Log-absorbancy/wave-length curves for solutions of potassium permanganate (linear scales) 30
10. Relative sensitivity curve for the eye 34
11. Colour comparator block 38
12. The Lovibond comparator _facing_ 38
13. Campbell Hurley comparator 39
14. The Duboscq-type colorimeter _facing_ 38
15. Leitz compensating visual photometer: diagrammatic _facing_ 40
16. Leitz compensating visual photometer _facing_ 40
17. Construction and equivalent circuit of photo-voltaic cell 41
18. Output, load and light intensity of Eel photo-voltaic cell 42
19. Equivalent circuit of photo-emissive cell 43
20. Intensity of illumination and anode current for typical vacuum photo-cell 43
21. Inverse feedback principle and circuit for photometer 44
22. Correction and amplification circuits for a photo-voltaic cell 45
23. Spekker Absorptiometer: diagrammatic 46
24. Spekker Photoelectric Absorptiometer _facing_ 46
25. Compensating circuit for photo-voltaic cells 47
26. Diagram of spectrophotometer 50
27. Spectrophotometer (Uvispek) _facing_ 50
28. Transmittancy curve for molybdenum blue in phosphate estimation 53
29. Knudsen pipette and burette 87
30. Apparatus for the preparation of Harvey's reagent 115
31. Micro-ammonia distillation (Krogh) 133
32. Micro-ammonia distillation (Riley) 136
33. Apparatus for the determination of dissolved organic nitrogen in sea water 143
34. Kjeldahl distillation apparatus 147
35. Arrangements for storing reagents in organic carbon estimation 169

36. Combustion apparatus for the determination of dissolved organic carbon *page* 170
37. The apparatus of Kay for carbon estimation 172
38. Details of the apparatus of Kay for carbon estimation 174
39. Circuit for amperometric titration 184
40. Results of amperometric titration 185
41. Syringe pipette and burette 190
42. Micro-gasometric estimation of oxygen 194
43. The Emery settling tube 263
44. Apparatus for the estimation of carbonates in sediments 265

INTRODUCTION

Details of the analytical methods used in chemical oceanography are, with the exception of some of the commonest procedures, widely scattered throughout the literature. At a time when the subject is expanding it would seem to be generally accepted that a compilation of these methods would be useful to many people. While there is general agreement as to what such a book should contain, there are differences of opinion regarding details. The subject is so wide, and techniques from so many diverse branches of science are used, that it is indeed difficult to decide on the essential contents. The following uses have been kept in mind. First, as a reference text and working handbook in a department of oceanography; the experts will be familiar with many of the techniques but they may appreciate having them collected and summarized. Secondly, as a reference text and working handbook in a laboratory largely given over to marine biology: biologists may perhaps have a less complete chemical background and it is hoped that the details will be adequate for their purpose; the requirements under this heading are, however, wide, and it has been difficult to know where to draw the line. Methods which are covered adequately in standard chemical or biochemical texts have not been included. Thirdly, as a text for use in new marine laboratories; there are many recently established institutes where library facilities are relatively inadequate. It is largely for this reason that it was felt desirable to include the first chapter, the information contained in which may largely be obtained from other texts.

In the simpler and better known methods the account is given largely in the imperative mood; in newer and more complicated procedures this mode of presentation has only been retained when convenient. Attention has not been restricted to the simpler procedures; new as well as more difficult techniques have been included, partly in the hope that they will be more frequently used and probably extended or simplified; further advances will require more than the all too common phosphate estimation.

The μg.-atom/L.(l.) is the officially recommended unit in chemical oceanography for the minor and trace constituents of sea water; it has largely been used. Nevertheless, when other modes of expression were deemed more desirable from the practical point of view they have been used without any hesitation.

Although I have personally had some experience of most of the procedures, it would be dangerous to issue a compilation such as this without advice from others. I have been most fortunate in my critics. Professor K. Kalle, Deutsches Hydrographisches Institut, Drs F. Koczy and N. Jerlov, Kungl. Fiskeristyrelsen, Göteborg, Dr B. H. Ketchum, Woods Hole Oceanographic Institution, Dr J. P. Riley, Department of Oceanography, The University of Liverpool, Dr N. W. Rakestraw of the Scripps Institution of Oceanography and Dr R. J. Robinson, Department of Chemistry, The University of Washington, have read the whole manuscript. Their critical comments have led to many improvements; Dr Riley has furnished details of methods he has developed but which are still unpublished. Professor Y. Miyake of the Central Meteorological Observatory, Tokyo, has drawn attention to the Japanese work and very kindly provided translations of some papers. Drs Richards and Creitz also of Woods Hole have made corrections in the section on pigment analysis. Dr L. H. N. Cooper and Mr F. A. J. Armstrong of the Marine Biological Association, Plymouth, have commented on Section 1. Dr R. A. Robb and his colleague, Mr Silvey, have increased the usefulness and precision of wording of Section 2. Dr G. Knowles and his colleagues of the Water Pollution Research Laboratory of the D.S.I.R. (Great Britain), have made valuable suggestions regarding Section 14. Dr J. D. Robertson, Department of Zoology, The University of Glasgow, has read and ensured the accuracy of Section 16, which is largely a compilation of methods he has developed. The section on sediment analysis has profited enormously by the detailed critical comments and advice of Professor K. O. Emery, University of Southern California, and has also been checked by Drs Mitchell and Williams of the Macaulay Institute for Soil Research, Aberdeen.

I have had many profitable discussions with my colleague, Mr J. Goodley; he has also been good enough to check many of the figures and to remove minor sources of error.

To all these, it is a pleasure and duty to express gratitude; that they did not always agree amongst themselves allows one to believe that it would not be possible to please everybody.

I have also to thank my wife, not only for making many of the drawings but also for her constant assistance in every way.

ACKNOWLEDGEMENTS

I wish to thank the following publishers, journals, and authorities for permission to reproduce, in part or entirety, plates, figures, and tables from their publications. Reference to these is made in the appropriate place: *Acta Academis åbo*; The American Chemical Society; Association of Physical Oceanography; The Biological Bulletin; Burroughs, Wellcome & Co. (The Wellcome Foundation Limited), London; The Chemical Society, London; Conseil international pour l'Exploration de la Mer; Council of the Marine Biological Association of the United Kingdom; Messrs Crosby Lockwood & Son Ltd., London; The Elsevier Publishing Company, Amsterdam; Evans Electroselenium Ltd., Harlow, Essex, England; Hilger & Watts Ltd., London; Ilford Limited, Ilford, London; Institut für Meereskunde der Universität, Kiel, Germany; Iowa State College Press, Ames, Iowa, U.S.A.; John Wiley & Sons, Inc.; *The Journal of Experimental Biology*; *The Journal of Industrial and Engineering Chemistry* (Analytical Edition); *The Journal of Marine Research*; *The Journal of Sedimentary Petrology*; Ernst Leitz G.m.b.H. Wetzlar, Germany; Merentutkimuslaitoken Julkaisu; Mullard Limited, London; Messrs Oliver & Boyd Ltd., Edinburgh, Scotland; Messrs Philip Harris & Co., Edmund Street, Birmingham, England; *The Review of Scientific Instruments*; The Tintometer Limited, Salisbury, England.

1
COLOUR COMPARATORS AND PHOTOMETRIC ANALYSIS

The estimation of most of the non-conservative substances present in sea water is usually achieved by means of so-called 'colorimetric' techniques (1, 15, 17, 43, 48, 50, 52, 53). In the presence of appropriate reagents the substance to be determined is made to yield a coloured compound, the 'intensity' of which is a function of the concentration of that substance. It was only subsequent to the development of reliable 'colorimetric' methods, by which a large number of sufficiently accurate analyses could be rapidly made, that any significant advances in the nutrient chemistry of the sea became possible.

There are several ways in which such colour reactions can be made to yield quantitative information. The colour may be compared visually with similar colours developed by the addition of the reagents to standard solutions of the substance concerned or, in place of the latter, permanent coloured solutions or coloured glasses may be used. Whilst these visual methods are still used, and in certain conditions may continue to be the only practicable technique, electrical instruments which measure the light transmitted by coloured solutions are now in more general use.

In physics the term colorimetry means the determination of colour as such, and a colorimeter is therefore an instrument used for this purpose. The 'colorimeter' of the analytical chemist does not measure colour; it only compares two colours and should be called a colour comparator. However, the term 'colorimeter', although to be deprecated, is still widely used. When the transmission of either 'white' light or light of a restricted spectral range is measured the instrument should be termed an absorptiometer, and when the measurements can be made at any selected wave-length within a given narrow spectral range the instrument becomes a spectrophotometer.

Desiderata for the Colour System

Colour reactions in analytical chemistry are not new—they have been used in a qualitative or semi-quantitative fashion for many decades. However, with the development of the colour comparator, by Jules Duboscq in 1854, they became increasingly used in a quantitative fashion. A considerable impetus to their use was given by the rapid expansion of biochemical work, in which, not only was it usual to

15

have relatively small quantities of material available for assay, but the only known specific reactions of many of the substances encountered were frequently colour reactions. The elimination of the subjective element in the colour comparator by the application of photoelectric techniques, together with general advances in instrumentation, have greatly increased the sensitivity and accuracy of these methods, the limitations of which are now determined rather by the available colour reactions themselves than by the instruments available to the analyst; for example, further advances in the chemistry of the nutrient elements will depend much upon devising suitable colour reactions for their study.

The substance to be estimated may itself be coloured (pigment extracts), it may be capable of forming a colour with the appropriate reagents (phosphate, silicate, nitrate) or it may affect the colour of another reaction (fluoride). We may consider the desirable characteristics of any colour system that is to be used for quantitative analysis.

1. The coloured substance should be stable for a sufficient time to permit accurate measurement. The time required will depend upon the instrument used. When there is a gradual yet slow change in colour it is usually possible to take the colour after a given time (*see* Harvey on phosphate, p. 154) or in some cases to take readings at known intervals and then extrapolate to zero time. This problem is encountered in an acute form in the estimation of vitamin A and ascorbic acid by colour reactions and the general problems involved in unstable systems have been considered by Brew and Scott (19).

2. The intensity of the colour should be high so that a reasonable sensitivity for the estimation is obtained.

3. The colour system, as far as possible, should be stable to slight changes in the conditions of the reaction. This requirement may frequently have to be sacrificed; thus many techniques for the estimation of phosphate are less sensitive to small changes of both pH and reagent concentrations than the stannous chloride reduction method, but the latter is almost the only method sufficiently sensitive for the small quantities of phosphate present in sea water.

4. When a visual instrument is used the wave-length of maximum absorption of the coloured solution should be in the spectral region to which the eye is most sensitive (*see* p. 34).

5. The coloured product should be readily soluble (or dispersed in some cases) in the solvent. This rarely presents any problems in the analysis of natural sea waters, but it may require consideration in experimental work, e.g. when the behaviour of heavy metals such as copper are being investigated.

6. Ideally, the system should conform to Beer's Law (*see* p. 21). This is usually the case over a limited range of concentrations and even when not applicable it only makes calibration and calculation of results more troublesome.

The reagents used to develop the colour should ideally have the following characteristics:

1. The reagent solutions should be stable. Reagents which are only moderately stable often have to be used (e.g. stannous chloride in phosphate analysis) although they are inconvenient.

2. The reagents should develop the colour rapidly. Apart from convenience, particularly in serial estimations, the effects of reaction time and temperature are usually more complicated in slow reactions. The most recent method for nitrites (18) has advantages in this respect over the older methods where conditions were not adjusted to give maximum speed of reaction.

3. Stoichiometric reaction of reagent and constituent should occur. If possible the reaction should go to 'completion', so that the amounts of added reagents (if they are colourless) are not critical. The difficulties in the thiocyanate method for iron are largely the result of the establishment of an equilibrium which is affected both by reagents and any added salts.

4. The reagents should not absorb in the spectral region in which the measurements are made; if coloured reagent additions are made they must be carefully measured out and the blank readings may then be high. These difficulties may be sometimes avoided, particularly with photoelectric instruments, by the use of appropriate filters.

5. The reagent should be specific for the constituent to be estimated. In some cases, although the reagent itself may not be specific, the conditions under which it is used can be adjusted to confer specificity on the reaction, e.g. in phosphate and silicate estimations, (*see* Sections 10 and 12).

It should be emphasized that the above are desiderata, particularly when the method is required for routine work in semi-skilled hands; as indicated, some of them may often have to be sacrificed in developmental work, and even in the ultimate method adopted.

General Precautions in Trace Analysis

Irrespective of the substance to be determined or of the methods to be used, certain general precautions common to all micro-chemical work and familiar enough to practising analysts, should be observed. In particular, the low level of concentrations involved in such work make it essential that adequate precautions are taken both before and during the analyses, against the contamination of sample, reagents, standards, all apparatus and glassware. Contamination may arise from various sources.

1. Gross contamination from dust should be avoided by clean over-all working conditions during the conduct of the analysis and during the preparation of the reagents. When possible all containers should be stoppered.

2. Contamination by dissolution from glass containers used either in the collection of the samples or during their analysis may be avoided by means which will vary according to the substance under consideration. For some estimations, e.g. silicate, plastic containers may be used; in the ashing process for phosphate and trace metals silica vessels are usually convenient.

3. The distilled water and reagents used in preparing solutions should be carefully tested for contaminants; the highest grade reagents available should be used, and if necessary purified. For example, particular care is necessary in the preparation of distilled water used in trace metal analysis (Section 18); oxidizing agents may have to be removed from sulphuric acid used in nitrate estimations (Section 6).

4. Filter papers are always suspect for certain substances, notably trace metals; they should be tested.

With the exception of gross uncontrolled contamination, allowance can often be made for the introduction of the material under analysis in the reagents, by adequate consideration of reagent blanks; these should, however, be kept minimal.

In addition to avoiding spurious increases by contamination, loss of trace constituents should be guarded against. Absorption of trace metals upon the surfaces of glass vessels is common (14); loss of strength of any dilute standards may be quite rapid. Choice of containers, rapid working and the use of freshly prepared working standards (made up from a preserved stock solution) help to avoid these errors.

All instruments must be carefully maintained and in particular the optical parts kept free from dust. Absorption cells, for the best quantitative work, have optical faces; these should be carefully cleaned before a reading is taken.

Terminology

In order to discuss various aspects of light measurement it is necessary to have a clear and precise definition of the terms used in this branch of physics and a set of well recognized symbols. There has been much confusion in the past, largely as a result of the varied interests in, and applications of, this subject; indeed, there is still no internationally recognized terminology. British practice now tends to conform to the recommendations of the British Standards Institution (21) which are largely in agreement with those of the Committee of the Physical Society's Colour Group (6, *see also* 2, 3 and 4). In the United States the *Letter Circular, LC-857* (5), sets out a restricted set of terms and symbols for use in transmission and absorption measurements and these are coming into general use; they have many advantages and avoid the use of non-Roman and complicated letters. The British and American systems will usually be given with any appropriate cross-references. Further information may be obtained in the reports of the Colorimetry Committee of the Optical Society of America (30–34) and in the report of the Commission Internationale de l'Éclairage (2).

For a person of normal vision, the eye is stimulated by radiation with wave-lengths between approximately 380 and 770 mμ and such radiation is termed light; it is inconsistent with this definition to speak of ultra-violet and infra-red light.

The luminous intensity is the property of the light source that determines the amount of light radiated per unit solid angle in any direction; its unit is the candela, the luminous intensity of an internationally agreed standard source. The luminous flux emitted in a unit solid angle of one steradian by a point source having a uniform intensity of one candela is one lumen. An illumination of one lumen per square metre is one lux and of one lumen per square foot is one foot-candle. A uniform diffuser emitting one lumen per square foot has a luminance of one foot-lambert. In some cases the integrated amount of radiant energy is measured, as for example, in the normal use of a photographic plate; more frequently it is the radiant flux which is measured as is the case with the eye, the phototube, and thermopile when ordinarily used with a galvanometer.

In spectrophotometry it is usual to measure the ratio of two quantities at a fixed wave-length or over a limited wave-band and it is often possible, as well as convenient, to ignore both the spatial and temporal variants of the radiant energy; this may then be used as the covering term and is denoted by I.

The Bouguer-Lambert Law

According to this law, each layer of equal thickness absorbs an equal fraction of the radiant energy of a given wave-length which traverses it, so that the decrease in the intensity of the radiant energy is proportional to that intensity; hence,

$$-\frac{\mathrm{d}I}{\mathrm{d}l} = a \cdot I,$$

where a is a constant, I the light intensity, and l the path length (b in U.S. system). Or,

$$-\frac{\mathrm{d}I}{I} = a \cdot \mathrm{d}l. \qquad \ldots(1)$$

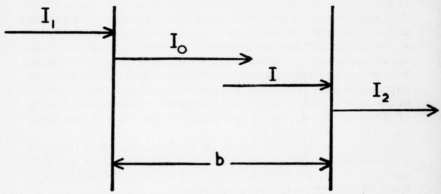

Fig. 1. Passage of light through a cell containing a coloured solution. Transmittance is I_2/I_1 and internal transmittance is I/I_0. (Redrawn from M. G. Mellon, *Analytical Absorption Spectroscopy*, John Wiley and Sons, Inc., 1950.)

Now let I_1 be the radiant energy incident upon the first surface, I_0 that entering the sample, I that incident upon the second surface and I_2 that leaving the sample (Fig. 1). Then,

$$T = \frac{I_2}{I_1} = \text{transmittance of the sample} \qquad \ldots(2)$$

and

$$T_i = \frac{I}{I_0} = \text{internal transmittance of the sample.} \qquad \ldots(3)$$

Integrating (1) between I_0 and I we have

$$-\log_e \frac{I}{I_0} = a \cdot l \qquad \ldots(4)$$

or

$$\frac{I}{I_0} = e^{-a \cdot l}. \qquad \ldots(5)$$

Using Briggsian logarithms, gives:

$$\log_{10} T_i = -\log_{10} \frac{I}{I_0} = K \cdot l$$

or

$$\frac{I}{I_0} = 10^{-K \cdot l}, \qquad \ldots(6)$$

where K is termed the extinction coefficient. The optical density, d, termed the absorbance A_i in the U.S.A. system is defined as

$$d = A_i = -\log_{10} T_i = \log \frac{I_0}{I} = K \cdot l, \qquad \ldots(7)$$

so that the extinction coefficient, termed the absorbance index is,

$$a_i = \frac{A_i}{l}. \qquad \qquad ...(8)$$

Beer's Law

This states that the absorption is proportional to the number of molecules of absorbing substance through which the radiation passes. If the absorbing substance is dissolved in a non-absorbing medium the absorption will be proportional to the molecular concentration of the dissolved substance. Combining this with equation (6) we have,

$$\frac{I}{I_0} = 10^{-\varepsilon.c.l}, \qquad \qquad ...(9)$$

where c is the molar concentration (g. mol./litre), ε is termed the molar extinction coefficient, and $\varepsilon . c = K$. The molar extinction coefficient, at a specified wave-length, should be used to describe the intensity of absorption of all pure substances in a stated solvent. From (7) the optical density is clearly $\varepsilon . c . l$.

In practice for analytical work it is usual to compare the solution in a given cell with the solvent contained in an identical cell in order to compensate both for absorption by the solvent and for radiation losses as a result of reflection and absorption by the cell windows. The American terms recommended for analytical work used are similar to those above but end in -ancy. Thus,

$$T_s = \frac{T_{\text{soln.}}}{T_{\text{solv.}}} = \text{transmittancy of the sample,} \qquad ...(10)$$

where the transmission values are the overall transmittances of the cell. (Note: T_s does not precisely equal $(T_i)_{\text{soln.}}/(T_i)_{\text{solv.}}$ but with end plates of refractive index greater than 1·5 the error is negligible for most purposes.) By analogy with equation (6),

$$A_s = -\log_{10} T_s = \log_{10} \frac{1}{T_s} = \text{absorbancy of the sample,} \quad ...(11)$$

and, if b is the path length and c the concentration in gram molecules per litre,

$$a_M = \frac{A_s}{b.c} = \text{the molar absorbancy index} \qquad ...(12)$$

which is the overall molar extinction coefficient.

The Validity of the Bouguer-Lambert-Beer Law

The Bouguer-Lambert law is considered to be strictly applicable to all homogeneous systems, so that any nonconformity of a colour system to the combined law is always attributed to deviations from Beer's Law. Kortüm (39 and 40, *see also* Kortüm and Seiler, 41) has pointed out that Beer's Law would not be expected to be valid over wide concentration ranges; it is a limit law for low concentrations. According to the theory of light dispersion Beer's Law states:

$$\log \frac{I_0}{I} = \frac{n}{(n^2+2)^2} . K . c, \qquad \text{(contrast equ. 9)}$$

where n is the refractive index of the solution. Since n generally increases with concentration, K cannot remain constant as c is varied. However, for concentrations less than about 0·01 M the change of refractive index rarely exceeds the accuracy of measurement and in this region, which covers most quantitative colour methods, the limit law (equation 9) is therefore valid.

'Apparent' deviations from Beer's Law take place; these usually arise from equilibrium changes involving the coloured substance whose absorption is being measured. A well-known example is the chromate-dichromate system, which is of particular interest because solutions containing these ions have been used as permanent standards for certain colorimetric methods (creatinine, silicate) and also for checking the photometric values of spectrophotometers. The effect involves the equilibrium represented by

$$Cr_2O_7^{--} + H_2O \rightleftharpoons 2HCrO_4 \rightleftharpoons 2H^+ + 2CrO_4^{--},$$

and is clearly sensitive to pH change (37).

Reciprocal interaction of the absorbing entities, either amongst themselves, with the solvent or with foreign substances, may also lead to apparent failure of the law. The 'salt effect' with indicator solutions used in the estimation of pH values, is a well-known example (22 and 43).

The concentration at which the limit law is no longer valid varies with the coloured substance concerned and with the position of the absorption band used; deviations may occur with some substances at concentrations as low as 10^{-6} M. Its validity for the substance in question, over the range to be used, should always be checked. It may be pointed out that an apparent deviation will occur if the amount of reagent added to develop the colour becomes inadequate at the higher concentrations; the reagent addition should be increased.

Apparent deviations from Beer's Law are also found as a result of a low degree of monochromaticity of the radiant energy used. If the principal wave-lengths of the illuminating light are restricted to one side of an absorption band, a linear relation between absorbancy (extinction) and concentration will not be found (Figs. 2 and 3).

Thus yellow solutions sometimes do not appear to obey Beer's Law because the blue or violet filters used are not sufficiently selective. Even when a monochromator is used, deviations from linearity may occur if the absorption maximum is very sharp and the slit width is

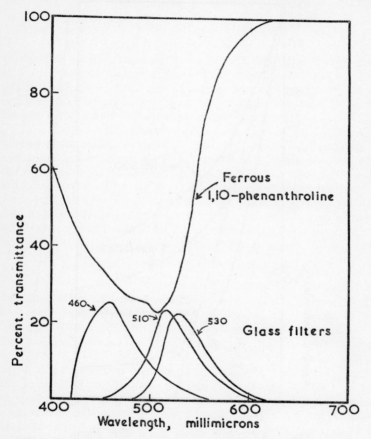

FIG. 2. Spectral transmittancy curve for the iron-phenanthroline complex: transmittance curves for three filters. (Redrawn from M. G. Mellon, *Analytical Absorption Spectroscopy*, John Wiley and Sons, Inc., 1950.)

too great, or if there is stray or scattered light in the emergent beam (*see* p. 52). On the other hand, it is easy to obtain a close approximation to linearity if the absorption band is broad and does not occur at the ends of the visible spectrum; suitable filters can then be obtained without much difficulty. For example, potassium permanganate solution which has a broad transmission band in the green can be easily made to give a linear curve by a green filter whose transmission is closely complementary to that of the permanganate

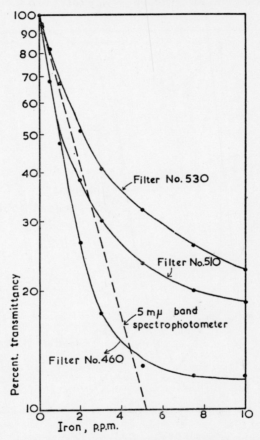

FIG. 3. Calibration curves for a filter photo-meter, using the three filters shown in Fig. 2. (Redrawn from M. G. Mellon, *Analytical Absorption Spectroscopy*, John Wiley and Sons, Inc., 1950.)

solutions (Fig. 4). The most exacting case to meet is the system which has a transmittancy curve with sharp minima and with the sides of the band asymmetrical. If the transmission (absorption) curve of a coloured solution is available the proper wave-length of illuminating light or filter may be chosen with exactness (*see* p. 52).

If such a transmission (absorption) curve is not available then, in general, a filter should be chosen of the complementary colour—although this is not always the correct choice, e.g. with molybdenum blue in phosphate estimations and with neodymium nitrate solutions.

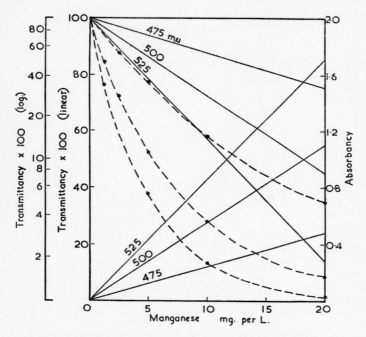

FIG. 4. Transmittancy and Beer's law curves for solutions of potassium permanganate at three wave-lengths. (Redrawn from M. G. Mellon, *Analytical Absorption Spectroscopy*, John Wiley and Sons, Inc., 1950.)

If several filters are available it is, of course, the one giving the highest transmittancy at the wave-length of maximum absorption of the sample which is usually chosen (*see, however*, p. 53). If the solution is coloured by a foreign substance or if such a substance develops a colour on the addition of the reagent it is sometimes possible to find a wave-length (not necessarily the peak of absorption) at which the required substance can be estimated, whilst the interfering colour has little influence. When two substances have widely differing absorption bands it is possible by the use of the appropriate filter, or better still by the use of a monochromator, to estimate both in the same solution.

Spectrophotometric Data

The laws considered above apply in the first instance to spectrally pure light, i.e. radiation of a given wave-length; in the discussion on Beer's Law, attention has been already drawn to the apparent deviations which may occur as a result of using light of a low degree of monochromaticity. For much analytical work it is only

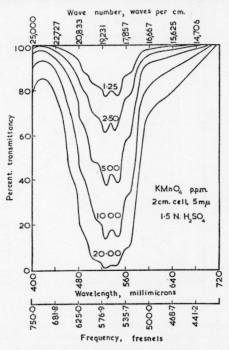

FIG. 5. Transmittancy/wave-length, transmittancy/frequency, and transmittancy/wave-number curves, for solutions of potassium permanganate (linear scales). (Redrawn from M. G. Mellon, *Analytical Absorption Spectroscopy*, John Wiley and Sons, Inc., 1950.)

necessary to know the optimal spectral region in which to work; a calibration can then be set up relating transmittancy and concentration from which the concentrations of unknowns may be read when their transmittancies have been determined. Such a calibration curve may be in quite arbitrary units and refer to a given cell. However, complete information about the absorbing properties of a coloured solution is only obtained by measuring the transmission over a wide spectral range. No full discussion of the data so obtained will be attempted, but the subject must be briefly considered since spectrophotometers are being increasingly used and a correct interpretation of the data is not only essential in their use but also in any application of the data to simpler instruments. (*See*, for example, Zwicker and Robinson (56) for a discussion of Harvey's nitrate reaction where a spectrophotometric study has improved the analytical procedure.)

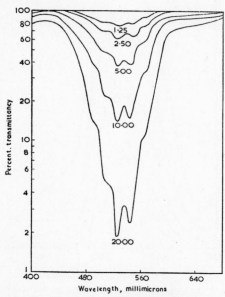

FIG. 6. Transmittancy/wave-length curves for solutions of potassium permanganate (semi-logarithmic scales). (Redrawn from M. G. Mellon, *Analytical Absorption Spectroscopy*, John Wiley and Sons, Inc., 1950.)

There is no internationally agreed method of plotting spectral transmission curves and there has been much confusion. If the units and conditions are clearly stated then it is possible to interpret published curves. Absorbancy, A_s (optical density, d; extinction, E), the absorbancy index a_s (extinction coefficient K); molar absorbancy index, a_M (molecular extinction coefficient) and their logarithms have all been used as ordinate. Since the direct measurement is that of the light received by the photoreceptor of the instrument, the transmittance, T_i, is a logical unit. Some instruments are calibrated directly in one or other of these units or their logarithms, whereas

others have their scales in terms of a 90° sector angle or a 45°
polarization angle which may be sometimes used as ordinates;
tables of these for conversion to other units have been given. The
abscissa is always the spectral region measured. Commonly wave-
length, λ (in mμ or Ångströms), is used, but frequently frequency, v

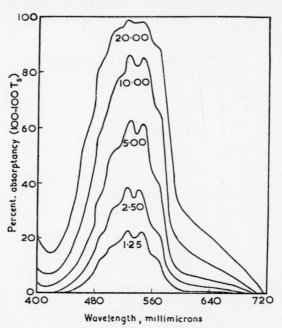

FIG. 7. Absorbancy/wave-length curves for solutions
of potassium permanganate. (Redrawn from M. G.
Mellon, *Analytical Absorption Spectroscopy*, John
Wiley and Sons, Inc., 1950.)

(in Fresnels), and wave-number, v' (in waves per centimetre), are employed. These units are related as follows:

$$\frac{1}{\lambda} = v' = \frac{v}{c},$$

the wave-length being in m$\mu \times 10^{-7}$, and c, the velocity of light,
3×10^{10} cm./sec. Curves for all three spectral units for potassium
permanganate are shown in Figs. 5–9.

Whilst it is undoubtedly true that confusion has resulted from the
lack of a standardized nomenclature and formulation of the data, it
is equally true that no one system is either adequate or convenient

for all the purposes to which the data may be put. It is therefore necessary to consider the advantages of some of the more common units for spectrophotometric data.

1. *Transmittancy*. This is usually the quantity obtained directly from the instrument and the presentation of the data is therefore a simple matter. Further, since the amount of light transmitted in

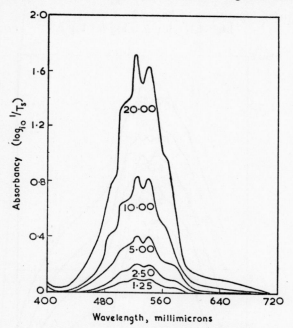

Fig. 8. Absorbancy/wave-length curves for solutions of potassium permanganate (linear scales). (Redrawn from M. G. Mellon, *Analytical Absorption Spectroscopy*, John Wiley and Sons, Inc., 1950.)

relation to wave-length determines the colour of the solution, transmittancy-wave-length plots are easy to interpret in terms of visual colour. The values are often plotted on semi-log paper, when the curves greatly magnify values below 10% in comparison with those above 70% (Fig. 6: compare Fig. 5).

2. *Absorbancy*. Curves plotted in absorbancy units have their absorption maxima magnified and therefore easily recognized. Such curves facilitate computations from one thickness to another since the relation is linear when Beer's Law holds. The curves often differ in shape for different thicknesses or different concentrations (Fig. 8)

but this may be eliminated by using log A_s (=log.log $1/T_s$) rather than absorbancy itself. This will be clear from the following. We have

$$T_s = 10^{-a_s \cdot b \cdot c}$$

and

$$A_s = \log_{10} \frac{1}{T_s},$$

so that using logarithms to base 10

$$\log (A_s)_1 = \log a_s + \log b + \log c.$$

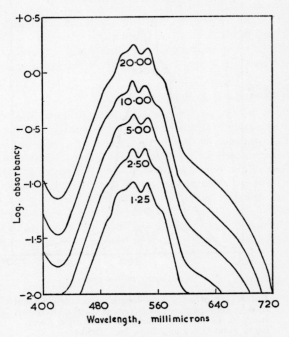

FIG. 9.   Log-absorbancy/wave-length curves for solutions of potassium permanganate (linear scales) (Redrawn from M. G. Mellon, *Analytical Absorption Spectroscopy*, John Wiley and Sons, Inc., 1950.)

Neither the concentration, c, nor the cell length, b, are functions of the wave-length and the shape of this curve will, therefore, depend solely on A_s. For a second concentration, $F.c$, where F is a numerical factor,

$$\log (A_s)_2 = \log a_s + \log b + \log F.c$$

$$= \log a_s + \log b + \log F + \log c,$$

which differs from the previous equation only by log F. The second curve log $(A_s)_2$, gives a curve a vertical distance log F from that of log $(A_s)_1$. This relation is implicit in Beer's Law.

3. *Frequency*. This is little used in analytical work, but in theoretical and interpretative studies on constitution and absorption it is the more fundamental quantity.

It is frequently difficult to interpret curves which are either not fully labelled or only labelled in agreement with the author's personal idiosyncrasy. The concentration of the solution, cell length, wavelength, solvent, temperature and presence of extraneous substances, together with the instrument used for the measurements should all be given. The publication of accurate curves carefully labelled is to be encouraged; the publication of individual calibration curves serves little useful purpose—only a tyro would fail to establish his own.

Sensitivity, Range and Accuracy

Again there is no well recognized terminology; the definition proposed by Sandell (48), namely that the sensitivity is the smallest weight of a substance which can be detected in a column having unit cross section, is one of the most satisfactory. It is definite and independent of the depth of the solution if Beer's Law is obeyed. Molar absorbancy indices are useful for a comparison of the sensitivities of different reactions with either the same or different constituents. The highest molar absorbancy indices commonly encountered are of the order of 35,000, e.g. for the azo dye formed in the Griess-Ilosvay reaction and for some metal dithizonates. The absorbancy index itself can be widely misleading for substances of very different molecular weights. To cover this point and facilitate practical work (where the actual weights are important) Wernimont (53) has proposed a 'specific absorbancy concentration' which is the weight in micrograms per litre required to give an absorbancy value of 1·00 for a 1 cm. cell.

The overall sensitivity of any particular method depends upon both chemical and instrumental factors. In visual methods, the visual acuity and spectral sensitivity are important, and in photoelectric methods the output of the photocells for a given light intensity and the response of the measuring device to changes of input must be taken into account. Assuming an adequate means of balancing a photo-electric instrument, then the overall sensitivity is measured by the response of the instrument-indicating mechanism to a given change in the concentration of the coloured substance concerned, that is by the slope of the calibration curve. The greater the slope, and therefore the greater the rate of change of the instrument reading with concentration, the greater the sensitivity both in detecting low concentrations and in distinguishing between concentrations of almost the same value.

The range and accuracy of a colour method are related to the sensitivity. If sensitivity were independent of the transmitted light, it would be clearly advantageous to work with high concentrations to reduce the percentage error. However, sensitivity falls off at high concentrations, so that, while the lower limit which may be determined depends directly upon the sensitivity, there is a loss of accuracy when working at high concentrations where the change of light transmitted per unit change of concentration becomes small. The optimum range has been dealt with for the visual method. The optimum instrumental condition depends upon the instrument. Since the relation between transmittancy and concentration is exponential it is evident that at high concentrations the change in transmittancy is small and the method will be inaccurate. As far as other considerations, such as presence of impurities, ease of manipulating the solution and so on are concerned, the working concentrations should be brought within the optimum range of the instrument used. For a spectrophotometer in which a solvent-filled reference cell is set to read 100% and balance obtained by a linear potentiometer, then the unbalance signal will be directly proportional to the absolute transmittancy unbalance; the optimum transmittancy can be shown to be 36·8%. In an instrument employing a Marten's photometer the optimum is at 28%. For visual instruments 10–20% has been given as the optimum. In general, satisfactory results will be obtained if the conditions are adjusted so that the transmission is kept within the range 10–50%.

Classification of Methods and Instruments

The methods currently employed, and to which brief reference has already been made in the introduction, may be conveniently classified as follows:

1. *Colour comparator methods.* In these, the colour developed in the unknown is compared visually, either with that developed at the same time in a standard solution of the constituent, or with permanent colour standards: the latter may take the form of coloured liquids or colour glasses. The method of colour comparison varies. It includes techniques using simple Hehner tubes and more expensive Duboscq colorimeters. Whilst visual colour comparators are being gradually replaced by photoelectric instruments for much of this type of work, in oceanography it is always advisable to retain (at least for emergencies) the relatively simple instruments. They can be

used under comparatively poor working conditions, require no complicated spare parts, are easily repaired and can be used by most people. Under certain circumstances, for example in the absence of an electrical supply, visual colour comparators may become indispensable. Hehner cylinders and the more complicated visual photometers such as the Pulfrich have been much used in the past for nutrient salt estimations. The Duboscq type of colorimeter cannot be used for many nutrient estimations, such as phosphate and silicate, because of the small length of the cells but it may be used in Harvey's strychnine method for nitrates (27) and his pigment extraction method for phytoplankton estimation (28).

2. *Photoelectric methods.* In these, the subjective element of the colour comparator is avoided by the use of photoelectric cells to measure the light transmitted by a coloured solution. If the instrument measures the transmission of either 'white' light or, by means of filters, that of a set of selected spectral ranges it is termed an absorptiometer; if it measures the transmission at a specified wavelength within a given spectral range it is termed a spectrophotometer. In the absorptiometer the light-sensitive element may be either a photo-voltaic (barrier layer) cell or a vacuum phototube. The merits of the two latter are discussed in detail later (*see* pp. 43–44). For many purposes, such as automatic recording and control, phototube instruments have inherent advantages.

COLOUR COMPARATORS

The Methods of Comparison

Four different methods of colour matching have been used.

1. *Standard series.* The unknown is compared with a series of standard solutions of the substance in question, or with a set of permanent calibrated standards in the form of coloured liquids or glass discs until a match is obtained. This method was used in Harvey's original technique for the nitrate estimation by strychnine and his phytoplankton estimation by pigment extraction. Less frequently it has been used with long tubes for the estimation of the nutrient elements.

2. *Duplication method.* This is a modification of the standard series method; known amounts of the constituents are added to a second container containing the reagents until a match is obtained. It is inconvenient and little used.

3. *Dilution methods.* In these a strong solution of the constituent, of known strength, is diluted until a match with the unknown is obtained. It is not much used.

4. *Balancing methods.* These are commonly used; they are the most convenient as well as the most accurate of the colour comparison methods. The unknown is compared with a single standard solution of the constituent to be determined which has been made up to about the same concentration as that of the unknown, a match being obtained by varying the depth through which one of the solutions is viewed; when the solutions are in match the concentrations are inversely proportional to the depths through which they are then viewed (*see* p. 78).

It should be pointed out that since in the standard series and duplication methods the concentrations of the two solutions being matched are practically identical, any deviations from Beer's Law are minimized. In the dilution or balancing methods readings must be corrected if Beer's Law is not valid for the solutions under test. Deviations from the law are easily detected by matching a standard solution against successive dilutions of the same solution; a correction curve may then be plotted from these readings.

Desiderata for Colour Comparators

The general requirements for quantitative colour reactions have already been set out (pp. 15–17). Some of these, however, assume a

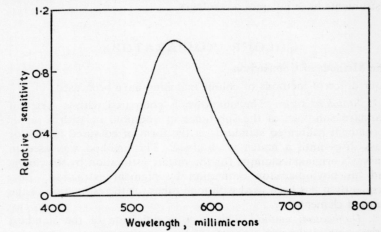

FIG. 10. Relative sensitivity curve for the eye. (Redrawn from M. G. Mellon, *Analytical Absorption Spectroscopy*, John Wiley and Sons, Inc., 1950.)

particular importance with visual methods. First, the colour should preferably be developed in that part of the spectrum to which the eye is most sensitive; secondly, the stability should be sufficiently great to allow replicate readings to be taken. The eye is best able to differentiate small changes in colour between 475 and 650 mμ (Fig. 10), and this region is, therefore, the best in which to make comparisons. Deep blues or reds are often difficult to duplicate within 15–20%, whereas green, orange and purple coloured solutions can be matched to about $\pm 2\%$. It should also be remembered that whereas, by choice of an appropriate filter it may be a simple matter to obviate the effect of any extraneous colour resulting from the reagent, side reactions or impurities when using a photoelectric instrument, this is not so easy with visual comparators.

Errors in Colour Comparators

These may be classified (excluding errors prior to colour comparison) thus:

1. *Equipment errors due to faulty instrument.* The instrument should be carefully maintained and the zero should be checked before use. Duboscq cups should always be examined for position; all optical surfaces should be kept scrupulously clean. Errors may arise in some instruments even when perfectly maintained as a result of different optical distributions in the two solutions under comparison, but such errors are virtually eliminated by competent design of the instrument. For example, in order that two solutions viewed in a comparator should appear identical they must be viewed at equal distances and the lines of the major axes must intersect at a point on or behind the retina. The eye compensates for this necessity. Further, since error would be introduced because of the apparent difference in size (truncated cone effect) of the upper and lower planes of the cylinder in which the solutions are viewed, the portions of the centres of the fields wherein the concentric rings of the top and bottom planes of the cylinder merge are closely juxtaposed in the best instruments. Such instruments also provide for viewing the fields at a considerable distance from the cylinders, and if the concentrations of the two solutions are not widely different, errors from this source become negligible. The use of similar concentrations for comparison also eliminates errors due to the difficulties of matching a long and a very short column (containing a concentrated solution), because the observed colour in the latter tends to become darker at the edge and a positive match is difficult to obtain. (*See* Yoe 54 for a detailed account.)

2. *Systematic errors.* These are inherent in the solutions and standards used, and are present therefore in all methods; they often assume such importance in visual methods that particular steps must be taken for their elimination. Every effort must be made to remove

extraneous colours due to reagents or any natural colour in the material being analysed since otherwise matching becomes difficult. This is the case in phosphate estimations when yellow colours develop in the solutions under test; it is sometimes possible to improve matters either by the addition of a similar-coloured liquid to the standard, e.g. Bismarck brown, or by the use of a filter placed over the eyepiece of the comparator or in front of the light source (11). Turbidity can be troublesome and difficult to allow for in visual methods since it changes the 'brightness' of the solutions under comparison.

3. *Working errors*, These include all subjective errors. Fatigue in using visual instruments should be guarded against; greens are much less tiring to the eye than blues and reds. Colour blindness, at least in its milder forms, is a much more common phenomenon than usually recognized.

The Advantages and Disadvantages of Comparator Methods

Visual methods at their simplest require inexpensive instruments— even ordinary test-tubes may be used to make an estimation; however, the better instruments are only a little cheaper than some using photoelectric cells. Apart from keeping clean, visual instruments require little or no servicing, they are easily repaired by relatively unskilled personnel, and may be used under quite adverse working conditions; if natural illumination is used they become independent of a supply of electricity.

On the other hand, unless a set of satisfactory permanent standards is available, a new set of standards must be prepared for each series of estimations and, as has already been stressed, compensation for the presence of interfering ions and colours is sometimes difficult. Since the method is subjective, the accuracy will usually be less than that obtained with a photoelectric instrument.

Standards

Under certain circumstances the only satisfactory standard is a solution of the substance being estimated prepared from a known quantity of that substance and treated with the appropriate reagents. Apart from the tediousness of having to prepare fresh standards for each set of estimations, much trial and error may be necessary when the concentration of the substance to be determined is not approximately known. Much effort has therefore been put into the preparation of so-called permanent standards. The solutions devised by Arny and co-workers have been much used (8, 9 and 10). These consist of the following:

Series a. 0·25 M-$CoCl_2$: 0·167 M-$FeCl_3$: 0·25 M-$CuSO_4$ in 1% HCl.

Series b. 0·01 M-$CoCl_2$: 0·00167 M-$(NH_4)_2Cr_2O_7$: 0·02 M-$CuSO_4$ in 2·8% NH_4OH.

Series c. Neutral 0·0002 M-$KMnO_4$: 0·00167 M-$K_2Cr_2O_7$.

Mixtures of these solutions within a series can be made to give almost any required colour except the deep reds and blues and much spectrophotometric data are available both for these mixtures (36) and for other artificial standards such as the mixtures of potassium chloroplatinate and cobaltous chloride used in the estimation of iron by thiocyanate (1). (It should be noted that the ammoniacal series (b, above) has only a limited stability compared with the others.)

Permanent standards should be kept in the dark when not in use, and if not completely sealed should at all times be kept free from dust and other contaminants. More convenient standards in the form of coloured glasses are now commonly used, and extensive investigations have been made on their optical properties, particularly those used in the more common estimations. Sets may be obtained for phosphate work.

There are certain objections to artificial standards no matter how perfectly they appear to match the required colour. For example, if the test colour fades, a natural standard of about the same strength will tend to fade at about the same rate and the results from the colour comparison will be directly valid; this is not so if a fading solution is compared with a permanent standard. Furthermore, the eye is variable in sensitivity to different wave-lengths; this may introduce errors since, although of the same apparent colour, the artificial standard will not have transmission properties identical with the substance which is being estimated.

Types of Colour Comparators

The type of instrument varies with the method employed for making the colour match; only the standard series and balancing methods will be considered.

Standard series instruments. These may vary from simple holders in which test-tubes containing the solutions are compared to quite complicated equipment with a precision optical system. The simplest is the block comparator (Fig. 11); the standards are held in a block at the sides of the unknown and the comparison made with back illumination. A second row of holes in the block allows self-coloured and turbid solutions to be compared. Aqueous coloured or turbid solutions are put in the back row and distilled water in the centre behind the unknown before the comparison is made. Standard specifications have been issued for comparator tubes for particular purposes—Nessler tubes, Eggertz tubes, and Julian tubes; particular attention is paid to bore and wall thickness.

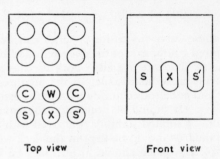

Top view   Front view

FIG. 11. Colour comparator block.

Even simpler is the use of a series of square bottles containing the standard solutions; these are set out in front of a light source, leaving room between them to interpose the unknown, which is then moved along the row until a match is obtained. In the more complicated instruments the standards are held in a movable rack whilst the unknown is maintained in a fixed position. The standards are in turn brought into juxtaposition with the unknown and viewed by means of a built-in light source, the images being brought together by an optical system. An artificial light is to be preferred since two solutions can give different results under different conditions of natural incident light, as a result of variations in the spectral composition of the latter. When colour glasses are used as permanent standards (Fig. 12) the instrument may be made much less cumbersome but is then somewhat less flexible. Particular attention has been paid in some of these instruments to the requirements for the estimation of pH.

The balancing type instrument. This may be simple or complex; balance may be obtained either by a real change in the length of the column of liquid or by an apparent change using an optical device viewing only a limited column. In the simplest form the liquids may be poured into and compared in graduated cylinders; Hehner tubes are cylinders with basal taps and the solution may be conveniently run out of one to obtain a match. The glass used in Hehner tubes must be free from defect, the wall thickness and internal diameters must match, and the graduations should be clear and reasonably close together. The tubes are preferably mounted in a closed dark box, with a removable top lid and with the taps projecting through holes in front, the light being reflected upwards from an inclined diffusing

[*Courtesy of The Tintometer Ltd., Salisbury, England*

FIG. 12. The Lovibond Comparator: disc with permanent colour standards rotating on central hub. Colour discs are interchangeable; samples viewed against light.

FIG. 14. The Duboscq-type colorimeter.

[*Courtesy of Hilger and Watts Ltd., London*

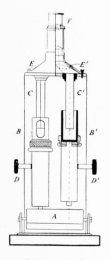

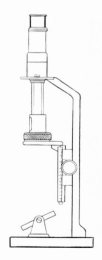

a. Schematic diagram of instrument.

b. Modern instrument; this includes built-in electric light source and scaled eyepiece giving direct readings.

mirror, situated under the tubes. The Campbell-Hurley comparator (Fig. 13) could well replace Hehner tubes. In this instrument one cylinder contains a fixed quantity of liquid while that in the other tube is varied by means of a separate reservoir and plunger device; the latter is all-glass and has a stop to prevent breaking the bottom of the reservoir. The tubes are illuminated by a built-in lamp and an optical system places two halves of the fields of standard and unknown in juxtaposition.

The most advanced instrument of the balancing type is the Duboscq comparator which in modern form is a precision instrument and should be treated as such. There are many variants but the same principle is used throughout. A mirror in the base reflects light up through the glass-bottomed comparison tubes into which fit two glass prisms moved by a rack and pinion, so that the viewing depth may be varied (Fig. 14). The two fields are brought together in a divided circular field. In the more expensive instruments facilities may be had for interchangeable tubes, illuminated vernier scales and an inclined eye-piece. Built-in lighting is now standard in a good instrument.

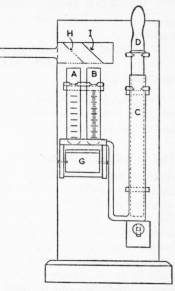

FIG. 13. Campbell-Hurley comparator. Constant volume maintained in cylinder (A); variable volume in (B) and (C) by means of syringe device (D). Built-in lighting (G) and device for giving juxtaposed fields of views, (H), (I). (Redrawn from M. G. Mellon, *Analytical Absorption Spectroscopy*, John Wiley and Sons, Inc., 1950.)

TRANSMISSION INSTRUMENTS

Analytical estimations using the relatively simple instruments so far considered have in all cases depended upon the matching of two colours: we must now consider that class of instrument in which the transmittancies of the solutions are measured. The essential requirements for this purpose are:

1. A suitable and adequately stabilized source of light or other radiant energy.

2. A set of spectral filters or some device for isolating selected parts of the spectrum.

3. An optical system to produce a parallel beam and mechanical provision for holding the cells containing the solution in the path of that beam.

4. A means of establishing photometric balance.

5. An instrument for indicating when the balance has been established.

To these may be added refinements such as convenient mechanical parts for handling the sample and, if required, automatic recording and control devices.

The Visual Filter Photometer

In this type of instrument the light source is usually a tungsten filament lamp (but auxiliary lighting may be available) and spectral selection is effected by the interposition of glass (or gelatin) filters in the beam of light. Such filters are often quite adequate for much analytical work since the absorption bands used are moderately broad. The eye is the sensitive receptor and a photometric balance is estimated visually. The direct measurement of a spectrophotometric ratio by eye is impossible; only a rough estimate of absolute photometric quantities can be made visually. Nevertheless, the eye can determine with considerable precision when two properly juxtaposed parts of a photometric field are equally bright. The visual filter photometer has therefore an arrangement for securing a uniformly bright two-part field and for varying one or both parts continuously and in a known manner. A balance is then obtained by comparison as the intensity of one half is changed and the desired photometric ratio thereby determined.

Visual filter photometers are more accurate than most colour comparators; they are more easily used with spectral filters, colour sensitivity of the eye is not involved, allowance for colour in the untreated solution is more easily made and standards are not required for comparison. Moreover, since these instruments are normally made to take long cells which usually require only a moderate quantity of the solution, they are very convenient for oceanography (*see* Kalle, 35). They are still subjective since the brightness comparison is made visually.

In the modern Leitz filter photometer (Figs. 15 and 16) which may be taken as typical of this type of instrument, the light beam from a tungsten filament lamp (L) is collimated by the lens (K) and then divided into two beams. These pass through cells, one of which contains the solution and the other solvent; the cells are readily

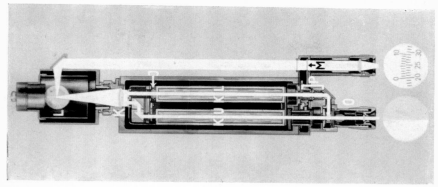

[*Courtesy of Ernst Leitz, G.m.b.H. Wetzlar, Germany*

FIG. 15. Compensating visual filter photometer (Leitz). Diagram of optical system.

Fig. 16. Compensating visual filter photometer (Leitz).

[*Courtesy of Ernst Leitz, G.m.b.H. Wetzlar, Germany*

a. General view, showing cells, and built-in light source.

b. Showing details of eyepieces and the micro-adaptor.

brought into fixed positions by means of stops. The intensity of the comparison beam (solvent cell) is reduced by the polarizing prism system (P) and the two rays are brought together in the photometric eye-piece (O) on the left. In setting up the instrument the two fields are first adjusted for brightness by a diaphragm connected to a scale which is read through the right eye-piece. Illumination for this scale is provided from the single light source by means of an inclined mirror. Both eye-pieces are on the same level and are inclined for convenience of observation. The two fields are semicircular and their dividing line may be focused by turning the mount of the eye-piece; the size of the measuring fields is made to correspond to the optimum angle of vision. After interposition of the coloured solution the adjustment of the fields to equal brightness is made by turning a large knob, the angle of rotation being read off on the scale in the right eye-piece. In this particular instrument the light intensity is controlled by means of a rotating polarizing prism; in others a neutral wedge is used.

The visual filter photometer is a useful instrument but in common with all visual instruments suffers from the disadvantages of a subjective element and the problems of fatigue. The inclusion of a photoelectric cell as a detector of the radiant energy and of a galvanometer as the instrument for detecting photometric balance is a logical development. Spectral isolation is effected by means of filters.

Photo-voltaic and Photo-emissive Cells

Almost all the photo-voltaic cells (the term barrier layer is now deprecated) at present on the market are 'selenium' cells. These are less sensitive to temperature changes and more stable in response over long periods of time than the original cuprous oxide cells. Selenium is a defect conductor and for its mode of action Mott (44)

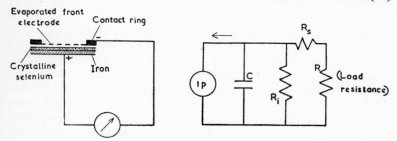

Fig. 17. Construction and equivalent circuit of photo-voltaic cell.

and Schottky (49) should be consulted (*see also* Lange, 42). The construction and equivalent electrical circuit is shown in Fig. 17.

If the primary photoelectric current is i_p and the load resistance R, then the current through the latter is

$$i = \frac{i_p \cdot R_i}{R_i + R_s + R}.$$

The series resistance R_s is almost entirely due to the top electrode. The capacity of the cell corresponding to that across the 'barrier

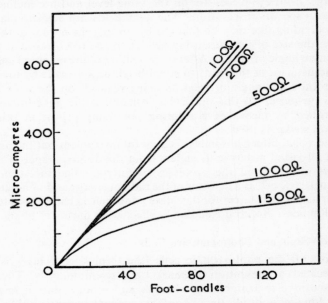

FIG. 18. Output, load and light intensity of Eel photo-voltaic cell. (Redrawn from leaflet of Evans Electroselenium Ltd., Harlow, Essex, England.)

layer' is high, amounting to several tenths of a microfarad. It is important to note that the internal resistance of the cell R_i is a function of the potential across the cell and hence of both of the intensity of illumination and external load. The wave-length of maximum response is close to that of the eye. For finite values of the load resistance R, the variation of current becomes increasingly non-linear as the internal resistance R_i decreases. Since current sensitivity is inversely related to the internal resistance the more sensitive the cell the less linear is the response to increasing illumination, parti-cularly at high levels of the latter. Current variation for increasing load is shown in Fig. 18 for an Eel cell.

Vacuum phototubes have a sensitive cathode (the sensitivity is a function of the wave-length of the radiation and special tubes are made for different purposes) and when illuminated under the influence of an applied potential E, an electron current i flows through the load R (Fig. 19). R may represent the resistance of an amplifier.

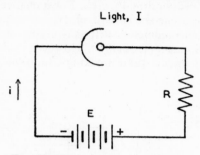

FIG. 19. Equivalent circuit of photo-emissive cell.

For a constant illumination the current i will increase with the applied potential until saturation is reached. If now a potential is applied adequate for saturation and the current is plotted against the intensity of illumination a straight line results (Fig. 20).

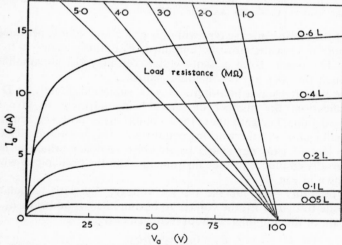

FIG. 20. Anode current plotted against total voltage for varying intensity of illumination of Mullard, 57 CV vacuum photocell. (Redrawn from leaflet of Mullard Ltd., London.)

In deciding upon which type of photocell to use in an absorptiometer the relative merits of the photo-voltaic and photo-emissive cells must be carefully considered. Without doubt the photo-voltaic cell leads to a simpler instrument. As already noted the output is linear at low levels of light intensity. Such a cell will have an output of the order of 120 μA. per lumen (per sq. cm. surface) which is the order of light intensity normally used. For a change in transmission of 1% we obtain a current change of 1·2 μA., and this is readily detected on a micro-ammeter such as is used, for example, in the Spekker Absorptiometer (*see* below). However, such a galvanometer can only be used under stable working conditions. By contrast, a

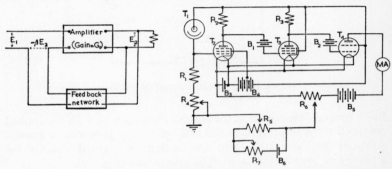

FIG. 21. Inverse feedback principle and circuit for photometer. (Modified from original. Rittner, E. S., *Rev. Sc. Instr.*, 1947.)

cell of the photo-emissive type will only give about 40 μA. per lumen: the output must therefore be amplified, if a sturdy meter is to be used. The output from a photo-voltaic cell may also be amplified, although the contrary is sometimes stated.

The output from a phototube may be subjected directly to D.C. amplification, the number of stages being adjusted to give the required gain. The gain under these conditions is, however, sensitive to small changes in the working conditions. This is minimized (with some loss of gain per stage) by negative feedback which is now universally employed in such instruments, and the principle of which is shown in Fig. 21.

A fraction $-\beta E_2$ of the output voltage, E_2, with a polarity opposite to that of E_1, the voltage to be amplified, is added to E_1. If the gain of the amplifier without feedback is G_0,

$$E_2 = G_0 (E_1 - \beta E_2),$$

and the gain of the feedback amplified becomes

$$\frac{E_2}{E_1} = \frac{G_0}{1+\beta G_0} \simeq \frac{1}{\beta}, \text{ since } \beta G_0 \gg 1.$$

For large amplification factors G_0 is determined by the circuit constants of the feedback network. The simplicity of amplification with the photo-emissive cell depends upon the fact that it has a high impedance which matches the load.

Since photo-voltaic cells are characterized by a high current sensitivity which, however, decreases rapidly as the load is increased, and since the linearity of response is impaired by increasing external load, the voltage sensitivity is low and conventional D.C. amplifiers have been little used in conjunction with these cells. If, however, the

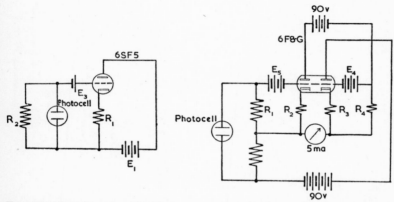

Fig. 22. Linearity correction for a photo-voltaic cell and photometric circuit employing cathode follower amplification. (Modified from original, Rittner, E. S., *Rev. Sc. Instr.*, 1947.)

potential is maintained constant, the sensitivity can be adequate despite a high value of the external resistance. If it is to be amplified a negative feedback amplifier such as a cathode follower must be used (Fig. 22). Since the voltage difference between the grid and the cathode remains practically constant independent of the input when the photo-voltaic cell is connected between these points in such a circuit, there is a constant potential across the cell and hence linearity of response to illumination. With amplification a larger response is, of course, obtained (Rittner, 46).

Photoelectric Filter Photometers (Absorptiometers)

When the ordinary spectral filters are used in conjunction with a tungsten filament lamp the current obtained from a photo-voltaic cell, used as the sensitive receptor, is adequate to operate a sensitive galvanometer (*see* p. 44): since, as already pointed out, such photocells require neither an external e.m.f. nor complicated electronic circuitry they are very frequently used in laboratory instruments. A single photocell may be used, in which case a calibration curve is set up in terms of the galvanometer readings; alternately a null method is employed using two photocells and restoring balance by a photometric device, the galvanometer being only employed as a null-point indicator. The readings are then taken from the calibrated diaphragm or shutter device that is used to restore the balance.

The Spekker Absorptiometer (Figs. 23 and 24) is typical of a modern precision instrument of the latter type.[1] The instrument is mains operated. Light from the tungsten filament lamp (G) passes

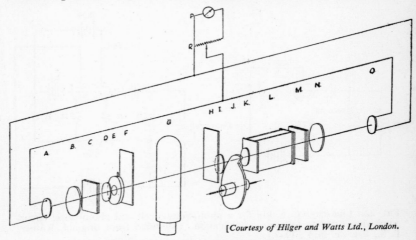

[*Courtesy of Hilger and Watts Ltd., London.*

FIG. 23. Spekker Absorptiometer. Diagrammatic.

on the left of the instrument through an adjustable iris diaphragm (E) to a photocell (A); on the right, it passes first through a calibrated shutter (J) and then through the solution to the second photocell (O). The two cells are connected in a bridge circuit so that the galvanometer (P) indicates zero when their outputs are balanced. Balance is first obtained with water in the cell by adjustment of the left-hand iris. The water is then replaced by the solution whose transmittancy is to be measured and balance re-established by means of the drum (fitted with a slow-motion friction device) which operates the shutter on the right. The drum is calibrated directly in terms of optical density and transmission. Heat-absorbing and spectral filters, mounted in a sliding carriage, are interposed on either side of the light source. A spring shutter mounted on the lamp house ensures that the photocells are only illuminated when taking a

[1] Instruments of this type are made by many well known firms; details should be sought in literature obtainable from the makers.

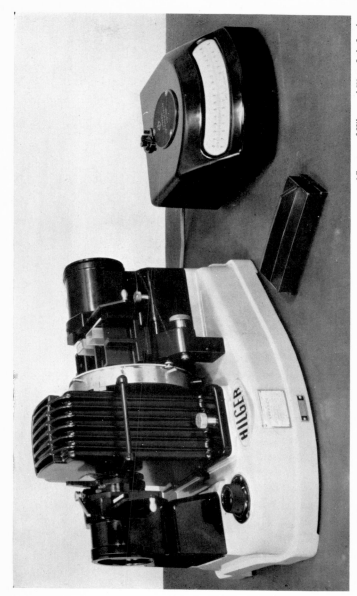

Fig. 24. Spekker Photoelectric Absorptiometer.

reading. The instrument takes a wide variety of cells, from micro-cells to cells 20 cm. in length. The volume of liquid required for the long cells is rather large but this may to some extent be reduced by the insertion of solid plastic liners fitting closely inside the cell walls.

The circuit of an instrument of this type may be balanced by means of a potentiometer and in making (as distinct from purchasing) an instrument for any particular purpose this possibility should be given serious consideration (the system is used in spectrophoto-meters, *see* pp. 48–51), since it obviates the necessity for a calibrated

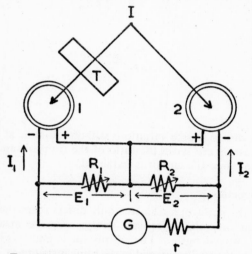

Fig. 25. Compensating circuit for photo-voltaic cells. (Redrawn from M. G. Mellon, *Analytical Absorption Spectroscopy*, John Wiley and Sons, Inc., 1950.)

slit, wedge, or polarizing prism to obtain photometric balance. With this arrangement there is no optical compensation and care must therefore be taken that compensation for source variations is inherent in the electrical circuit. Brice (20) has discussed such problems, and a convenient circuit fulfilling these requirements is shown in Fig. 25. Adopting the lettering given on the figure, we have,

$$i_1 = kTI \quad \text{and} \quad E_1 = kTIR_1,$$
$$i_2 = kI \quad \text{and} \quad E_2 = kIR_2.$$

At balance $E_1 = E_2$, hence

$$kTIR_1 = kIR_2$$

or

$$T = \frac{R_2}{R_1}.$$

The resistor R_2 may be a precision potentiometer or a Kohlrausch slide wire and R_1 an ordinary potentiometer. The slide wire is set at 100 without the sample and balance is established with R_1. The sample is then introduced and balance re-established with the slide wire. Both resistors should have low values. We may note that the current through the galvanometer is,

$$i_g = \frac{E_2 - E_1}{r_g} = \frac{kIR_2 - kITR_1}{r_g},$$

$$\frac{di_g}{dI} = \frac{kR_2}{r_g} - \frac{kTR_1}{r_g},$$

for a minimum,

$$\frac{di_g}{dI} = 0,$$

so that

$$T = \frac{R_2}{R_1}.$$

Fluctuations due to source variations will therefore be at a minimum when the resistors are set in the ratio of the transmittance, which is the condition when the circuit is balanced.

Spectrophotometers

In principle, the spectrophotometer only differs from the absorptiometer in that the relative radiant energy may be measured as a function of wave-length. The ultra-violet and visible regions (200–700 mμ) are usually covered in the same instrument; work in the infra-red requires somewhat different techniques and apparatus. This type of instrument has all the advantages of the absorptiometer and in addition enables a complete absorption curve to be plotted and any part of that curve to be used. The optimum conditions may therefore be chosen for any particular set of transmission measurements. Furthermore, wave-length selection enables more than one constituent to be estimated in a solution by transmission measurements at the appropriate wave-lengths.

The requirements listed (pp. 39–40) are complied with as described below. The radiant source is either a tungsten filament lamp or for the ultra-violet region, a hydrogen discharge tube (which gives a virtually continuous spectrum of adequate intensity between 200 and 400 mμ).

Although there are some visual instruments it is modern practice to employ a vacuum phototube as the detector and a galvanometer as an indicator of photometric balance.

Both prisms and diffraction grating have been used for spectral dispersion and isolation; modern practice for most of the instruments employed in analytical work inclines to prism dispersion; both 'telescope' and 'collimator' are fixed and the wave-length is changed simply by rotating the prism. Apart from simplicity and convenience in manipulation this has the advantage that the rays accepted for measurements are close to minimum deviation regardless of wave-length; the disadvantage, namely greater light losses in the optical system, is of less importance as a result of modern improvements in phototubes and methods of amplification.

The extent of pure spectrum transmission by an exit slit of constant mechanical width varies throughout the spectrum with a prism instrument; at the longer wave-lengths, it is several times greater than at the shorter wave-lengths. Hence, the longer the wave-length at which it is desired to work the smaller must be the mechanical slit-width to obtain the same purity of spectral band, and if it is required to maintain a constant spectral purity over the whole range, then, either the slit width must be continually changed mechanically or a cam arrangement must be fitted to do it automatically.

In order to obtain a pure spectrum the entrance slit should ideally be of infinitesimal width but for sufficient spectral energy the slit must be finite; it has become customary to set entrance and exit slits to the same width. With a continuous spectrum source this results in an extension of the transmitted range of wave-length beyond that for a pure spectrum. The band-pass, that is 'amount of spectrum' at a particular slit width, is usually expressed in terms of wave-length units. Most of the present-day instruments have a direct-reading scale in $m\mu$ and when carefully adjusted the error need not exceed ± 1 $m\mu$.

There are many commercial instruments available; they differ in detail but the general principles may be illustrated by reference to the Uvispek (Hilger and Watts) instrument (Figs. 26 and 27). The light from a tungsten filament lamp (or hot cathode hydrogen discharge lamp for the ultra-violet region) passes through a slit to the monochromator which employs a Littrow dispersion system consisting of a concave collimating mirror and a $30°$ prism with a back reflecting surface. Both quartz and glass prisms are available and interchangeable, since although a quartz prism will cover the whole range from 200 to 1000 $m\mu$, glass gives a much higher dispersion in the visible range. Wave-length selection is obtained by rotating the prism, the wave-length being indicated directly on a calibrated scale. Special arrangements are made for accurate wave-length setting. After dispersion, the light is returned to the mirror which focuses it in the plane of the exit slit after reflection in a small plane mirror.

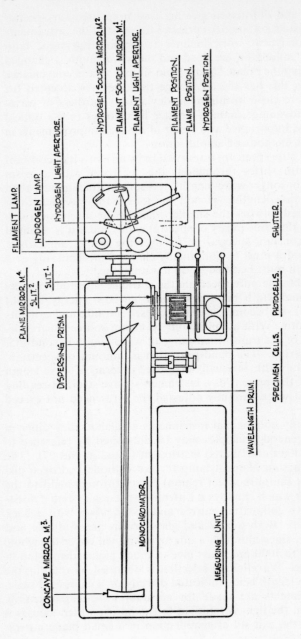

FIG. 26. Diagram of spectrophotometer.

[Courtesy of Hilger and Watts Ltd., London.

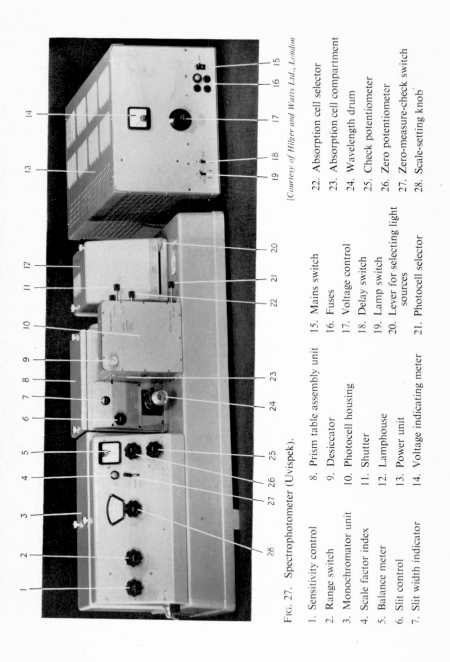

FIG. 27. Spectrophotometer (Uvispek).

[Courtesy of Hilger and Watts Ltd., London]

1. Sensitivity control
2. Range switch
3. Monochromator unit
4. Scale factor index
5. Balance meter
6. Slit control
7. Slit width indicator
8. Prism table assembly unit
9. Desiccator
10. Photocell housing
11. Shutter
12. Lamphouse
13. Power unit
14. Voltage indicating meter
15. Mains switch
16. Fuses
17. Voltage control
18. Delay switch
19. Lamp switch
20. Lever for selecting light sources
21. Photocell selector
22. Absorption cell selector
23. Absorption cell compartment
24. Wavelength drum
25. Check potentiometer
26. Zero potentiometer
27. Zero-measure-check switch
28. Scale-setting knob

In this particular instrument the prism is placed at a lower level than the plane containing the slits and the concave mirror; this allows the mirror to be used more readily on an axis which ensures that there is no significant broadening of the spectral slit image and no loss of spectral purity. The light passes from the exit slit through the reference or test solution to the photocells—a pair of interchangeable cells for the ranges 200–625 mμ and 625–1000 mμ. The signal is amplified (the first stage being mounted in the photocell housing) by a D.C. amplifier. Balance is obtained by opposing the photocell current by a potentiometer, calibrated directly (with five overlapping ranges) in optical density and percentage transmission. This instrument is mains operated, but in others batteries are used. Various sizes and types of cells are employed, and they may be water jacketed. Provision is made for attachment of subsidiary units for measurement of diffuse reflection and fluorescence; a separate attachment is used for flame photometry.

Errors in Spectrophotometry

The importance of the various kinds of error to which this type of instrument is subject will depend very much on the use to which the instrument is being put. In measuring transmittancies in a routine analytical procedure any error in the actual reading of the wave-length indicator will, if it is always the same, be of little importance when the results are interpreted from a calibration curve obtained with standards at the 'erroneous' wave-length. If, however, a spectrophotometric curve is being prepared such wave-length errors are of fundamental importance.

All commercial instruments now have direct-reading wave-length scales and according to Gibson (in Mellon, 43) the deviations on such instruments seldom exceed ± 1 mμ when properly adjusted. Wave-length selection may be of great importance in transmission measurements taken for analytical purposes (see below).

The photometric scale may be checked by the use of certificated filters issued by some Standards Institution or by standard solutions whose absorption curves have been carefully determined. Again, errors of this type, if constant, are of less importance in analytical work where a direct calibration curve is used. Stray energy, arising from a variety of sources in the instrument and often a general mixture of all wave-lengths emitted by the source, is reduced to a minimum by careful instrument design.

Slit-width errors depend primarily upon the effective width of the entrance and exit slits (with a continuous spectrum) and the curvature, as distinct from the slope, of the spectral distributions being isolated. The errors will be greatest where the curves are sharpest.

(*See* Mellon, 43, for a detailed discussion.) It is far better to keep the slit width sufficiently narrow so that correction is unnecessary (for the purpose in hand) than to apply slit-width corrections which at the best are only approximate. In chemical oceanography, however, fairly wide absorption bands are usually used and slit-width errors need, therefore, hardly be considered.

Choice of Working Region

The great advantage of working with a spectrophotometer is that a narrow region of the spectrum may be selected at which to make the transmittancy measurements. Under ideal working conditions the wave-band of maximum absorption would be used to ensure maximum sensitivity; there may, however, be factors present which should modify such a choice and these will now be considered.

1. *Wave-length errors.* In taking a measurement, a wave-length setting is made at the selected point and the transmittancy determined. If, as is sometimes the case, it is difficult to repeat the wave-length setting accurately, and if at the same time the transmittancy of the solution is changing rapidly at the selected point, then any slight error in the wave-length setting may result in considerable error in the results. It would be better under these circumstances to choose a working wave-length on a flatter portion of the absorption curve.

2. *Transmittancy errors.* The optimum transmittancy has been already discussed (p. 32). With a spectrophotometer the sensitivity varies with the wave-length, and in general the accuracy is greatest in those spectral regions where the photoreceptor is most sensitive. If possible, it is therefore better to work in this region just as with a visual instrument it is better to work in a region to which the eye is sensitive, say at about 500 mμ. For example, although the molybdenum blue complex is determined by the eye as visual blue it is usually determined with a photo-electric instrument with a red filter (*see* Fig. 28), although with a spectrophotometer the absorption is measured either at 705 mμ or even at 820 mμ, where the photocell is near its maximum sensitivity.

3. *Solution effects.* Some part only of the absorption curve gives additive absorbancies and freedom from large effects of, say, salt and other pH. This region should, if the required sensitivity can be obtained, be chosen.

4. *The absorbancy index.* With a limited cell length the greater this value the more sensitive is the method and an absorption maximum is therefore favourable.

5. *Resolution.* With a narrow slit width the absorbancies are more likely to be additive and it is, therefore, best to work in the region

where the instrument has the greatest resolution. Again, it should be stressed that narrow band-widths are usually not required in the methods used in chemical oceanography.

6. *Impurities.* It may, if the added reagent or the solution itself is coloured to any great extent, be desirable to choose a wave-length where absorption by these 'impurities' is minimal.

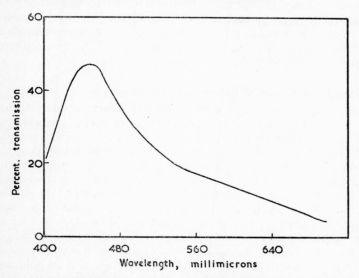

Fig. 28. Transmittancy curve for molybdenum blue in phosphate estimation General Electric Recording spectrophotometer: band-width 10 mμ. Reduction by hydroquinone. (Redrawn from Kitson, R. E., and Mellon, M. G., *Ind. Engng. Chem. (Anal.)*, 1944.)

It is evident from the above that the choice of a maximum in the absorption curve as the point at which to work is by no means axiomatic. Other considerations must be taken into account and only when this has been done will the optimal working conditions be obtained for any particular analytical method. It should, however, be stressed that in most of the analytical methods used in chemical oceanography the measurements are made at the wavelength of maximum absorption (one exception is the yellow silicomolybdate complex where the absorption spectrum of the blank overlaps at λ max., p. 164).

Work with Multi-component Systems

One of the great advantages of the spectrophotometer over the filter photometer (absorptiometer) is the possibility of carrying out multi-component analysis by selecting suitable wave-lengths for the transmittancy measurements. With the appropriate precautions systems which do not obey Beer's Limit law may also be adequately dealt with. The methods require a good deal of computation and for details reference should be made to Mellon (43, *see also* Section 18).

In the future much might be done in pigment analysis and the analysis of other soluble micro-nutrients by the application of these techniques. Recently Richards and Thompson (45) have estimated chlorophyll a, b and c, astacin and non-astacin type carotenoids in acetone, extracts of plankton using a Beckman D.U. spectrophotometer and working at five different wave-lengths.

Desiderata with Special Reference to Oceanography

If the samples are brought back to the laboratory for analysis then the choice of instrument is largely a matter of finance and personal preference. Most analysts would now prefer an objective spectrophotometric instrument, and there are many reliable products on the market. If finance were not a limiting factor a spectrophotometer would be chosen. When an absorptiometer, which is quite adequate for many purposes, is used, there is much to recommend the simpler instrument employing photo-voltaic cells and a sensitive galvanometer. It is essential that all instruments should be capable of taking cells sufficiently long to obtain the required sensitivity and, in view of the limited volume of the sample usually available, it is very desirable that these cells should not require an undue quantity of solution; frequently commercially available instruments either do not take long cells or the long cells provided require a large volume of solution—sometimes as much as 500 ml. It is for this reason that many prefer to make their own instrument; for laboratory work that described by Harvey (29) is simple to make and reliable. Any instrument specifically designed for use at sea may of course be used.

The problems are more severe in designing a satisfactory photoelectric sea-going instrument. The desiderata may be listed:

1. The instrument should be unaffected by constant high humidity and a salt-laden atmosphere over long working periods.

To this end, wherever possible, the photoreceptors, the indicating galvanometers and any electronic components should be mounted in sealed containers carrying silica-gel driers. Leads should be of stout modern design (*see* Roberts, 47; Cox, 24).

2. It should be mechanically robust and easy to operate under adverse conditions.

Robustness may be secured by careful mounting. In general it will be preferable to have a compact instrument. The use of a movable light source tends to a long instrument. Ease of working may be ensured by an adequate lay-out, which has not always been carefully considered; for example, the cells should be readily removable from the apparatus and when in the instrument should be so positioned as to reduce the tendency for spilled liquids to fall on electrical or other sensitive parts.

3. Electrically, it should be as simple as possible, and easy to repair by semi-skilled personnel with limited workshop facilities. It should be easily checked.

Electrical simplicity is a very subjective concept. To many, amplifiers and electronic equipment in general are inherently complex, and the simpler photo-voltaic cell absorptiometer is often preferred. Roberts (47) has described a direct-reading instrument using a microammeter which he states works adequately at sea. However, with amplification a more robust indicating instrument may be used. Cox has used an ammeter and Ford (25a) a magic eye indicator, which is not sensitive to motion. Dr B. H. Ketchum, who has had much experience with Ford's instrument, finds it very satisfactory for work under ship-board conditions; it is, however, better to have the Perspex rod in this instrument fixed in position and to insert a conventional cell of the desired length. The orientation of the latter is somewhat critical; it should always be held in the same position by reference to a small mark scratched on the cell.

Dr ZoBell writes that a Beckman D.U. spectrophotometer has been in constant use for several years (covering some 55,000 sea miles) by members of the Scripps Institution of Oceanography, although Snodgrass, Carritt and Wooster (51) note that it is slightly affected by the motion of the ship. These authors have developed a sea-going servo-operated filter photometer which cannot, however, be considered a simple instrument to service.

Two further considerations may be discussed. First, whichever type of photoelectric instrument is used some form of power is required for illumination, and in the case of instruments with photo-tubes and amplification, for the electronics; there is much to be said for batteries. Alternatively constant current transformers or electronic devices may be used (*see* Cox, 24). Secondly, in making an instrument, careful thought should be given to the question of balance. A direct-reading instrument (single photocell) is simple and obviates this difficulty and, if adequate means of checking zero are available, has much to recommend it. If a null method with its well-known advantages is to be employed, some means of restoring balance is essential. Optical compensation may be effected by a precision slit and an accurate mechanical means of measuring the slit movement. Ford (25a) has used a logarithmic slit and a micro-meter gauge. Alternatively the principle of a movable source or photocell may be employed, but this makes the instrument unduly long. There would seem to be much in favour of electrical balance; the appropriate precision resistance can be purchased and fitted into the instrument compactly and easily.

REFERENCES

1. American Public Health Association and others, 1955. *Standard Methods for the Examination of Water, Sewage and Industrial Wastes*. Amer. Publ. Health Ass. Inc., New York, 10th ed., 1955, 522 pp.
2. Anon., 1937. *Commission Internationale de l'Éclairage. Recueil des Travaux et Comptes rendus des Séances*, 1935. Cambridge, 679 pp.
3. ——, 1937. 'Physico-chemical symbols.' Report of a Joint Committee of the Chemical Society, the Faraday Society and the Physical Society. *Analyst*, 62, 800–5.
4. ——, 1942. 'Spectrophotometric terms and symbols.' Report of a panel appointed by the Publication Committee. *Analyst*, 67, 164–5.
5. ——, 1947. National Bureau of Standards, *Letter Circular, LC-857*, Washington, D.C.
6. ——, 1948. *Report on colour terminology*. By a Committee of the Colour Group of the Physical Society. London, 56 pp.
7. Armstrong, F. A. J., 1951. 'The determination of silicate in sea water.' *J. Mar. biol. Ass. U.K.*, 30, 149–60.
8. Arny, H. V., 1913. 'International standards for coloured fluids.' *J. Amer. pharm. Ass.*, 2, 76–80.
9. ——, and Ring, C. H., 1915. 'Colour standards and cudbear.' *J. Amer. pharm. Ass.*, 4, 1294–9.
10. ——, and Taub, A., 1923. 'Standardized colored fluids and some official colorimetric tests'. *J. Amer. pharm. Ass.*, 12, 839–49.
11. Atkins, W. R. G., 1923. 'The phosphate content of fresh and salt waters in its relationship to the growth of the algal plankton.' *J. Mar. biol. Ass. U.K.*, 13, 119–50.
12. ——, 1932. 'Nitrate determination in sea water and its estimation by means of diphenyl benzidine.' *J. Mar. biol. Ass. U.K.*, 18, 167–92.
13. ——, and Wilson, E. G., 1926. 'The colorimetric estimation of minute amounts of compounds of silica, of phosphorus and of arsenic.' *Biochem. J.*, 20, 1223–8.
14. Barnes, H., 1946. 'The estimation in sea water solutions of micro quantities of mercury in the presence of copper by means of dithizone.' *J. Mar. biol. Ass. U.K.*, 26, 303–11.
15. ——, 1949. 'Analytical Chemistry; 5. Analysis of Sea Water.' *Annual Reports of the Chemical Society for 1948*, 45, 338–44.
16. ——, 1954. 'The estimation of nitrite.' *Mem. Ist. Ital. Idrobiol.*, 8, 73–9.
17. ——, 1955. 'The analysis of sea water.' *Analyst*, 80, 573–92.
18. ——, and Folkard, A. R., 1951. 'The determination of nitrites.' *Analyst*, 76, 599–603.

19. Brew, W., and Scott, M. B., 1946. 'Chemical determination of Vitamin A in mixed feeds and feedstuffs.' *Industr. Engng. Chem.* (*Anal.*), **18**, 46–8.
20. Brice, B. A., 1937. 'A compensating circuit for blocking-layer photo-electric cells.' *Rev. sci. Instrum.*, **8**, 279–87.
21. British Standards Institution, 1953. *Glossary of terms used in illumination and photometry.* British Standard 233: 1953, 17 pp.
22. Clark, W. M., 1920. *The Determination of Hydrogen Ions.* London, 3rd ed., 1928, 717 pp.
23. Cooper, L. H. N., 1932. 'The determination of nitrate in the sea by means of reduced strychnine.' *J. Mar. biol. Ass. U.K.*, **18**, 161–6.
24. Cox, R. A., 1954. 'A filter photometer for use at sea.' *J. sci. Instrum.* **31**, 374–6.
25. Evans, R. M., 1948. *An Introduction to Colour.* John Wiley & Sons, Inc., New York, 340 pp.
    [This deals with colour in general terms.]
25a. Ford, W. L., 1950. 'Seagoing photoelectric colorimeter.' *Analyt. Chem.*, **22**, 1431–5.
26. Hardy, A. C. (Ed), 1936. *Handbook of Colorimetry.* Massachusetts Institute of Technology. Cambridge, Mass. 87 pp.
    [The physics of colorimetry.]
27. Harvey, H. W., 1926. 'Nitrate in sea water.' *J. Mar. biol. Ass. U.K.*, **14**, 71–88.
28. ——, 1934. 'Measurement of phytoplankton populations.' *J. Mar. biol. Ass. U.K.*, **19**, 761–73.
29. ——, 1948. 'The estimation of phosphate and total phosphorus in sea waters.' *J. Mar. biol. Ass. U.K.*, **27**, 337–59.
30. Jones, L. A. *et al.*, 1943. 'The concept of colour.' *J. opt. Soc. Amer.*, **33**, 544–54. (Chapter II of the forthcoming Colorimetry Report.)
31. ——, 1944. 'Physical concepts: radiant energy and its measurement.' *J. opt. Soc. Amer.*, **34**, 183–218. (Chapter V of the forthcoming Colorimetry Report.)
32. ——, 1944. 'The psychophysics of colour.' *J. opt. Soc. Amer.*, **34**, 245–66. (Chapter VI of the forthcoming Colorimetry Report.)
33. ——, 1944. 'Quantitative date and methods for colorimetry.' *J. opt. Soc. Amer.*, **34**, 633–88. (Chapter VII of the forthcoming Colorimetry Report.)
34. ——, 1945. 'Colorimeters and color standards.' *J. opt. Soc. Amer.*, **35**, 1–25. (Chapter VIII of the report of the Committee on Colorimetry of the Optical Society of America.)
35. Kalle, K., 1931. 'Meereskundliche Chemische Untersuchungen mit Hilfe des Zeisschen Pulfrich-photometers. I. Apparatus.' *Ann. Hydrogr., Berl.*, **59**, 313–7.
36. Kasline, C. T., and Mellon, M. G., 1937. 'Solutions for colorimetric standards. VIII. Arny's series.' *J. Amer. pharm. Ass.*, **26**, 227–30.
37. Kitson, R. E., and Mellon, M. G., 1944. 'Color of aqueous potassium dichromate solutions.' *Industr. Engng. Chem.* (*Anal.*), **16**, 42–4.
38. ——, ——, 1944. 'Further studies of the molybdenum blue reaction.' *Industr. Engng Chem.* (*Anal.*), **16**, 466–9.
39. Kortüm, G., 1936. *Das Optische Verhaltengelöster Electrolyte.* Enke, Stuttgart.
40. ——, 1936. 'Das optische Verhalten gelöster Ionen und seine Bedeutung für die Struktur elektrolytischer Lösungen. V. Lichtabsorption

und Dispersität organischer Farbstoffionen in wässeriger Lösung.'
Z. phys. Chem., B, **34,** 255–74.

41. Kortüm, G., and Seiler, M., 1939. 'Die kritische Auswahl colorimetrischer, spectralphotometrischer und spectrographischer Methoden zur Absorptionsmessung.' *Angew. Chem.,* **52,** 687–93.

42. Lange, B., 1938. *Photo-elements.* Reinhold Publishing Corporation. New York, 297 pp.
   [A very useful adjunct to Zworykin and Ramberg's book on *Photo-electricity:* it is written at a more elementary level and is less up to date.]

43. Mellon, M. G. (Ed.), 1950. *Analytical Absorption Spectroscopy.* John Wiley & Sons, Inc., New York, 618 pp.
   [This is an excellent modern work on colorimetry, absorptiometry, and spectrophotometry. The general principles of the methods are dealt with and there is much theoretical and practical detail regarding the instruments and their use.]

44. Mott, N. F., 1939. 'Note on cuprous oxide photocells.' *Proc. roy. Soc.,* Ser. A, **171,** 283–5.

45. Richards, F. A., and Thompson, T. G., 1952. 'The estimation and characterization of plankton populations by pigment analysis. II. A spectrophotometric method for the estimation of plankton pigments.' *J. Mar. Res.,* **11,** 156–72.

46. Rittner, E. S., 1947. 'Improvement of the characteristics of photovoltaic and photo-conductive cells by feedback circuits.' *Rev. sci. Instrum.,* **18,** 36–8.

47. Roberts, C. H., 1950. 'A photo-electric cell comparator for colorimetric analyses at sea.' *J. Cons. int. Explor. Mer,* **17,** 17–24.

48. Sandell, E. B., 1944. *Colorimetric Determination of Traces of Metals.* Interscience Publishers, Inc., New York, 487 pp.
   [A general account of trace metal analysis is given and details, with particular reference to dithizone techniques, for the estimation of metallic radicals.]

49. Schottky, W., 1947. 'Simplified and extended theory of the barrier layer rectifier.' *Z. Phys.,* **71,** 717–27.

50. Snell, F. D., and Snell, C. T., 1948–54. *Colorimetric Methods of Analysis.* D. van Nostrand Co. Inc., New York. Vol. I (1948), 239 pp.; Vol. II (1949), 950 pp.; Vol. III (1953), 606 pp.; Vol. IV (1954), 676 pp.
   [Volume I gives an account of the theoretical principles of analysis and of the various types of instrument. Volume II deals with inorganic analysis; Volumes III and IV are given over to organic analysis.]

51. Snodgrass, J. M., Carritt, D. E., and Wooster, W. S., 1954. 'Automatic servo-operated filter photometer.' *Analyt. Chem.,* **26,** 249–50.

52. Urbach, C., 1937. *Stufenphotometrische Trinkwasseranalyse.* Emil Haim & Co., Wien und Leipzig.

53. Wernimont, G., 1948. 'A proposed method of expressing extinction coefficients of photometric test methods.' Third Analytical Symposium, Analytical Division of Pittsburgh Section, American Chemical Society, February 1948. (See *Analyt. Chem.,* **20,** 277, 1948.)

54. Yoe, J. H., 1928. *Photometric Chemical Analysis.* John Wiley & Sons, Inc., New York. 2 vols., 771 and 337 pp.
   [This is similar in scope to Snell and Snell. Volume II is given

over to nephelometry. There is a good account of principles and old equipment and an extensive bibliography.]

55. Zworykin, V. K., and Ramberg, E. G., 1949. *Photo-electricity and its Application.* John Wiley & Sons, Inc., New York. 494 pp.
[An authoritative account of the subject: should be consulted for information, theoretical and practical, concerning the application of photocells.]

56. Zwicker, B. M. G., and Robinson R. J., 1944. 'The photometric determination of nitrate in sea water with a strychnidine reagent.' *J. Mar. Res.*, **5**, 214–32.

2

ERRORS AND PRECISION

The method of recording the precision—often incorrectly termed the accuracy—of an analytical method, has, in the past, varied greatly. Most frequently in reporting results, it is stated that they are accurate to, say, $\pm 1\%$; usually the level at which the analyses have been made is also stated or may be inferred from the data. Nevertheless, what is intended by such a statement is not always clear; it is usually taken to mean that on a series of test analyses carried out under the stated conditions of the method, replicate results have all been within $\pm 1\%$ of the average value or of an added known quantity. This type of statement, in spite of the statistical criticisms which follow, is meaningful to the practising analyst; to him with his background of technical experience, it expresses the range over which he would accept a result as reliable (4). For example, when material containing 100 mg. of a substance has been subject to replicate analyses, all the values have lain within 100 ± 1 mg., and if a value outside this range were obtained, it would be suspect; further, were two new samples analysed and the second differed from the first on analysis by much more than 1% the analyst would probably regard the samples as differing in their content of the substance in question; on the other hand, if a new method were being tested the analyst would expect his replicates to lie within the stated 1%. The expression $\pm 1\%$ is then a measure of the spread of the results, that is, the range, and if a sufficiently large number of test analyses have been made it may be a reasonably reliable one. It is not, however, a statistically efficient estimate of the range, and it is difficult to use for comparative purposes since, not only do more extreme values tend to be encountered as more observations are made, but also inferences regarding the range may easily be distorted by extreme values.

More recently, in analytical work, the mean deviation has been used to indicate precision; this is the average of all the deviations from the mean *irrespective of the sign of the differences*, i.e. $(\Sigma x - \bar{x})/n$, where x is an individual result, $\bar{x}$ is the mean and n the number of observations. Like the range, this mean deviation is a measure, and indeed a rather more satisfactory measure, of the spread of the results. While not entirely satisfactory, it may be used for comparative purposes for it does in fact indicate the region in which slightly more than half the results will fall on either side of the arithmetic mean.

60

These methods of expression should be discontinued and their place taken by more efficient statistics. (In subsequent sections it will not always be possible to indicate the precision in accordance with this suggestion since the practice has not yet been always adopted in published work.) When this is done it becomes possible to make exact predictions based on probability theory and to state the results rigorously.

Suppose the results of a large number of analyses carried out by the same technique on a given quantity of uniform material, are available. The total range of these results may be divided into equal sub-ranges or class-intervals; if the number of results falling within each of these class-intervals is arranged in ascending order of the latter, a frequency distribution is obtained. In general as the number of analyses considered become larger and larger and at the same time the width of each class-interval is made smaller and smaller, the frequency distribution of the results will approach a definite form known as the normal distribution. This is completely defined by two constants—the arithmetic mean and the standard deviation of the distribution. The arithmetic mean, μ, of the normal distribution approached in the above manner by the frequency distribution of the results of repeated analyses may be interpreted as the average result given by the technique employed. The standard deviation, σ, of this normal distribution measures the spread about the average of the results of repeated analyses and is a measure of the precision of the technique. Thus with a given technique it is possible to associate two constants, μ the mean of the technique and σ, the standard deviation (S.D.) of the technique. The square of the standard deviation is called the variance of the technique.

The two constants μ and σ associated with a technique define a normal distribution also associated with it. This means that it is possible to calculate the percentage of cases in which, in the long run, the result x of an analysis by a technique with mean μ and standard deviation σ will differ from μ by more than any stated fraction of σ. The quantity $d=(x-\mu)/\sigma$ is called the normal deviate. Table 3 (p. 278) has been prepared from which it is possible to determine the percentage of values for a normal distribution falling between any selected values of d. It is more useful for our purpose to calculate the proportion of observations which will exceed the true mean by a stated fraction of the standard deviation: an alternative Table (p. 278) for this is available. For example, it may be stated that 95% of all the values will lie between $\pm1\cdot96\sigma$ and 99% of the values between $\pm2\cdot58\sigma$ of the true mean μ.

It will be seen that since, in practice, the number of replicate analyses whose results are available is necessarily limited, the normal distribution approached by the frequency distribution of repeated analyses is never known exactly: i.e. the mean μ and standard deviation σ associated with a technique are never known precisely. It then becomes necessary to estimate the constants μ and σ from the limited number of replicate analyses available.

If n replicate analyses are available with results $x_1, x_2, ..., x_n$ then the best possible estimate of μ is $\bar{x} = (1/n)\Sigma x$ and the best possible estimate of σ is $s = \sqrt{\left\{\dfrac{1}{n-1}\Sigma(x-\bar{x})^2\right\}}$; $\bar{x}$ is the mean of a sample of n analyses and s the standard deviation of this sample (s^2 is termed the sample variance). Associated with the estimate s of σ is the number $(n-1)$ called the degrees of freedom of s. $\bar{x}$ and s vary from one sample of n analyses to another such sample. For most samples $\bar{x}$ will be relatively near μ and s will be relatively near σ. If n is very large, then the estimates $\bar{x}$ and s are so likely to be very close to μ and σ respectively that we may say we know effectively their values. Thus extended experience of an analytical technique may enable us to consider that we know its mean μ and standard deviation σ.

Now suppose we have a method of analysis and many replicate analyses on a given quantity of uniform material have shown the mean of the technique to be 100 mg. and its standard deviation ±6 mg. Then on 95% of occasions the result of analysis by this technique would lie between 88 and 112 mg., i.e. $100\pm2\times6$ mg. If a second analyst finds on repeating such an analysis that the result is 120 mg., then he may assume that he has not mastered the technique or that his materials and equipment have been at fault, for if he has mastered it and his materials are adequate there is only a 1 in 20 chance of his getting a result outside the range 88–112 mg. With the above result, there is only a 1 in 20 chance that his assumption of not having mastered the technique is wrong. The second analyst's result is said to be significantly different from the technique mean at the 5% (1 in 20) level of significance. Note that the choice of significance level is arbitrary. Generally either 5% or 1% is used.

The Comparison of Variances

It is now evident that a comparison of the precision of two methods should always be made by means of their standard deviations. If the results of all possible observations were available, i.e. the population values σ_1 and σ_2 were known, then any departure from unity in the ratio of the standard deviations would indicate a difference of precision. However, only an estimate, s, of σ is ordinarily available. It is usual to compare the estimated variances rather than the standard deviations, and tables are available of the variance ratio showing the percentage of trials in which a given ratio will be exceeded by chance, the tables being entered for the number of degrees of freedom upon which each variance estimate is based (Tables 6, 7, pp. 280–3).

For example, suppose we have two methods for estimating silicate; the standard deviation, at a given level of analysis, based upon ten estimations in each case is stated to be ± 6 units for the first method and ± 5 units for the second method; can the precision of the second method be said to exceed that of the first? Is it worth any extra labour involved in using the second method with its lower standard deviation? At the 5% probability level Table 7 (p. 282) gives a value of 3·18, when there are 9 degrees of freedom for each variance estimate, i.e. the ratio 3·18 will be exceeded 1 in 20 times by chance when the precision of the two methods is the same. The calculated variance ratio $6^2/5^2 = 36/25 = 1\cdot44$ does not exceed 3·18, and the precision of the second method cannot be considered greater than that of the first. It is also evident from the Table that for the second method to be considered better than the first (with the estimated variances again based on ten results) a standard deviation of less than $\pm 3\cdot36$ units $(36/s^2 = 3\cdot18)$ is required.

The Pooling of Variances

It is frequently not possible to make a long series of observations from which to calculate the variance of an estimate. If several sets are obtained, then, if they are not significantly different, they should be pooled to give a better estimate of the population variance. The pooled variance of the sets is

$$s^2_{pool} = \frac{\Sigma(x - \bar{x})^2 + \Sigma(y - \bar{y})^2 \ldots}{(n_1 - 1) + (n_2 - 1) \ldots}.$$

For example suppose two sets of ten replicates were made on 100 mg. of material and the variances in the two cases were 16 and 9 units. The ratio is 1·78 and as seen above the first cannot be considered significantly greater than the second. We should, therefore, pool the variances in order to get a better estimate of the population variance to compare, for example, with the variance of a second method. Thus, the pooled value would be

$$s^2_{pool} = \frac{(16 \times 9) + (9 \times 9)}{9 + 9} = 12\cdot5.$$

The Variance of Sums and Differences

The variance of the sum or difference of a series of independent measurements is the sum of their variance, thus

$$s_{x+y}^2 = s_x^2 + s_y^2 = s_{x-y}^2.$$

In the estimation of organic phosphorus in sea water total phosphorus and inorganic phosphorus are measured in separate aliquots of the sample and the organic phosphorus found by difference. The estimation of inorganic phosphate is usually made on board ship and is less precise than the laboratory estimation of the total phosphorus. Suppose at one place we find 100 units of inorganic phosphorus and 120 units of total phosphorus, and at a second place 100 units of the former and 115 units of the latter, with the standard deviation of the inorganic phosphorus estimation ± 5 units and that of the total phosphorus ± 3 units. The organic phosphorus by subtraction is 20 units at the first place and 15 units at the second; can these be considered significantly different? From the above statement the variance of the difference is given by $5^2 + 3^2 = 34$, so that the standard deviation is $\sqrt{34} = 5 \cdot 83$ and $\pm 2s$ is $\pm 11 \cdot 66$. Clearly the second organic phosphorus value cannot be considered significantly different from the first.

We may give another example: with simpler analytical methods the blank due to reagents alone is sufficiently constant to make no contribution to the precision of the actual estimation. When a complicated procedure is involved this may not be the case. Under these circumstances the contribution of the blank to the precision of the estimation may be calculated. If on replicate experiments the variance of the blank were 2 units and of the estimation, say, 4 units, then the precision of the estimate obtained by subtracting the blank from the actual value estimated would be $2^2 + 4^2 = 20$ units and its standard deviation 4·47 units.

The Difference between Means

(1) *Standard deviation of the technique known.* We have said above that the mean, $\bar{x}$, of a sample of n analyses by a given technique varies from sample to sample. Just as we associated a mean, μ, and standard deviation, σ, with an analytical technique, so we associate a mean and standard deviation with $\bar{x}$ the mean of a sample of n analyses. For a technique with mean μ and standard deviation σ, the mean of $\bar{x}$ is μ and its standard deviation is $\sigma/\sqrt{n}$. Also $\dfrac{x - \mu}{\sigma/\sqrt{n}}$ is a normal deviate and from tables of the normal deviate we can find, e.g. that 95% of the samples of n analyses will have means lying in the range $\mu \pm (2\sigma/\sqrt{n})$. The standard deviation of a mean is alternatively called its *standard error*.

Suppose now two samples, one of n_1 analyses and one of n_2 analyses by the same technique on the same material, have means $\bar{x}_1$ and $\bar{x}_2$ respectively. The standard error of $\bar{x}_1$ is $\sigma/\sqrt{n_1}$, that of $\bar{x}_2$

is $\sigma/\sqrt{n_2}$ and it follows that the standard error of the difference $\bar{x}_1 - \bar{x}_2$ is $\sigma\sqrt{(1/n_1 + 1/n_2)}$. Furthermore, the quantity $\dfrac{\bar{x}_1 - \bar{x}_2}{\sigma\sqrt{(1/n_1 + 1/n_2)}}$ is a normal deviate and we can say that 5% of pairs of samples, the first of n_1 analyses and the second of n_2 analyses will give a numerical value of $\bar{x}_1 - \bar{x}_2$ greater than $2\sigma\sqrt{(1/n_1 + 1/n_2)}$. This result can be used to compare two means.

For example extended experience of a nitrate method has shown its standard deviation to be ± 3 μg.-atom NO_3-N/l. Suppose the mean of a sample of six analyses at 5 m. is 60 μg.-atom NO_3-N/l and that of a sample of six analyses at 100 m. is 55 μg.-atom NO_3-N/l. Do these figures indicate any difference in nitrate content at the two depths?

If in fact the nitrate content is the same at both depths, then on only 5% of occasions will the difference in the means of two samples, each of six analyses, be greater than $2 \times 3\sqrt{(1/6 + 1/6)} = 3 \cdot 46$ μg.-atom NO_3-N/l. The actual difference in means found is 5 μg.-atom/l. So either the nitrate content is the same at both depths and an unusual event has occurred, or the nitrate content differs at the two depths. We accept the latter alternative and say that the sample means are significantly different at the 5% level.

(2) *Standard deviation of technique unknown.* When σ, the standard deviation of a technique is known we have seen that, if $\bar{x}$ is the mean of a sample of n analyses by the technique, the quantity $\dfrac{\bar{x} - \mu}{\sigma/\sqrt{n}}$ is a normal deviate.

If σ is not known, but only the sample standard deviation s (which estimates σ), then it is natural to consider the quantity $t = \dfrac{\bar{x} - \mu}{s/\sqrt{n}}$. t varies from one sample of n analyses to another, because of variations in *both* $\bar{x}$ and s, and t is not a normal deviate. The extent of the variation in t from one sample to another depends on $(n-1)$, the number of degrees of freedom associated with s. For each value of $n-1$, we can imagine associated with t a frequency distribution describing how t varies over a very large number of samples of n analyses, and tables of this distribution have been drawn up, for various values of $n-1$. From Table 5 (p. 279) we find, e.g. that if $n-1=5$, then only 5% of samples of six analyses will give a value of t numerically greater than $2 \cdot 575$ and only 1% a value of t numerically greater than $4 \cdot 035$. Thus we can conclude that for 95% of samples of six analyses the mean μ of the technique will lie in the interval $\bar{x} \pm 2 \cdot 575 s/\sqrt{6}$. If, for a particular sample of six analyses with mean $\bar{x}_0$ and standard deviation s_0, we state that μ lies in the interval

$\bar{x}_0 \pm 2 \cdot 575 s_0 / \sqrt{6}$, there is only a 5% chance of this statement being wrong.

If $n-1 > 30$ then t is nearly a normal deviate and we can obtain proportions from tables of the normal deviate. Similarly in comparing the means $\bar{x}_1$ and $\bar{x}_2$ of two samples of n_1 and n_2 analyses, respectively, it is natural to use the quantity $t = \dfrac{\bar{x}_1 - \bar{x}_2}{s\sqrt{(1/n_1 + 1/n_2)}}$, where s is a pooled estimate of the standard deviation σ of the analytical technique. Thus

$$s^2{}_{\text{pool}} = \left(\frac{1}{n_1 + n_2 - 2}\right)\left[(n_1 - 1)s_1{}^2 + (n_2 - 1)s_2{}^2\right],$$

where s_1 and s_2 are the sample standard deviations. The number of degrees of freedom associated with s_{pool} is $n_1 + n_2 - 2$.

Suppose in the above example on a nitrate method, the standard deviation of the method had not been known to be ± 3 μg.-atom NO_3-N/l but the sample variances $s_1{}^2$ and $s_2{}^2$ were known to be 16·0 and 9·0 respectively. Then the pooled estimate of σ^2 is

$$s^2{}_{\text{pool}} = \left(\frac{1}{6 + 6 - 2}\right)\left[(5 \times 16) + (5 \times 9)\right] = \frac{125}{10}$$

and

$$t = \frac{60 - 55}{\sqrt{(125/10)}\sqrt{(1/6 + 1/6)}} = 2\cdot 45.$$

We find from tables of t, entered with 10 degrees of freedom, that 5% of pairs of samples of six analyses of uniform material will give values of t greater than 2·28. Hence the value of t obtained is significant at the 5% level, i.e. we conclude that there is a difference in nitrate content at the two depths.

It cannot be emphasised too strongly that the above argument only applies to deductions concerning the solutions analysed—as they stand, so to speak, on the bench; we are only considering the precision of the analytical techniques. There will also be sampling variations when these water samples are drawn from a water mass; replicate analyses of a single outside sample cannot increase our information regarding the primary sampling variations and if the latter are large it is generally advisable to replicate the primary samples rather than replicate the analyses on a single primary sample.

Errors contributing to the Overall Precision of Analysis

Before considering the contribution of various common sources of error to the overall precision of an analytical method we must stress that we are dealing, in the first place, only with its variability as defined above, i.e. by its standard deviation; Conway (1) calls this the variable error. In addition to this variability, the mean of a series of analyses may differ constantly from the amount of added material. Thus when 100 mg. are taken for analysis a return of 105 $\pm$ 2 mg. (S.D.) may be obtained in a series of replicate test runs. Statistically this is bias; Conway calls it the constant error, and others refer to it as a systematic error. It is quite a different category of error from variability; it may be caused, for example, by basing the calculations on a '10 ml.' pipette which delivers, say, 10·1 ml., or by always over-shooting an end-point in a titration to the same amount. This type of error will be considered separately.

The precision of an analytical technique as indicated by its standard deviation is determined by errors arising from all possible sources throughout the analysis. We may divide these errors into those associated with the equipment and those arising from the chemical reactions involved in the analytical procedure. Equipment errors may result either from faults inherent in the construction of instruments and apparatus or from personal errors in their use. Chemical errors may be taken to include those which are purely manipulative such as contamination or loss due to improper working conditions, as well as more strictly chemical errors such as are inherent in the chemistry of the reactions involved; for example, incomplete precipitation, volatility (as in the case of reactions involving iodine) and difficulty of judging the end-point in a titration, will all lead to variability (and indeed may also give rise to bias). The contribution to the total variability of any of these sources of error may be determined by an appropriately designed set of experiments, followed by a so-called variance analysis, but it will suffice to consider two pieces of equipment—pipettes and burettes—whose use is common to so much analytical work. The following treatment follows closely that of Conway (1), from whom most of the figures quoted are taken and to whom reference should be made for a further consideration of the problems dealt with below; he also gives an extension of the arguments to techniques using very small quantities.

We must stress the previous statement that the contributions of several uncorrelated sources of error is determined by the addition rule for variances:

$$s^2{}_{\text{total}} = s_1{}^2 + s_2{}^2.$$

It will often be found convenient, especially when comparing the performance of different sizes of similar equipment, to use the coefficient of variation (C.V.) rather than the standard deviation, where

$$C = \frac{s}{v} \times 100\%.$$

This gives the precision relative to the working level. (C will be used throughout for the coefficient of variation.) This is clearly a more useful estimate when comparing, for example, the precision of delivery of, say, a 10 ml. and a 1 ml. pipette.

In general these variable errors are normally distributed but it must be pointed out that some of them (if considered separately) give a rectangular distribution. The standard deviation of a rectangular distribution is $s = l/\sqrt{12}$, where l is the length of the rectangle. The variances of such distributions may be added as for normal distributions, but the same conclusions cannot be drawn regarding the distribution of sample values and means of samples, because the probability of an observation falling in any part of the range is the same over the whole range, l, of a rectangular distribution. However, the summation of a number of rectangular distributions rapidly approaches a normal distribution, and without significantly affecting our deductions the variable error may, therefore, be considered as a normal distribution.

PIPETTES

Overall Precision

In delivering fluid from a pipette the chief sources of variability arise from:

1. the amount of fluid left on the walls;
2. the adhesion of droplets to the tip;
3. the adjustment of the meniscus to the mark.

Even gross maladjustment of the meniscus, for example ± 1 mm. in a 2 ml. standard pipette, will only affect the total standard deviation by 10%; with normal precautions the meniscus can easily be adjusted to within a tenth of this range and the error from this source may, therefore, be neglected. The other two errors are related to the mode of use of the pipette, about which there has been much argument and not a little confusion. Three methods are commonly used; after normal flow from the pipette has ceased:

(a) the tip is pressed against the glass wall of the receiving vessel immediately on cessation of delivery and the drop blown out sharply, rotating the tip in contact with the glass then quickly withdrawing;

(b) the tip is held for 15 seconds at a slight angle to the wall of the container and then withdrawn;

(c) the tip is held for 15 seconds just touching the fluid into which delivery has been made and then withdrawn.

Conway (*loc. cit.*) has shown that the first two methods give almost identical variances whilst that from (*c*) is greater. In general (*a*) saves time and should be adopted.

An estimate of this variability may readily be obtained for moderate-sized pipettes by weighing the water from replicate deliveries of the pipette, the water temperature being maintained uniform throughout. With small pipettes a titration method is used: successive deliveries from, say, a 0·1 ml. pipette, are made with N hydrochloric acid and each delivery titrated with carbonate-free 0·1 N alkali from a 2 ml. burette. This is repeated with a 1 ml. pipette (whose precision is known by the method of weighing) using this time 0·1 N-HCl but again titrating the deliveries with 0·1 N alkali. Only the delivery errors then enter the calculation since all other errors are the same. We have,

$$C_{p_1}^2 - C_{p_2}^2 = C_{t_1}^2 - C_{t_2}^2, \qquad \ldots (1)$$

where the C_p's are the coefficients of variation for the two pipettes and the C_t's are those of the actual titrations. From this C_{p_1}, the coefficient of variation of the 0·1 ml. pipette may be calculated. Furthermore,

$$s_p = C_p \cdot v,$$

where v is the mean volume of delivery and s_p its standard deviation.

If v, as is usual, is expressed in ml. and s_p in c.mm. this becomes

$$s_p = 10 \cdot v \cdot C_p. \qquad \ldots (2)$$

Conway (1) has shown that the total variable error of 25, 5 and 2 ml. Grade A (National Physical Laboratory) pipettes, with tips whose terminal surface are at right angles to the axis, is given by the relation

$$s_p = 1 \cdot 3v, \qquad \ldots (3)$$

where v is expressed in millilitres.

Factors Contributing to the Overall Precision

The important factor determining this overall variability is the liquid left on the walls of the pipette and Conway has shown that provided the meniscus does not fall faster than 15 cm./sec. the standard deviation is proportional to the wall fluid, with

$$s_p = 0 \cdot 05 f_p, \qquad \ldots (4)$$

where f_p is the wall fluid in c.mm.

The amount of wall fluid is a function of:

(*a*) the delivery time;
(*b*) the internal surface;
(*c*) the bore of the tube.

Conway has found that the wall fluid is inversely proportional to the square root of the delivery time, and for any given pipette

$$f_w = \frac{a}{\sqrt{t}}, \qquad \qquad ...(5)$$

where a is a constant dependent upon the shape and size of the bulb of the pipette. For a standard 25 ml. pipette a is about 580 c.mm., t being expressed in seconds.

The delivery time should therefore be as slow as reasonable; further there is no point in allowing long after-drainage periods if the delivery time is kept constant. It is simplest to adopt procedure (*a*) already given (*see* p. 68) and blow out. The use of increased delivery time to improve the precision, especially of a micro-pipette, should always be borne in mind: with very rapid delivery, the precision with such pipettes may only be 0·4%, but by increasing the delivery time to about 40 seconds for a meniscus descent of 16 cm. this precision may be increased to the order of 0·03%. The wall error may of course be eliminated by rinsing the pipette about five times, although care should be taken that titration errors are not thereby increased as a result of the increased volume of liquid which it will be necessary to titrate.

Temperature affects the amount of wall fluid, but within normal working limits the error is negligible (note this is not true of the effect of temperature on the bias or mean volume delivered).

BURETTES

Analogous to the pipette there are delivery errors; in addition, however, the meniscus must be adjusted at the beginning and read at the end of a titration. These constitute manipulative errors. To these must be added the end-point emergence error.

The Delivery Error

As with a pipette this is determined largely by the fluid left on the walls which in turn is a function of the delivery time, the rate of fall of the meniscus and the bore of the burette. Conway has shown that, as with a pipette, the amount of wall fluid is inversely proportional to the time of delivery and that the relation between wall fluid, time of meniscus descent, and tube bore is given by the equation

$$q = 1·1 \sqrt{\frac{d}{t}}, \qquad \qquad ...(6)$$

where q is the c.mm. of wall fluid per sq. cm. surface, t the time in seconds for 1 cm. descent of the meniscus, and d the bore in cm. The total amount left on the walls is

$$q_t = \pi \cdot d \cdot l \times 1 \cdot 1 \sqrt{\frac{d}{t}}$$

$$= \frac{3 \cdot 45 \cdot d^{1 \cdot 5} \cdot l}{\sqrt{t}}, \qquad \ldots(7)$$

where l is the length of the tube. Hence, per sq. cm. of surface, from equations (4) and (6),

$$s_b = 0 \cdot 05 \times 1 \cdot 1 \sqrt{\frac{d}{t}}$$

$$= 0 \cdot 055 \sqrt{\frac{d}{t}}. \qquad \ldots(8)$$

The coefficient of variation is

$$C_b = \frac{0 \cdot 022}{\sqrt{dt}}. \qquad \ldots(9)$$

Equation 9 is fundamental to the design of precision burettes; the relative delivery error remains unchanged if the rate of meniscus descent is altered in an inverse relation to the tube diameter. It is also evident from this statement that errors will result if the titration fluid is run out at different rates (varying t in the above equations) by adjusting the cock during titration; for accurate work the tap should be fully open; this requires a knowledge of the approximate position of the end-point.

After-drainage Time and Precision

After closing the cock, the liquid will drain down the walls of the burette, and the meniscus will rise. Drainage is slow at first, then rises and later falls off (3). Such after-drainage has no significant effect on the variable error if the burette is read immediately after delivery. For example, even at a fast rate of delivery (18 seconds for a full 50 ml. burette) no significant drainage takes place during the first 30 seconds (Lindner and Haslwanter, 2). With a delivery time of 40 seconds no appreciable drainage occurs in the first two minutes.

With micro-burettes the after-drainage error becomes more important; the absolute drainage error is increased per unit surface and this must be considered relative to the total volume delivered; reduction of drainage errors is one of the major advantages of the horizontal Rehberg-type micro-burette.

The Manipulative Error of the Burette: the End-point Emergence

For a 50 ml. burette the end-point emergence is usually taken as 1 drop, which with a well-made tip should not exceed about 40 c.mm. With micro-burettes, the use of a drop as a unit should be avoided completely. With a suitable tip, fractions of drops are easy to manipulate and with a well-made 2 ml. burette an end-point emergence of 4 c.mm. may be obtained.

It is easier to adjust a meniscus to a given mark than to read its position between two divisions. The manipulative error *per se* is distributed in the rectangular form but, as measured, other small errors, such as lack of discernment of the bottom of the meniscus and initial adjustment errors contribute to it, so that in practice it may be treated as normal variable. Indeed, the total manipulation error including the end-point emergence error may be treated together. It may be pointed out that avoidance of parallax errors and the use of a uniform background are two essentials for the accurate reading of a burette. This total manipulative error is clearly independent of the total fluid delivered and is relatively greater, therefore, with small volumes.

The Combined Delivery and Manipulative Error

As has been seen, the magnitude of the delivery error is proportional to the volume delivered but, by contrast, that of the manipulation error is independent of this volume: stated as percentages the converse is of course true: the manipulation error may always be expressed in c.mm. For the total of these two errors, we have

$$C_b{}^2 = C_d{}^2 + \left(\frac{s_m}{10v}\right)^2, \qquad \ldots(10)$$

where C_b is the coefficient of variation of delivery plus manipulation, C_d is that for delivery, s_m is the standard deviation for manipulation, expressed in c.mm., and v is in ml. It should be remembered that

$$C_d = \frac{0 \cdot 022}{\sqrt{dt}}.$$

Clearly the relative contributions of these two sources of error will vary according to the volume of the liquid delivered, and a comparison is given in the following Table I for a 50 ml. standard burette with a meniscus descent of 1 cm. per second and a 2 ml. Bang burette, bore 0·24 cm. also with a meniscus descent of 1 cm. per second.

TABLE I (*adapted from Conway, 1*)

Factors	Burette	
	50 ml.	2 ml. Bang
C_d	0·021	0·045
Manipulation error	15 c.mm.	1·3 c.mm.
Volume required for delivery error to equal manipulation error	72 ml.	3 ml .
Volume required for delivery error to equal ½ manipulation error	36 ml.	1·5 ml.
Volume when manipulation error dominant	0–36 ml.	0–1·5 ml.

THE TOTAL VARIABLE GLASS ERROR IN A TITRATION

The total variable glass error of a titration is given by,

$$C_g{}^2 = C_p{}^2 + C_d{}^2 + \left(\frac{s_m}{10v}\right)^2, \qquad \ldots(11)$$

where C_p=C.V. of pipette error, C_d=C.V. of delivery error of burette, s_m=manipulation error of burette in c.mm., and v=volume delivered in titration (ml.).

Values for a standard 50 ml. burette with glass tap and the 2 ml. Bang burette are given in Table II when used over 50% of their range (25 and 1·0 ml.) to titrate the delivery from a 25 and 1·0 ml. pipette respectively.

TABLE II (*adapted from Conway, 1*)

Factors	Burette	
	50 ml. burette 25 ml. pipette (25 ml. used in titration)	2 ml. Bang burette 1 ml. standard pipette (1 ml. used in titration)
C_p%	0·025	0·13
C_d%	0·022	0·045
s_m (c.mm.)	15	1·3
C_g%	0·07	0·19

It is clear that with a 50 ml. burette the most important error is that of manipulation namely, 0·06%: by increasing the volume used in the titration to 45 ml. this error could be reduced to about one-half of this (0·033%) and the total glass error to 0·047%. To fill the burette twice would increase the error in the all-important meniscus adjustments; the practical way to increase the accuracy is to reduce the manipulation error by lowering the end-point emergence error using fractions of a drop. If this is reduced to half a drop the total error with a 25 ml. delivery would be reduced from 0·07 to 0·05% and with a 45 ml. delivery from 0·05 to 0·04%.

For a 2-ml. Bang burette (with a meniscus descent of 1 cm. per second) and a 1 ml. standard pipette with a delivery of 1 ml., i.e. 50% of the burette, the total glass error is 0·19% (C.V.), i.e. three times that of the preceding technique. Two steps may be taken, quite simply, to bring the precision of this latter technique close to that of the former. First, the large manipulation error must be reduced. This may be easily brought from 1·3 c.mm. to 0·7 c.mm. by employing a sufficiently fine tip. Secondly, the pipette error may be reduced by lowering the drainage time. This also may easily be done; for example, a straight tube pipette (16 cm. long) delivering 0·7 ml. in 40 seconds will do so with a precision of 0·029%, so that with a burette precision of 0·045% and a manipulation precision of 0·7 c.mm. (with 1·5 ml. used in the titration), the total glass error would then become 0·068%, i.e. identical with that of the 50–25 ml. technique when one drop is taken as the end-point emergence.

THE CONSTANT GLASS ERRORS

So far we have only dealt with the precision; unless the calibration figure of the makers is accepted the volume contained or delivered by the glassware must be determined. Any difference from the assumed mean, or the specified volume, is constant bias.

The constant error, if any, is usually determined by measuring the weight of water delivered or contained by the apparatus when used under the standard conditions. Five replicates are sufficient for this purpose. It is only then necessary to apply the appropriate corrections for temperature to obtain the density of the water. These corrections are as follows:

1. *The density correction.* If the weight of a given volume of water *in vacuo* is W, then,

$$V = \frac{W}{\rho}, \qquad \qquad ...(12)$$

where V is the volume and ρ is the specific gravity. ρ is frequently written as $(1 - S/100)$ so that

$$V = W \left(1 + \frac{S}{100}\right). \qquad \qquad ...(13)$$

2. *The air displacement correction.* The weight in air will always be smaller than the weight *in vacuo* by the weight of the air displaced

by the water in excess of that by the brass weights. This correction, though small is larger than appears, being 0·1 % of the total weight. If V is the volume of water then $V(1-\rho_w/\rho_b)$ is the volume of air displaced, where ρ_w is the density of water and ρ_b is the density of the brass weights. This volume of air multiplied by the density of the air (ρ) at the given temperature and barometric pressure will give the necessary correction.

The full expression for the weight of air displaced by 100 ml. of water in excess of that of the weights then becomes

$$a=100(1-\rho_w/\rho_b)\times\rho_a\times\frac{273}{T}\times\frac{P}{760}, \qquad \ldots(14)$$

where ρ_a is the density of air at $0°$C., and T and P are the absolute temperature and the barometric pressure ($\rho_b=8\cdot4$ and $\rho_a=0\cdot00129$). For ordinary purposes, differences of barometric pressure may be neglected and the volume of the water may be taken as equal to the weight of the water. Tables of the correction, a, are available. (In Table 8, p. 284, a is given per 100 g. of water, i.e. 100 times that for 1 g. water.) The equation may now be written

$$V=W_a\left(1+\frac{S+a}{100}\right), \qquad \ldots(15)$$

where W_a is now the weight in air and V the volume.

3. *The correction for the expansion of glass.* The volume delivered or contained varies with the temperature as a result of the expansion of the glass and the glassware should, therefore, be standardized at a known temperature and the results expressed at an arbitrary standard temperature usually taken as $20°$C. The coefficient of cubical expansion of glass is $0\cdot000026$ per ml. per $°$C. so that for V ml. at $t°$ we have for the excess volume at $20°$ C,

$$(20-t°)\times0\cdot000026V,$$

and for 100 ml., i.e. 100 g. practically of water

$$(20-t°)\times0\cdot0026. \qquad \ldots(16)$$

The volume now becomes

$$V=W_a\left(1+\frac{S+a+g}{100}\right), \qquad \ldots(17)$$

and g has been tabulated. For most practical purposes it may be neglected.

4. *The correction for changes of wall fluid with temperature.* This error applies only to delivery apparatus and not to volumetric flasks which are made up to a mark. The residual wall fluid increases as the

temperature decreases because of an increase in the viscosity of the fluid. For every 100 ml. delivered the wall fluid decreases 0·0064 ml. for each degree rise in temperature (*see* Table 8, p. 284, correction *f*). The basic equation then is

$$V = W_a\left(1 + \frac{S+a+g+f}{100}\right). \qquad \ldots(18)$$

The following types of observations require different corrections; these are now listed for convenience (Table 9, p. 285).

(i) Actual volume of a weighed quantity of water at any room temperature.

Here *S*, the density correction, and *a*, the air displacement correction, have to be considered. Both are positive; hence

$$V = W_a\left(1 + \frac{\alpha}{100}\right), \qquad \ldots(19)$$

where $\alpha = S + a$.

(ii) Standardization to 20°C. of a volumetric flask, the weight of the filling being taken at *t*°, a different temperature.

The coefficients *S*, *a* and *g*, must all be considered. The sign of *g* in the equation (20) below is kept positive by adjusting the sign in the table according to whether *t* is greater or less than 20°C. We have then

$$V = W_a\left(1 + \frac{\beta}{100}\right), \qquad \ldots(20)$$

where β is $(S + a + g)$.

(iii) Standardization of pipette or burette mean delivery at a temperature *t*°C. to a standard temperature of 20°C. Here *S*, *a*, *g* and *f* must be considered, so that,

$$V = W_a\left(1 + \frac{\gamma}{100}\right), \qquad \ldots(21)$$

where γ is $(S + a + g + f)$.

(iv) A volumetric flask standardized for 20°C. is used at some other temperature, *t*°; the volume correction is wanted.

The sum of the corrections for (iv) and (ii) must give that for (i). Hence

$$V_t = V_{20}\left(1 + \frac{\delta}{100}\right), \qquad \ldots(22)$$

where δ is $(S + a) - (S + a + g) = -g$.

(v) A pipette or burette standardized for 20°C. is used at some other temperature *t*°; the volume correction for delivery is required.

Here as with (iv) the sum of the corrections in (ii) and (v) must give that in (i), so that we may write

$$V_t = V_{20}\left(1 + \frac{\varepsilon}{100}\right),$$

where ε is $(S+a)-(S+a+g+f)$ or $-(f+g)$.

The values of α, β, γ, δ and ε are entered in Table 9 (p. 285) against temperature.

For all except the highest standard of working α is the only correction that need be applied, so that for β and γ we may write α and consider δ and ε as negligible. α is of course the percentage factor for converting a weighed quantity of water to a volume under stated conditions of temperature and pressure.

REFERENCES

There are many books of general statistical methods; Fisher, R. A., *Statistical Methods for Research Workers*, (Oliver and Boyd); Snedecor, G. W., *Statistical Methods*, (Iowa State College Press); Yule, G. U., and Kendall, M. G., *An Introduction to the Theory of Statistics*, (Griffin & Co., Ltd.) are well known standard texts.

1. Conway, E. J., 1939. *Microdiffusion Analysis and Volumetric Error.* Crosby Lockwood and Son, Ltd., London. Second edition, 1947, 357 pp.
2. Lindner, J., and Haslwanter, F., 1929. 'Über den Einfluss der Ablaufzeit und des Nachlaufes auf die Messungen mit Büretten.' *Z. angew. Chem.*, **42**, 821–5.
3. Stott, V., 1928. *Volumetric Glassware.* Witherby, London, 232 pp.
4. Youden, W. J., 1951. *Statistical Methods for Chemists.* John Wiley & Sons, Inc., New York, 126 pp.

3

THE CALCULATION OF RESULTS: CALIBRATION CURVES

A great number of the methods to be described are absorptiometric and to save repetition under each section, the method of calculating the results is given here.

Visual Comparison Methods

The balancing method is most frequently employed, and whether this is done with a Duboscq type colorimeter (as in Harvey's method for nitrate) or with Hehner cylinders, the principles involved are the same. If at balance

L_1=length of column of known concentration, c_1,

L_2=length of column of unknown concentration, c_2

then

$a_s L_1 c_1 = a_s L_2 c_2$, where a_s is the absorbancy index so that

$$c_2 = \frac{L_1 c_1}{L_2},$$

from which c_2 may be calculated.

It is usually necessary to correct for colour either inherent in the reagents alone or developed by them as a result of impurities: blank values must be determined. For this purpose comparison must be made with very dilute standards.

In the first instance, assume that the blank is due to the reagents only. Suppose that to 98 ml. of a standard solution of the substance under test containing x μg.-atom/l. and to 98 ml. of distilled water are added in each case 2 ml. of a reagent, and the two solutions are then matched in 100 ml. Hehner cylinders. Let the standard match 100 ml. of the distilled water blank at l. If Δx is the equivalent of the blank in μg.-atom/l., then the true content of the cylinder containing the standard is $x+\Delta x$ μg.-atom/l. and of the distilled water cylinder Δx μg.-atom/l.

$$\frac{\Delta x}{x+\Delta x} = \frac{l}{100}$$

or

$$\Delta x = \frac{l.x}{100-l},$$

from which Δx may be calculated.

78

Suppose now an unknown solution (y μg.-atom/l.) be matched against a standard in distilled water containing x_1 μg.-atom/l., 2 ml. of reagent being added to 98 ml. of solution in each case. Let the solutions match at 100 ml. of standard to l_1 of unknown.

The blank value Δx is present in both standard and unknown, hence

$$\frac{y+\Delta x}{100}=\frac{x_1+\Delta x}{l_1},$$

so that when Δx has been determined as above, y, the unknown, may be calculated.

Under certain circumstances both the distilled water in which the standards are made up and the reagents, which are added to both solutions, may make a contribution to the blank. The distilled water will not contribute to the unknown when the latter is a natural water sample and the blanks must therefore be evaluated separately.

Let the procedure be carried out as above, all concentrations being expressed in the same units, and also

Δx=blank due to distilled water,

Δy=blank due to reagents,

l_1=reading of standard (concentration x_2)

again 100 for distilled water + reagents.

Then

$$\frac{l_1}{100}=\frac{\Delta x+\Delta y}{x_2+\Delta x+\Delta y}.$$

Clearly both Δx and Δy cannot be obtained from this one equation and it is necessary to match the distilled water plus reagents against a second dilute standard solution x_3. Let this match the distilled water plus reagents at l_2. Then

$$\frac{l_2}{100}=\frac{\Delta x+\Delta y}{x_3+\Delta x+\Delta y}.$$

We now have two equations and Δx and Δy may be separately evaluated.

It may of course be found that Δx or Δy or even both are negligible. Assuming this is not so, and that a distilled water standard containing p units is matched at 100 by a sea-water sample of unknown value q units at l_3. Then

$$\frac{l_3}{100}=\frac{p+\Delta x+\Delta y}{q+\Delta y},$$

from which q may be determined if Δx and Δy have been evaluated as described above.

The method is straightforward when the colour developed in distilled water is qualitatively and quantitatively identical with that developed in sea-water solutions of similar concentration to the standard. If this is not so, then the values obtained by comparing unknowns developed in sea water with standards prepared in distilled water will be subject to a so-called salt-error, for which a correction must be applied. The appropriate correction factor must be determined by comparing the increment obtained by adding a known quantity of the solute to sea water with that given by the addition of the same increment to distilled water.

Suppose we have sea water with moderately low content of the unknown, x_4 which balances at 60 against 100 of a standard solution in distilled water containing x_5 units. We now increase the concentration x_4 by a small increment $\Delta_1 x$ (best added by a micro-pipette so as to leave the volume virtually unchanged). Let the two solutions now match at 50 to 100 of standard. The same increment $\Delta_1 x$ is added to the distilled water standard which is compared with the original; let it match at 80 to 100 of the original.

Now, neglecting any blank corrections,

$$\frac{x_4}{x_5}=\frac{100}{60}=1\cdot 67$$

and

$$\frac{x_4+\Delta_1 x}{x_5}=\frac{100}{50}=2\cdot 0.$$

For the distilled water comparison

$$\frac{x_5+\Delta_1 x}{x_5}=\frac{100}{80}=1\cdot 25.$$

In the first comparison $\Delta_1 x=0\cdot 33 x_5$ and in the second, $0\cdot 25 x_5$. The salt-error factor is therefore, $0\cdot 33/0\cdot 25=1\cdot 32$. All values obtained by comparing sea water with distilled water standards must be corrected by this factor. In theory blank corrections should be applied to the above results, but the difference between the blank in sea water compared with that in distilled water is neglected.

If sea water free from the component for which the analyses are being made is available, it is of course simpler to make the standards up in it, in which case the salt-error does not come into question.

ABSORPTIOMETERS
AND SPECTROPHOTOMETERS

When an absorptiometer or spectrophotometer is used, the results are frequently evaluated from a calibration curve. This is set up by determining the transmission values of a series of solutions of the substance in question at graded concentrations with a stated wavelength setting (or filter) in an optical cell of given length. The transmission measurements are usually made against the pure solvent. A curve is then constructed in which transmission values are plotted against the concentration of the substance; once the transmission value of a solution has been determined its concentration may be obtained by reference to such a working curve. The actual form in which the transmission values are recorded depends upon the instrument used; the concentrations may be read off a working curve in which the transmission values are plotted in any convenient units. It is usually most convenient to plot such a calibration curve in terms of absorbancies because, when the Bouguer-Lambert-Beer Law is valid, a linear relation exists between concentration and absorbancy (*see* p. 21). An example is given in Table I. In this calibration, the instrument has been set at 0·400, a point appropriate to the concentrations being used in this particular series.

TABLE I

Instrument set at 0·400

Concentration μg./l	Reading	Transmittancy	Absorbancy
0	0·400	1·00	0·00
0·5	0·328	0·82	0·15
1·0	0·208	0·52	0·30
1·5	0·140	0·35	0·45
2·0	0·088	0·22	0·60

Instead of having to read the concentration of an unknown from a calibration curve it is convenient when the relation is linear to calculate the absorbancy index or, if a constant cell length is employed for a series of estimations, a factor $1/b.a_s$. Since (*see* p. 21)

$$a_s = A_s/b.c$$

$$= \log_{10} \frac{1}{T_s} \div b.c,$$

where a_s is the absorbancy index, A_s is the absorbancy ($=\log_{10} 1/T_s$),

b is the cell length, and c is the concentration of the solution; then

$$c = \frac{1}{b \cdot a_s} \cdot \log_{10} \frac{1}{T_s},$$

so that the concentration corresponding to any transmittancy is readily calculated.

In order to avoid estimating a blank, some workers measure transmittancies against distilled water plus reagents rather than against distilled water (or solvent). This may be considered bad practice: it is better to estimate the blank separately and subtract its absorbancy from that of the absorbancy of a given solution before either plotting the calibration curve or calculating the absorbancy index. The latter is then given by

$$a_s = \left(\log_{10} \frac{1}{T_s} - \log_{10} \frac{1}{T_B} \right) \div b \cdot c,$$

where T_B is the transmittancy of the blank. A blank is then run for each series of estimations; in this way any serious contamination of the reagents between sets of estimations, any long-term trend in the reagent blank due to changes in the reagents, reaction with containers or their contamination, are more easily detected. In addition to the reagent blank, absorption may arise from turbidity present in the raw sample; a blank should always be determined, therefore, before addition of the reagents and in calculating the result this value is added to that for the reagents (T_B).

Frequently the intensity of colour depends upon the temperature of the solution so that, unless the test solutions are always kept at the same temperature as that at which the calibration was set up, a correction must be applied to the results. This must be particularly borne in mind in marine work where estimations are done on board ship and deep-water samples may have a different temperature from surface samples or the ambient temperature of the laboratory. In order to determine a temperature-correction curve, calibration curves are constructed for, say, three known temperatures. It is then possible to determine the relation between the absorbancy index at any temperature in relation to the standard curve at one temperature. It is usually a linear relation of the type

$$(a_s)_{t_1} = P(a_s)_{t_2} + K.$$

In the estimation of the concentration of an unknown measured at a given temperature the absorbancy index is first calculated from the measured transmittancy; the temperature correction is then applied to give the absorbancy index at the standard temperature, from which the concentration may be calculated.

If the method is subject to a salt-error and the calibration is set up using distilled water solutions then a correction must be applied to determinations in sea water; the same procedure as already described for visual comparators may be used. The increment in absorbancy for a known addition to sea water and to distilled water is determined, and all sea-water absorbancies to be read against a distilled-water calibration multiplied by the factor obtained from these incremental additions. It is simpler to set up the original calibration in sea water free from (or low in) the constituent being determined. The concentration-absorbancy curve will not pass through the origin but will cut the absorbancy axis at the concentration of the constituent in sea water used. The slope of the curve is, however, unchanged and from this the absorbancy index may be calculated. Sodium chloride solutions, or artificial sea water (according to the source of the salt-error) may be used to replace sea water for such calibration if they can be freed of the constituent being estimated; trouble is frequently encountered, however, because of impurities in the materials used.

4

CHLORINITY (‰)

Because of its complex composition, the total quantity of dissolved solids in any given sample of sea water is difficult to determine by direct analysis, and reproducible results are not obtained by evaporative methods. These difficulties have been avoided by an arbitrary definition of the total salt content, termed the salinity (S‰). This was originally defined as the weight in g. (*in vacuo*) of the solids that can be obtained from 1 kg. of sea water (likewise measured *in vacuo*), when all the carbonate has been converted to oxide, the bromine and iodine replaced by chlorine, all organic matter oxidized and the remainder dried at 480°C. to constant weight.

Dittmar (5) established that the ratio between the concentrations of the major ions was constant and independent of the total salt content in ocean water unaffected by land drainage (*see* below); the estimation of a single constituent will, therefore, suffice to determine the total salt content. The major 'constituent' most easily estimated is the silver-precipitable halides, which may be determined directly by titration with silver nitrate, using potassium chromate as indicator. A factor, termed the chlorinity (Cl‰), was therefore defined as the weight in g. (*in vacuo*) of the chloride ion contained in 1 kg. of sea water (likewise measured *in vacuo*) when all the bromide and iodide ions have been replaced by chloride ion. To the above definition must be added a proviso that the reference standard is Normal Water (*see* below), and the titration result must be calculated using Knudsen's Hydrographical Tables (14). The following equation was established to express the relation between salinity and chlorinity:

$$S‰ = 0 \cdot 03 + (1 \cdot 805 \times Cl‰). \qquad \qquad \ldots(1)$$

It will readily be appreciated that this definition of salinity introduces a chlorine equivalent dependent upon the atomic weights of the elements present in the standard solution. In oceanography we are interested in widely separated areas and in making comparisons between the salinity at different places and different depths, often over long intervals of time. It is, therefore, essential that the apparent chlorinity of the oceans shall not vary as any revisions of atomic weights affect the appropriate gravimetric factors used in its calculation. This can only be done by maintaining an international standard for chlorinity that is independent of atomic weight changes; it has been effected in the past by standardization of all solutions against so-called Normal Water (*Eau de Mer Normale*), which has its chlorinity adjusted to about 19·4‰, and which is accurately standardized either directly or indirectly against the 1902 standard on which equation (1) was based. This standard sea water is prepared and distributed by the Hydrographic Laboratories at Copenhagen. More recently Jacobsen and Knudsen (9) have established a permanent standard for chlorinity by standardizing Normal Water against the mass of silver required completely to precipitate the halogens in 1 kg. of such water. On the basis of this work a new definition of chlorinity may be given; the number giving the chlorinity in grams per kilogram of sea-water sample is identical with the number giving the mass in grams of 'atomic weight silver' just necessary to precipitate the halogens in 0·3285233 kg. of the sample of sea water. This new definition makes the chlorinity independent of any atomic weight changes, and the empirically established relation (equation 1) between salinity and chlorinity still remains valid.

THE TITRATION METHOD FOR CHLORINITY

The standard method for estimating chlorinity is titration by the Mohr method, that is, with silver nitrate using potassium chromate as indicator, and taking Normal Water as standard reference substance; the results are calculated using the Tables of Knudsen (14). We shall only consider this method; alternative methods and those employing continuous reading instruments will be dealt with elsewhere.

As already stated the method is empirical and it cannot be rigorously checked by an alternative method as a matter of routine. Meticulous attention to detail is therefore essential if results of the required accuracy are to be obtained; furthermore it is essential that all laboratories should adopt a standard procedure so that all results will be comparable. Detailed instructions have been published by Thomsen (21), and these will be quoted in the following account, and supplemented particularly by the remarks of King (13), which are based on many thousands of samples analysed in the Government Laboratory, London.

The principle of the method consists in taking equal volumes of the standard sea water and of the sample and determining the volumes of a given silver nitrate solution required to precipitate completely the halogens. Let

N = chlorinity of the standard water,

Cl = chlorinity of the sample,

S=density of the standard water at the working temperature,

s=density of the sample water at the working temperature,

A=volume of AgNO$_3$ required to precipitate the standard water,

a=volume of AgNO$_3$ required to precipitate the sample.

Then,

$$\frac{Cl.s}{N.S}=\frac{a}{A}$$

or

$$Cl=N.\frac{a.S}{A.s}.$$

The results are calculated by Knudsen's Tables.

Apparatus

1. *The Knudsen pipette* (Fig. 29). This allows the delivery of a constant volume (about 15 ml.) of fluid with precision. It consists of an ordinary bulb pipette fitted with a two-way tap, and a double entry. With the tap in the appropriate position the sample is sucked up the pipette into the limb (B). When the liquid reaches the limb (B) the tap is turned off, and when turned a second time to put the liquid in communication with limb (A) the pipette delivers a fixed volume of liquid, i.e. that below the tap. It is recommended that new pipettes should be calibrated with distilled water by weighing a series of successive deliveries using the standard procedure given below (p. 90). The precision of the delivery is thereby obtained.

2. *The Knudsen burette* (Fig. 29). The silver nitrate solution contained in a reservoir is delivered from a special burette, with an automatic zero. With the tap (G) open to the overflow (I), the burette is put into connection with the silver nitrate reservoir by tap (E), and the solution allowed to pass the tap (G) towards (I) when the tap (E) is turned off. The tap (G) is then turned to put the burette in communication with the atmosphere (as with the pipette) and the volume below the tap used for the titration, by the burette stop-cock (H), in the usual manner.

Since the volumes required for titration normally extend over a limited range, the major portion of the titration fluid may be run out rapidly from a non-graduated bulb (F), so allowing the stem to be more finely graduated. The unit of graduation is the double millilitre, the graduations beginning at 16·00 and going to 22·50 or 23·50; this range is adequate for all normal ocean waters. (It may not be so for low-salinity waters such as the Baltic.)

A certificate of accuracy should be supplied with the burette;

otherwise it must be calibrated. It is particularly important to calibrate between the 16·00 and 20·00 marks.

The burette should be read using a parallax avoiding device.

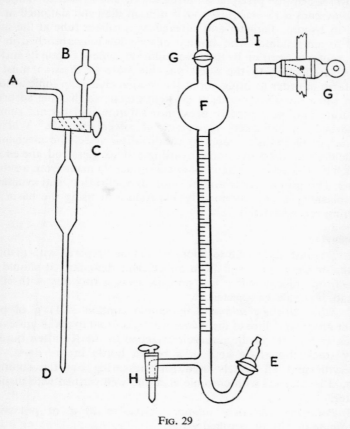

FIG. 29

Knudsen Pipette.   Knudsen Burette.

3. *Titration vessel*. Thomsen recommends a thick-walled conical vessel (tumbler), 5 cm. wide at the base, 7 cm. at the top, and about 10 cm. high. King (13) prefers a 7-in.-wide porcelain round-bottomed dish of almost truly hemispherical shape as the titration vessel. It is easier to disperse the precipitate with a rubber-tipped glass rod in such a dish and observation of the colour and its comparison with a preceding titration may be easily carried out. There is some risk of splashing in such a vessel but long experience has

shown that the careful worker can avoid this and that in general there is a gain in accuracy using a dish.

4. *Agitation of the solution.* It is essential to agitate thoroughly and break up the precipitate during the titration process. Thomsen recommends a 17 cm. glass rod, 5 mm. in diameter flattened at the end to 16 mm. diameter and covered by a rubber tube at the other end to aid holding. The amount of chloride ions absorbed in the first stages of titration by the silver chloride, depends upon its surface area. Reduction to the finest possible state of division must be uniform in order to bring about the sudden change in ionic adsorption when the silver nitrate is in slight excess, so that the adsorbed chloride ions pass rapidly back into solution and do not remain adsorbed by unbroken aggregates of silver chloride. When a white porcelain dish is used as the titration vessel the mechanical difficulties are best overcome by using a thick glass rod, the end of which is inserted into a hemispherical rubber tip made from a rubber bung. This grinding necessitates vigorous application, and avoidance of splashing is only attained by experience in using the basin and stirring rod advocated.

Reagents

1. *Distilled water.* All solutions should be prepared with distilled water or water prepared from an efficient deioniser: it should be free from chlorides; if a test portion gives a turbidity with silver nitrate it should be rejected.

2. *Silver nitrate solution.* This should contain 37·11 g. of pure silver nitrate in 1 litre of distilled water; it is usual to make up several litres, to be kept in the reservoir attached to the Knudsen burette. Any stock should be kept in a brown bottle in the dark. The reservoir and all vessels used for measuring out the solutions should be cleaned with chromic acid and well washed with distilled water.

3. *Potassium chromate solution.* Dissolve 20 g. of potassium chromate in 250 ml. distilled water.

4. *Eau de Mer Normale.* This is supplied by the Laboratoire Hydrographique, Charlottenlund Slot, Charlottenlund, Denmark, in ampoules, containing about 250 ml. The chlorinity, always about 19·38‰, is indicated on the ampoule the value being given to three decimal places. For use, the ampoule is opened at one end by means of a glass knife and a clean bottle rinsed with the standard water; the rinsings are rejected. The ampoule is then inverted over the bottle and the other end broken when the water passes into the bottle. The latter is then tightly closed with a rubber stopper. It is recommended that two bottles of normal water are used, one as a check on

evaporation; when the first is almost finished it is checked against the second to ensure no loss by evaporation has taken place.

5. *Tap grease.* Oxner (18) has recommended a tap grease made by melting together seven parts of ordinary rubber, three parts of pure vaseline and one part of paraffin. Commercial preparations may be used, but a constant check on the taps is necessary. On no account should a silicone grease be used.

Preparation of the Instruments

The pipette and burette should be cleaned and then thoroughly washed with distilled water. Chromic acid cleaning fluid was recommended by Thomsen, but King finds that if the apparatus is first filled with sodium hydroxide in ethanol (8% solution) allowed to stand a few minutes, drained, and then washed with a little concentrated nitric acid the cleaning is quicker and more effective. Some workers dislike this latter technique considering it a little dangerous; some allow the glassware to stand overnight after filling with a mixture of equal volumes of sulphuric and nitric acid. If at any time the solutions tend to stick to the glass the apparatus should be re-cleaned. The taps are then greased and put in place. Thomsen recommends that the upper taps of both the pipette and burette should be greased with a little glycerin, and the lower taps of the burette with an appropriate commercial grease. The minimum quantity of grease should be used. The burette is placed in position on the bench and connected to the silver nitrate reservoir by clean rubber tubing; a small vessel to collect any overflow is placed in position. Dr J. P. Riley recommends black PVC (polyvinyl chloride) tubing for these connections; unlike ordinary rubber tubing it does not perish, and once in place does not readily slip off. The silver nitrate in the reservoir should be thoroughly agitated and the burette rinsed out several times with this solution. King recommends that at intervals air, passed through two wash bottles of water, should be rapidly blown through the silver nitrate solution to prevent any stratification. It is essential to check that the tap (E) after closing does not leak and thereby force silver nitrate solution into the burette during the titration: this is done by taking a reading with the liquid in the burette at a mark and with the tap (G) closed, and reading again after five minutes' interval. Vessels which have been contaminated with silver chloride may be first washed with dilute ammonia before acid cleaning.

The Titration

It is desirable that all titrations should be carried out with extreme care and under standard conditions; it has therefore been thought desirable to append what is substantially a translation of Thomsen's instructions, again adding comments of King from experience in the Government Laboratory.

(a) *Rinsing of the pipette.*

The pipette must always be rinsed with the liquid to be titrated. This operation must be repeated for each sample.

1. Close the tap to cut off the body of the pipette from the two branches (A) and (B).
2. Dry the point of the pipette with a soft cloth or scrap of filter paper.
3. Place the tip of the pipette in the sample of liquid previously stirred.
4. Suck at (B) with the mouth, turning the tap at the same time to establish connection with this branch; suck until the pipette is about one-third full: close the tap.
5. Take the pipette out of the sample, shake a little, open the tap to branch (B), and allow the liquid to drain.
6. Repeat the rinsing in exactly the same way. *Note.* When running out the rinsing fluid the tap must be turned as indicated so that the branch A is closed; this limb should *always* remain perfectly dry.

(b) *Taking of the sample of sea water.*

1. Repeat 1–3 as given above.
2. Repeat 4 above but sucking the liquid a few cm. past the tap.
3. Withdraw the pipette and lightly wipe downwards with a soft cloth or small piece of filter paper: stopper the flask containing the sample.
4. Introduce the point of the pipette to the bottom of the titration vessel and turn the tap to open the pipette to the air. As the liquid is delivered the pipette is gradually withdrawn, always keeping the tip a few millimetres below the level of the liquid.
5. When the delivery is finished slowly withdraw the pipette from the liquid; again dip the tip several millimetres below the surface of the liquid and then finally withdraw slowly. Constant drainage time is important; a period of 15 seconds from the end of the delivery is adequate.
6. Close the tap, dry the tip gently and return to stand.

Notes A. During manipulation never touch the body of the pipette with the hand, since any resultant heating would change the volume of the liquid. Keep the hands well away.

B. In order to ensure that drainage is the same in all estimations always hold the pipette vertically and ensure that the time between opening the tap and the final withdrawal is always the same.

C. Make sure that the pipette empties completely; if any drops of liquid adhere to the glass, the surface is greasy and the pipette should be cleaned.

D. When turning the tap, press in gently.

(c) *The titration.*

1. Add to the liquid in the reaction vessel a few drops of the potassium chromate solution. Take care not to splash the liquid. King finds it an advantage to titrate using a daylight lamp in a partially darkened room: the colour vision of all workers is tested. He considers the previous instructions for the addition of potassium chromate are not precise. He finds that the end-point is most accurately judged when 0·05 g. is present in 50–55 ml. of final volume of fluid; this agrees with theoretical studies but is more than recommended by Thomsen. He confirms the observation of Dupré that a sharper end-point is obtained when the titration is observed through a yellow or orange filter, but continuous working in such a light is unpleasant. The difference in the amount of potassium chromate advocated by different workers appears to be a light filter phenomenon, the worker unconsciously using the supernatant potassium chromate as a filter for sharpening the end-point. Since Thomsen's technique uses a straight-sided beaker, his depth of solution through which the orange-coloured silver chromate is observed, is greater than that when a porcelain dish is used and the quantity of potassium chromate for optimum precision may be less.

2. Fill the burette until the solution passes the upper tap (G) and ensure that the tap (H) is full: if a drop of liquid passes the tap, remove it carefully with a piece of filter paper.

3. Place the titration vessel under the delivery tap of the burette: open the upper burette tap to the air and titrate. Use an even jet and avoid splashing. At the same time stir the liquid vigorously (*see* p. 88).

4. When it is estimated that about 2 ml. of solution is required to complete the titration close the tap and remove the titration vessel from under the burette, incline and swirl to wash down the sides and then agitate.

5. Replace the titration vessel and add more silver nitrate drop by drop, all the while stirring vigorously.

6. When the liquid has a faint red tinge, remove the titration vessel from under the burette, rotate about its axis, and rub the sides of the vessel with the stirring rod. Stir energetically for 15 seconds.

7. Replace the titration vessel and add one or two drops of the solution until the liquid has a definite red colour.

8. The burette is read exactly two minutes and a half after the beginning of the titration. This interval may be modified, for example with low salinities, but in order to remove drainage errors each titration should take the same time.

Precautions. It is essential that the temperature of the room should not change during standardization and titration; King recommends that titrations should be carried out in a roughly controlled constant temperature room. The samples to be titrated should be kept in the room for several hours prior to the estimations.

The analysis of a series of samples. Since considerable time is spent in preparing the apparatus it is an advantage to perform titrations in a long series. The first titration should be repeated for practice and to ensure the apparatus is in satisfactory order. All titrations should be carried out in exactly the same way, and with the same time intervals for all phases of the work; only then will the results be satisfactory. Only when two titrations within 0·01 burette reading are obtained can the operation be considered satisfactory.

After the analysis of two or three samples of a series, a repeat of the standard water should be made and further repeats carried out during the series. In the Government Laboratory sub-standards are prepared by retaining samples whose chlorinity approaches that of the latest issue of Normal Water, blending them until they are of precisely the same chlorinity as the Normal Water. Intermediate checks can then be made with this sub-standard water. If the titration of any series is interrupted or if any change of temperature is suspected, then Normal Water should again be titrated.

At the end of a day's work it is recommended that the rubber connection to the silver nitrate reservoir be closed off with clips to prevent evaporation or loss through accident.

If the apparatus is left for several days take care to see that no crystals of silver nitrate have formed around the taps of the burette.

Calculation

Let

N = the chlorinity ‰ of the Normal Sea Water,

Cl = the chlorinity ‰ of the sample which it is required to determine,

A = the burette reading for the titration of the Normal Sea Water,

a = the burette reading for the sample.

Then,

$$\alpha = N - A,$$
$$k = Cl - a.$$

For each standardization with Normal Water, determine α, and from Knudsen's Tables find the appropriate value of k for this value of α and the titration figure of the sample, a. The chlorinity is found by subtracting this value of k from the burette reading of the sample. For example suppose

$$N = 19 \cdot 386\text{‰},$$
$$A = 19 \cdot 52,$$
$$a = 21 \cdot 10,$$

then

$$N - A = \alpha = -0 \cdot 134.$$

For $\alpha = 0 \cdot 134$ and a titration, $a = 21 \cdot 10$, the value of k from the Tables is $-0 \cdot 19$.

The required chlorinity is therefore,

$$Cl = k + a = 21 \cdot 10 - 0 \cdot 19 = 20 \cdot 91\text{‰}.$$

Remarks

1. The accuracy required for general work is $\pm 0 \cdot 02\text{‰}$. Routine workers reach this standard of accuracy if the instructions are carefully followed throughout all the estimations. Experienced workers reach an accuracy of $\pm 0 \cdot 01\text{‰}$.

2. With regard to Knudsen burettes, King has made the following comments about various patterns which have been in use.

The Knudsen pattern burettes of German manufacture that were issued from Copenhagen for many years, though of excellent workmanship and made from carefully selected glass tubing, were not of the uniform bore of the modern precision tubing. On recalibration, errors of at least 0·02 ml. were frequent, but these are not of great importance provided changes in the bore are not sudden, and that these rapid changes do not occur at points on the burette where readings are taken. Furthermore, it frequently happens that the standard and sample are read at nearly the same point on the burette. These burettes were originally calibrated at 17·5° C., an appreciably lower temperature than the modern figure of 20° C. now used for all volumetric glassware in this country. This is not important provided that the sea water, standard and unknown, as well as the silver nitrate solution are at the same temperature, although there may be slight differences in the coefficient of expansion of the two liquids and between the glass of which the burette and pipette are made. Much more serious is the difficulty in delivering precisely the same volume of the silver nitrate solution as indicated by a given burette reading on all occasions. The filling of the burette for its calibration and for working purposes must be carried out in precisely the same way. Some of the burettes issued from Copenhagen were constructed so that the upper jet was bent at an angle, and ground so that drops of silver nitrate solution could not form. Another pattern had the tip pointing upwards, and this enabled drops of unequal size to be retained on the orifice after filling, unless precautions were taken to remove them. It is essential to have the exterior of this jet thoroughly clean and wetted with silver nitrate solution. The drop which forms on filling is then gently removed by touching the side of the jet with a glass rod in the same way as that used in detaching the drop from the bottom jet immediately before carrying out a titration. The error given by neglecting this precaution may amount to 0·02‰ Cl. The time taken for each titration must be uniform, and in calibrating the burette the liquid should be delivered for weighing exactly as though a titration was in progress. It is preferable to use the silver nitrate solution for this calibration.

3. Hand stirring is recommended by Thomsen as already described. Many workers now prefer to use a mechanical stirrer of the conventional type or a magnetic stirrer. In the latter the motor may be mounted under the bench, the titration vessel fitting into a recess in the bench over the motor unit.

4. Giral (6) has questioned the desirability of storing standard sea water in glass ampoules, but at least within the limits of the Mohr titration the practice is satisfactory. This is true in spite of the fact that alkaline saline solutions on long contact with some forms of glass deposit minute crystals often with the solution of quantities of silica.

5. The effects of storage have been discussed by Wüst (24), who concluded that there is a definite tendency for the chlorinities to increase on storing; with unopened bottles coated with paraffin wax the increase was negligible. Thomson (22) has examined samples stored for four months taken at several depths in the Bermuda region and finds no significant changes in the chlorinity. He also considers Wüst's statement, that evaporation during examination outweighs the advantages of repeated titration, to be unjustified. He found that samples which had come to temperature equilibrium with the laboratory showed no measurable change in chlorinity after being left open for four hours and he considers the erratic results obtained in repeated titrations are more probably due to contamination through inadequate manipulation. Nevertheless, samples should not be unduly exposed to the air. Quite large changes can of course occur with faulty stoppers.

6. Polythene bottles have come into use for the storage of water samples for various purposes; they are light, non-breakable and readily labelled with wax pencil. However, Cox (3) has shown that water is lost from these bottles on storage; with elevated temperatures of a ship's hold the change could be of the order of $0.1‰$ salinity in a matter of a few months. Such bottles should not be used for storage over long periods. Dr J. P. Riley (personal communication) has also carried out such tests on polythene bottles; he found (by titration) an average change of $0.005‰$ Cl per week at $30°$C., $0.002‰$ Cl at $20°$C., and no detectable change over several months at $5°$C.

7. Sund (20) has described a slide rule for the calculation of salinity and density and Kalle (12) a circular slide rule, simpler to use than Knudsen's Tables, although giving only salinity.

8. The method given above is the standard titration method for determining the chlorinity of sea water. It should be pointed out that it is less accurate than the Volhard method which was used by Jacobsen and Knudsen in standardising the Urnormal 1937 water (9). The latter method, owing to the necessity to wash the silver halide precipitate is not suitable for routine work. Bather and Riley (1) (*see also* West and Robinson, 23; Hermann, 8) have described volumetric methods in which the end-point is determined potentiometrically; the methods are easy to use and give results with a standard deviation about $0.005‰$.

9. McGary (15) has emphasised the fact that Knudsen's Tables are based on a reference solution of chlorinity $19.38‰$ and the 'Table of Titration' can only be used with reference solutions within the range $19.31–19.45‰$ Cl. Any sub-standards must be brought within this range by the addition of either sodium chloride or distilled water. The addition of substantial quantities of sodium chloride is undesirable because the densities of sample and reference solution enter into the calculations, and the coefficients of thermal expansion of natural sea water and sodium chloride solution are not identical; when the estimations are made at very high or very low temperatures errors will result. He has therefore given a method, with graphs and tables, by which sub-standard solutions outside this range may be used.

10. The above instructions apply to all determinations when accurate results are required. For some purposes, for example in tide pool studies, a simpler method may be used (Harvey, 7; *see* Kalle, 10). Titrate 10 ml. of the sea-water sample with a solution containing 27.25 g. silver nitrate per litre using potassium chromate as indicator, and employing an ordinary burette; take the standard precautions of volumetric analysis. The volume of silver nitrate used will be almost equal to the salinity; a more accurate value will be

obtained by applying to the result the appropriate correction given in Table I.

TABLE I

Salinity corrections (Ref. 7)

Salinity, $S\%_0$ found	Correction to be applied	Salinity, $S\%_0$ found	Correction to be applied
40	−0·15	22	+0·22
38	−0·08	20	+0·23
36	−0·03	18	+0·23
34	+0·03	16	+0·23
32	+0·07	14	+0·20
30	+0·11	12	+0·19
28	+0·15	10	+0·16
26	+0·17	8	+0·15
24	+0·20		

11. Recently a sub-committee of the Conseil International pour l'Exploration de la Mer have considered the possibility of a revision of the foregoing Oxner-Knudsen method as described by Helge Thomsen (21). The following is a summary of their preliminary report, based on information collected by this sub-committee from various laboratories and made available through Dr F. Koczy, Miami, Fla.

(a) The essential requirements of any method for the routine determination of salinity are simplicity, speed and accuracy. From the point of view of simplicity and speed the Mohr-Knudsen method is most convenient and gives an accuracy of $\pm 0·02\%_0 S$.

(b) The Mohr-Knudsen method may be modified to increase speed by use of mechanical, especially magnetic, stirring without loss of accuracy (1).

(c) The chromate indicator of the Mohr-Knudsen method may be replaced by sodium fluoresceinate with a slight increase in accuracy.

(d) A limiting factor in the accuracy of a titration method is the volumetric error. A major increase in accuracy cannot be expected unless this is reduced, for example by weighing the sample or treating the glassware with a water-repellent coating. For a routine method, weighing cannot be used and treatment with silicone water repellents has not in general been found satisfactory.

(e) In order to facilitate the detection of the end-point some laboratories are using a potentiometric method, which has the advantage of increasing precision and reducing eye-strain associated with the standard methods. Potentiometric methods are of greatest application in non-routine work, where the samples are weighed, but they could be used for routine work to reduce fatigue to the operator.

These methods do not, in general, increase the speed of the determination. A potentiometric end-point has been used in an Automatic Chlorinity Titrator (ACT) developed in the U.S.A. This instrument requires a well-trained operator.

(*f*) A semi-micro method has been devised by Miss Saruhashi (19) in Japan. This involves titration with silver nitrate using uranin indicator, and requires only one-tenth of the quantities of sample and reagents as the Mohr-Knudsen method. It is said to be fast and accurate, but insufficient experience has been gained by other workers. Nevertheless, it is considered that the method should be more widely studied. The use of uranin has been described by Miyake (16, 17). 5 ml. of uranin (sodium fluoresceinate) solution are mixed with 100 ml. of 1 % starch solution which serves as a protective colloid. 2 ml. of indicator are used per 15 ml. of sea water. The colour changes from pale greenish-yellow to pink at the end-point when the fluoresceinate ion is adsorbed on the silver chloride; it is essential to watch the precipitate not the solution. The starch serves as a protective colloid to prevent coagulation of the silver halide precipitate. The mean error is stated to be less than 0·015‰; the time required for the titration is shorter. Since the colour change at the end-point is very clear, in the presence of a protective colloid there is little danger of under-titration of the solution. The method checks well with potentiometric titrations.

(*g*) Determination of salinity by means of density, electrical conductivity and refractive index measurements have been developed, but only the density methods of Cox (4) and of Kalle (11) and the conductivity method using a Wenner bridge give the required accuracy of $\pm 0·02$‰. An electrical conductivity method is the common means by which continuous recording of salinities have been obtained *in situ*.

(*h*) Experience with polyethylene bottles has shown that they are unsatisfactory for the storage of sea-water samples.

REFERENCES

1. Bather, J. M., and Riley, J. P., 1953. 'The precise and routine potentiometric determination of the chlorinity of sea water.' *J. Cons. int. Explor. Mer*, **18**, 277–86.
2. Christie, A. A., and Newman, O. F., 1955. 'The use of a magnetic stirrer in the determination of the salinity of sea water.' *J. Cons. int. Explor. Mer*, **21**, 3–5.
3. Cox, R. A., 1953. 'Water transmission of Polythene bottles.' *J. Cons. int. Explor. Mer*, **19**, 297–300.
4. ——, 1954. 'An apparatus for determining the salinity of sea water.' *J. Cons. int. Explor. Mer*, **20**, pp. 9–17.

5. Dittmar, W., 1884. 'Report on researches into the composition of ocean water collected by H.M.S. *Challenger*.' *Challenger Report, Physics and Chemistry*, **1**, 1–251.
6. Giral, J., 1926. 'Quelques observations sur l'emploi de l'eau normale en océanographie.' *Publ. Circ. Cons. Explor. Mer*, No. 90.
7. Harvey, H. W., 1955. *The Chemistry and Fertility of Sea Water.* Cambridge University Press, Cambridge, 224 pp.
8. Hermann, F., 1951. 'High accuracy potentiometric determination of the chlorinity of sea water.' *J. Cons. int. Explor. Mer*, **17**, 223–30.
9. Jacobsen, J. P., and Knudsen, M., 1940. 'Urnormal 1937 or Primary standard sea water 1937.' *Publ. sci. Ass. Océanogr. phys.*, No. 7. The University, Liverpool.
10. Kalle, K., 1951. 'Einige Vereinfachungen der Chlor-Titration für biologische und Wasserbaukundliche Zwecke in Küstengewässern.' *Dtsch. hydrogr. Z.*, **4**, 13–16.
11. ——, (in press).
12. ——, 1955. 'Einkreisförmiger Rechenschieber zur Bestimmung des Salzgehaltes bei der *Cl'*-Titration des Meerwassers.' *Dtsch. hydrogr. Z.*, **8**, 29–30.
13. King, J., 1950. 'Some notes on the determination of the chlorinity of sea water by comparison with the international standard.' *J. Cons. int. Explor. Mer*, **16**, 167–74.
14. Knudsen, M., 1953. *Hydrographical Tables.* G.E.C. Gad, Copenhagen, 1953.
15. McGary, J. W. 'Substandard reference solutions in chlorinity determinations by the Knudsen method.' *J. Mar. Res.*, **13**, 245–53.
16. Miyake, Y., 1939a. 'A new indicator for the determination of chlorinity in sea water.' *Geophys. Mag.*, Tokyo, **12**, 299–300.
17. ——, 1939b. 'Chemical studies of the western Pacific Ocean. I. The chemical composition of the oceanic salt. Part I.' *Bull chem. Soc., Japan*, **14**, 29–34.
18. Oxner, M., 1920. 'Manuel pratique d'analyse de l'eau de mer. I. Chloruration par la méthode de Knudsen (avec un préface de M. Knudsen).' *Bull. Comm. Int. Expl. Scient. Médit.*, Monaco. No. 3.
19. Saruhashi, K., 1953. 'The chlorinity determination of sea water by micro-analytical method.' *Rec. Oceanogr. Wks. Jap.*, New Series, **1**, 52–4.
20. Sund, O., 1929. 'An oceanographical slide rule.' *J. Cons. int. Explor. Mer*, **4**, 1.
21. Thomsen, H., 1954. 'Instructions pratiques sur la détermination de la salinité de l'eau de mer par la méthode de titrage de Mohr-Knudsen. *Bull. de l'institut Océanographique.* No. 1047, 20 pp.
22. Thomson, E. F., 1940. 'Effect of delayed titration on the salinity determination.' *J. Mar. Res.*, **3**, 268–71.
23. West, L. E., and Robinson, R. J., 1941. 'Potentiometric analysis of sea water. I. Determination of chlorinity.' *J. Mar. Res.*, **4**, 1–10.
24. Wüst, G., 1932. 'Das Ozeanographische Beobachtungsmaterial, *Deutsche Atlantische Exped.* '*Meteor*', *1925–7, Wiss. Erg.* **4**, Part 2, 4–13.

5

THE POTENTIOMETRIC DETERMINATIONS OF pH

THE MODERN CONCEPT OF pH

Definitions

In order to understand the precise meaning of the term pH we must first define certain quantities in accordance with modern electrochemical theory. This subject has recently been dealt with in an exhaustive and accurate manner by Bates (5) and this section is largely based on his treatment.

1. When current is drawn from a galvanic cell a reaction takes place with the transformation of chemical into electrical energy. A reversible electrode can suffer either an oxidation or a reduction when it either supplies or removes electrons.

2. The potentials of the two electrodes with respect to one another determine the direction of flow of the current, and the difference in potentials (e.m.f.) constitutes the driving force of the reaction.

3. The reversible e.m.f., E, multiplied by the quantity of electrical charge that must be transferred to bring about the unit amount of reaction, gives the maximum work that this amount of chemical reaction is capable of producing at constant temperature, pressure and concentration. This is the decrease in free energy, $-\Delta F$; hence

$$-\Delta F = n\boldsymbol{F} \cdot E, \qquad \qquad ...(1)$$

where $\boldsymbol{F}$ is the Faraday and n is an integer.

4. While differences of potential can be readily measured, an absolute scale of electrode potentials cannot readily be established. This is the practical difficulty in pH work where attention is focused upon the half reaction that occurs at the electrode reversible to hydrogen and upon the half-cell potential. The validity and accuracy of an absolute scale of potential, in spite of much work, cannot be considered to have been established.

5. An arbitrary zero of potential has been defined as the potential of a reversible hydrogen electrode in contact with hydrogen gas at 1 atmosphere pressure and immersed in a solution containing hydrogen ions at unit activity (*see* below)

$$\text{Pt; } H_2 \text{ (g, 1 atm.), } H^+ \text{ } (a=1). \qquad ...(2)$$

This is taken as zero at all temperatures and the scale of which it forms the basis is termed the hydrogen scale. The potential of a single electrode on the hydrogen scale is the e.m.f. of a complete cell of that electrode and the standard hydrogen electrode. In fact, the hydrogen electrode defined as above is not convenient from a practical point of view and potentials on the hydrogen scale are usually measured by other electrode combinations.

6. As systems are not usually ideal, the chemical potentials are usually expressed in terms of the activity, a, instead of concentrations. In the standard state the activity is unity.

The choice of standard states is to a large extent arbitrary; for solutions with which we are largely concerned it is chosen so that $a/m=1$ when $m=0$, i.e. at zero molality or infinite dilution of the solute. The activities of substances in solution, particularly when they are electrolytes are not equal to the molalities. The ratio of its activity to its molality is the activity coefficient

$$f_m = \frac{a_i}{m_i}.$$

When ions are under consideration the activity coefficients of individual ions cannot be uniquely determined; conventional ionic activity coefficients are therefore used.

7. It may be shown that for the reaction,

$$aA + bB = uU + vV,$$

$$\Delta F = \Delta F^\circ + RT \log \left(\frac{a_U{}^u . a_V{}^v}{a_A{}^a . a_B{}^b} \right), \qquad \ldots(3)$$

where ΔF° is the change in free energy when all the substances are in their standard state.

From (1) and (3)

$$E = E^\circ - \frac{RT}{nF} \log \left(\frac{a_U{}^u . a_V{}^v}{a_A{}^a . a_B{}^b} \right). \qquad \ldots(4)$$

The Definition of a pH Scale

The equilibrium between hydrogen and hydroxyl ions in an aqueous medium is given by

$$H_2O \rightleftharpoons H^+ + OH^-. \qquad \ldots(5)$$

If solutes are present in such small quantities that the activity of water is for all practical purposes unity, then

$$K_w = m_{H^+} . m_{OH^-} . f_{H^+} . f_{OH^-}, \qquad \ldots(6)$$

where m and f are the respective molalities and activity coefficients and K_w is the dissociation constant for water. The dissociation of pure water is extremely small, and in the absence of solutes the activity coefficients are virtually unity; hence at 25°C., when $K_w = 1·008 \times 10^{-14}$, we have

$$m_{H^+} = m_{OH^-} = \sqrt{K_w} = 10^{-7}. \qquad ...(7)$$

The hydrogen-ion concentration is usually extremely small, and normality, C_{H^+}, is therefore expressed in a logarithmic value where

$$C_{H^+} = 10^{-p} = \frac{1}{10^p}.$$

This is usually written

$$-\log C_{H^+} = p\text{cH}. \qquad ...(8)$$

As a means for measuring pH values Sørensen chose the cell, Pt; H_2, Soln. X| Salt Bridge| 0·1 N calomel electrode, applying a correction for liquid junction potentials. For the difference in e.m.f. between two cells of the above type in terms of hydrogen-ion concentration we have

$$E_1 - E_2 = \frac{RT}{F} \log \frac{C_{H_2^+}}{C_{H_1^+}}. \qquad ...(9)$$

If $C_{H_2^+}$ in the second solution is fixed (unity) E_2 would have a definite value at each temperature.

Designating this standard potential, $E^{\circ\prime}$, we have

$$E_1 = E^{\circ\prime} + \frac{RT}{F} \log \frac{1}{C_{H_1^+}} \qquad ...(10)$$

$$= E^{\circ\prime} + \frac{2·3026RT}{F} . p\text{cH}. \qquad ...(11)$$

If E_1 is determined for a solution of known hydrogen-ion concentration then $E^{\circ\prime}$ may be calculated. Sørensen used solutions of hydrochloric acid-sodium chloride mixtures, assuming that

$$C_{H_1^+} = \alpha_1 c_1,$$

where c_1 was the normality of the acid and α_1 the classical dissociation constant calculated from measurements of conductivity.

There are two reasons for the failure of this method—although it has been widely used. First, equation (9) holds only for ideal solutions so that activities should replace concentrations and also the residual junction potential must be zero. Secondly, the hydrogen-ion concentration is equal to c_1 rather than $\alpha_1 c_1$ in a strong monobasic acid.

However, Sørensen's pH unit (psH) has been most widely used; it is arbitrary and measures neither the concentration nor the activity of the hydrogen ion. It is a conventional scale defined in terms of a method and a conventional formula; at 25° C.

$$p\text{sH} = \frac{E - 0.3376}{0.05916}. \qquad \qquad ...(12)$$

Extensive data for the psH values of buffer mixtures are available.

The fact that the activity of a single ionic species cannot be determined necessitates the establishment of a conventional scale. Using Sørensen's standard cell as a basis,

$$E = E° - \frac{2.3026RT}{F} . \log a_{\text{H}^+} . a_{Cl^-} + E_j \qquad ...(13)$$

or

$$p\text{aH} = \frac{F(E - E° - E_j)}{2.3026RT} + \log a_{Cl^-}, \qquad ...(14)$$

where paH is the hydrogen-ion exponent on the activity scale, and E_j is the algebraic sum of liquid junction potentials. The standard potential on this scale refers to the standard state of unit activity instead of unit concentrations as on the Sørensen scale.

On certain reasonable assumptions this equation gives

$$p\text{aH} = \frac{E - (E_0' + E_j)}{0.05916}. \qquad \qquad ...(15)$$

This is clearly of a similar form to equation 12 and psH and paH differ by a constant amount; substituting the appropriate values gives

$$p\text{aH} = p\text{sH} + 0.04.$$

(There is *no* constant difference between paH and pcH since these two quantities differ by $\log f_{\text{H}^+}$ which is a function of the ionic strength.)

The choice of a pH scale must take into account both the theoretical and practical aspects of the problem: while the convenient routine measurement of the theoretically desirable scales is not possible, the pH obtained by conventional experimental technique has no simple exact meaning.

The practical method still most convenient and widely employed to determine the acidity of a solution is still that of Sørensen with a glass electrode replacing the Pt-H half-cell.

In practical work an operational definition has been internationally accepted

$$p\text{H} = p\text{H}_s + \frac{(E - E_s)F}{2.3026RT}, \qquad ...(16)$$

where pH$_s$ is $-\log a_{H^+}$ and a_{H^+} the conventional hydrogen-ion activity of the reference solution, arbitrarily chosen and internationally agreed upon.

In this equation pH$_s$ is the pH assigned to the standard, and E and E_s are the values of the e.m.f. of a pH cell with the electrode immersed in an unknown fluid and the standard respectively.

It may be noted that the standard potential E_H° is by definition zero at all temperatures and therefore measurements of hydrogen-electrode potentials can give no exact comparison between hydrogen-ion activity at two different temperatures. pH measurements still give reproducible comparisons but for this purpose the assembly should always be standardized at the temperature of the test solutions.

pH Standards

In principle the great bulk of practical pH estimations are based upon measurements of the e.m.f. of a cell of the type

Hydrogen electrode, Soln. X $|$KCl (satd.)$|$ Reference electrode.

From the equation

$$pH = -\log a_{H^+} = \frac{E-[(E^{\circ\prime}+E_j)]F}{2\cdot3026RT},$$

it is only necessary to establish conventional values for $E^{\circ\prime}$ and E_j to permit conventional pH values or hydrogen-ion activities to be determined. Electrode assemblies vary and they are best standardized from time to time with a solution of known a_{H^+} (or pH$_s$) replacing the solution X in the cell. If the reference potential and the liquid junction potential remain unchanged upon replacement of the standard by the unknown, then

$$pH_x = pH_s + \frac{(E-E_s)F}{2\cdot3026RT}.$$

In the standardization of commercial pH assemblies day-to-day changes in the cell potential are compensated by manual adjustment of resistances in the meter circuit. In this way the correct pH of the buffer standard is obtained and E_j+E is not evaluated; the assignment of a value of pH$_s$ to a particular buffer solution fixes the value of $E^{\circ\prime}+E_j$. Primary reference solutions are preferred to the use of a fixed standard potential since:

1. saturated calomel reference electrodes are not highly reproducible;
2. the potentials of glass electrodes vary rather widely and the asymmetry potentials may vary from day to day;
3. the meter is usually calibrated to read in pH units.

The American (N.B.S.) standards (1) are given in Table 24. The British standard scale is consistent in nearly all respects with the N.B.S. scale already given, the 0·05 M solution of potassium hydrogen phthalate being taken as the primary standard by the former authority (2).

BUFFER SOLUTIONS

The presence of buffers in solution increase the amount of acid or alkali that must be added to give a certain change in pH. They make accurate regulation of H-ion concentrations possible. The intensity of buffer action is termed the buffer capacity. If a buffer solution is to be effective in regulating the acidity it should be insensitive to dilution of its components; this is measured by its dilution value, the change in pH on dilution with an equal volume of water. The addition of a neutral salt to a buffer solution affects the pH since it lowers the activity coefficients of the ions. Further the pH will be affected by temperature.

The buffer solutions recommended by the U.S. Bureau of Standards for setting up a pH assembly are given in Table 24, p. 305. Buffer solutions have been devised for many special purposes and a selection covering various ranges is given in standard text-books. The following notes refer to the buffer standards.

Recommended Buffer Standards (National Bureau of Standards, 1)

1. *0·05 M potassium tetroxalate.* (pH 1·68, 25°C.) Recrystallize the salt from water; no crystals should be allowed to separate above a temperature of 50°C. Dissolve 12·7 g. of the salt $KH_3(C_2O_4)_2 . 2H_2O$ in water and make up to 1 litre. This buffer shows a more pronounced change with concentration than the other standards but no appreciable error is likely to result from variations in the composition of the salt.

2. *Saturated potassium hydrogen tartrate* (pH 3·56, 25°C.). Prepare a saturated solution of the reagent grade salt in distilled water; a 10% error in the concentration changes the pH by only 0·01 unit and elaborate precautions to ensure saturation are therefore unnecessary. The solution should be filtered before use.

3. *0·05 M potassium hydrogen phthalate* (pH 4·01, 25°C.). Dry reagent grade acid potassium phthalate at 110°C. and cool in a desiccator. Dissolve 10·211 g. in distilled water and make up to 1 litre. This has the lowest buffer value of the standards, and should be carefully protected against contamination.

4. *0·025 M potassium dihydrogen phosphate and 0·025 M disodium hydrogen phosphate* (pH 6·86, 25°C.). Dry reagent grade anhydrous

potassium dihydrogen phosphate at 110°C. and reagent grade disodium hydrogen phosphate at 130°C. and cool in a desiccator. Dissolve 3·44 g. of the former and 3·55 g. of the latter in water and make up to 1 litre with distilled water.

5. *0·01 M sodium borate* (*p*H 9·18, 25°C.). Dissolve 3·814 g. of reagent grade borax (sodium tetraborate decahydrate) in distilled water and make up to 1 litre. The water content of borax tends to fall on storage unless the container is tightly sealed, but the dilution value of the borax buffer is very small. The solution should be well stoppered to prevent absorption of carbon dioxide.

Buffer solutions should be stored in resistance glass or polythene bottles. A small crystal of thymol may be added as preservative.

THE DETERMINATION OF pH BY MEANS OF THE GLASS ELECTRODE ASSEMBLY

Various electrode systems have been used to measure pH; essentially the following set-up is required:

Electrode reversible to hydrogen ion; unknown solution	Salt Bridge	Reference Electrode.

For the reversible electrode, the ultimate standard is the hydrogen electrode, i.e. hydrogen gas bubbled over a platinized electrode. Both the quinhydrone and the antimony electrodes have been used as secondary standards. For practical purposes, however, these have been displaced by the glass electrode and this is now almost invariably used for sea water; attention will be confined to such measurements. Some type of calomel electrode, i.e.

$$\text{Hg (liquid), } Hg_2Cl_2 \text{ (solid), } Cl^- \text{ (solution),}$$

is almost invariably used as the reference electrode.

The Glass Electrode

In its common form this consists of a thin glass bulb inside which is mounted a reference electrode, frequently a silver chloride or calomel electrode in hydrochloric acid. The potential of the electrode in the unknown solution is measured with respect to the external reference solution. The exact mechanism by which the surface potential develops is not completely understood but the conditioned electrode serves as a site for proton transfer between the solution and the reservoir of protons in the surface of the glass; the potential of the surface changes as protons are acquired or lost.

There are many types of electrode available and makers' catalogues should be consulted. It may be pointed out that electrodes taking small quantities of solution and with semi-automatic washing are available.

The care of glass electrodes. A new electrode or one that has been left dry for some time should be soaked 1–2 hours or preferably overnight before use; phosphate buffer near pH 7·0 or distilled water may be used. If the use of a new or inadequately soaked electrode cannot be avoided, the pH assembly should be repeatedly standardized during the early estimations with that electrode. Storage of an electrode in distilled water prolongs its life.

Although the pH-sensitive tip or bulb may be dried without damage, care must be taken that it does not become scratched or cracked. Standardization of an assembly with two known buffers will readily reveal any defects in the electrode.

Electrodes should not be placed in chromic acid or other dehydrating liquids. Contact with non-aqueous liquids should be avoided and after any such contact the electrode should be reconditioned. Old electrodes can sometimes be restored to their normal response by treatment with 6 M hydrochloric acid followed by washing with distilled water.

The Calomel Reference Electrode

As already pointed out this consists essentially of mercury, mercurous chloride and the chloride ion; the chloride solution is saturated with calomel at the surface of the mercury and is maintained so in spite of any temperature changes by the presence of excess calomel. The chloride, KCl, may be 0·1 N, N or saturated. Connection between the reference electrode and the solution under test is made by a salt bridge, which is now normally incorporated into the calomel electrode assembly. Since the salt bridge is saturated potassium chloride solution the reference electrode now most conveniently employed (which avoids a second liquid junction) is the saturated calomel electrode, although in some respects it is less satisfactory (temperature coefficient, reproducibility) than the 0·1 N calomel electrode.

The junction is now normally of either the impeded flow or static junction type. Of the former the sleeve type, or of the latter those with a porous plug are commonly used. Facilities are provided for flushing in both cases.

The pH Meter

The internal resistance of the glass electrode cell is very high and the potential changes are therefore measured with vacuum-tube electrometers. The pH meter is in reality a voltmeter with a high input resistance, high zero-stability, low scale-length error and compensation for temperature changes at the electrodes (10). Commercial instruments may be divided into the potentiometric (slide-wire) and the direct-reading instruments. In the former the vacuum-tube amplifier is used as a null-point detector; the latter has a vacuum-tube voltmeter of the deflection type. The potentiometric instruments are capable of greater accuracy. For details of circuitry the maker's catalogues and instruction sheets should be consulted since details vary with the instrument.

Errors with pH meters. These have been summarized by Perley (in Bates, 5, p. 286) as follows, the maximum limit of error being given in terms of percentage of the scale reading.

Leakage errors	0·01
Stability and sensitivity of detector	0·01
Calibration and adjustment of temperature compensation	0·10
Zero adjustment	0·10
Potentiometric type	
Calibration of slide wire	0·30
Adjustment of standardizing current	0·10
E.m.f. of standard cell	0·05
Direct-reading type	
Calibration of deflection meter	1·00

Adjustments and repairs to pH meters. A large majority of the difficulties encountered in the operation of pH assemblies can be traced to the electrodes, with worn-out batteries and defective valves following next in order of importance. Failures of the other components of the circuits and any effects of humidity are less frequent causes of trouble. According to the Beckman Company (4), nearly all troubles arise from one or more of the following causes:

1. Scratched or cracked bulb of glass electrode.
2. Cracked or broken internal assembly of the glass or calomel electrode.
3. Electrodes not properly cleaned.
4. Contamination of the potassium chloride solution of the calomel electrode or salt bridge.
5. Interruption of the flow of potassium chloride solution from the calomel electrode by clogged aperture.
6. Inaccurate buffer solution.
7. Instability of sample being tested or unusually high resistance of the solution.
8. Worn-out batteries.

9. Imperfect or incorrect battery connections.
10. Defective or worn-out valves.

Location of difficulties. Unfortunately, faulty operation of a pH meter is not always at once evident, and the operator may not be aware that incorrect values are being obtained. For this reason, it is strongly recommended that at least two reliable standard buffer solutions, differing in pH by at least two units, should be available, and that as a routine procedure the instrument should be standardized against both. A reading for the pH of the second solution, after the meter has been standardized with the first, will serve as a check on the satisfactory functioning of the *entire* assembly.

If this double standardization reveals operating difficulties, it must be decided whether the fault lies with the meter or with the electrodes. The most common meter troubles render it impossible to balance the amplifier, even when the electrodes are entirely out of the circuit. If the amplifier of a battery-operated instrument cannot be balanced properly, the voltages of the batteries should first be measured under load, i.e. with the meter turned on and all the batteries connected. Batteries should be replaced, as a rule, when they have dropped 10 to 15% below their rated voltage.

If the batteries are found to be in order one of the valves may be at fault. An unsteadiness or oscillation of the meter needle is a frequent indication of valve failure. Proper operation of the electrometer valve should be verified by substituting a new valve. The performance of most other valves can be checked adequately with a radio valve tester. It is advisable, however, to make a secondary check at lower filament voltages to simulate the actual conditions under which many of these valves are used in pH meters.

The manufacturers of pH instruments usually supply circuit diagrams and instructions for locating amplifier difficulties and for making simple repairs. The literature on the particular instrument should be consulted if amplifier troubles persist after replacement of any defective batteries or valves.

If no difficulty is experienced in bringing the amplifier to a satisfactorily constant zero setting, the trouble may lie in the electrodes and solutions. An extra pair of electrodes, known to be in good condition, should always be kept available for test purposes. Only in this way is it easy to check on the electrodes. If this simple replacement test cannot be made, or if it is found that the electrodes are at fault, the condition of both glass and calomel electrodes should be carefully examined.

Inspect the glass electrode for scratches, cracks, or any surface deposit. Clean the electrode by immersion in dilute hydrochloric acid followed by thorough rinsing and gentle rubbing with soft absorbent tissue. Ensure that the electrical circuit within the calomel electrode itself is not broken by any air bubbles that appear when the level of the potassium chloride solution in the salt bridge becomes too low. A break in the calomel-mercury column itself usually does no harm. The air bubbles can sometimes be removed by gentle evacuation of the salt bridge chamber or by warming the electrode in hot water. Make sure that the potassium chloride solution can flow freely from the electrode and that a few crystals of solid potassium chloride are present in the salt bridge. A hard mass of salt is to be avoided. If contamination is suspected, renew the chloride solution; dry the electrodes and leads carefully, and replace the electrodes in the holder. Insulation leakage, a defective valve, and a change in the grid bias may make it impossible to adjust the meter to the pH of this buffer solution by means of the standardization (asymmetry potential) control, even though good electrodes are used. A drift or lack of stability may have the same origin or may be caused by poor contacts in the various controls. Leakage is most pronounced in humid atmospheres but may occur at normal humidities if the glass-electrode terminal is not kept clean. In very dry atmospheres, earthing the case of the meter is sometimes helpful in reducing fluctuations caused by static charges.

It may happen that no difficulty is experienced in standardizing the instrument with the first standard but the reading for the second solution is in error. This is a common experience when the glass electrode is cracked or when, because of unusual attack or ageing, it is not displaying the theoretical response. An improperly adjusted or defective temperature compensator may also be the cause. In meters of the potentiometric type, a change in the e.m.f. of the standard cell may be responsible.

Simple remedial measures such as the replacement of batteries and valves, the elimination of electrical leakage, and the proper care of electrodes may be readily made, but repairs to the instrument should only be made by those with both the technical skill, experience and a full understanding of the function and requirements of a vacuum-tube electrometer.

PROCEDURE FOR THE DETERMINATION
OF pH VALUES

The determination of pH values is guided by the following considerations:

1. The pH assembly is designed to indicate a difference between the pH value of a standard buffer and an unknown or test solution, both of which are at the same temperature.

2. The accuracy of the instrument over the pH range of the test solutions should be demonstrated after standardization by determining the pH of a second standard solution. If possible, the two standards should bracket the pH of the unknowns.

3. Errors caused by changes in temperature and by the residual liquid-junction potential are minimized by standardizing the assembly at a pH value close to that of the test solution.

The following recommendations are largely those set out by the American Society for Testing Materials (3).

Standardization of the Assembly

Switch on the instrument and allow to warm up thoroughly and then bring the amplifier to electrical balance in accordance with the manufacturer's instructions. Wash the electrodes and sample container three times with distilled water, and then with the appropriate buffer. Form a fresh liquid junction, if the salt bridge is not of the continuous-flow type. Note the temperature of the unknown or test solution, and adjust the temperature dial of the meter to the proper setting.

Choose two standard buffer solutions to bracket, if possible, the pH of the unknown. Warm or cool these solutions as necessary to match within $2°$C. the temperature of the unknown. Immerse the electrodes in a portion of the first standard. Engage the operating button, or turn the range switch to the proper position, and rotate the standardizing or asymmetry potential knob until the meter is balanced at the known pH of the standard (pH$_s$), at the appropriate temperature, as given in Table 24 (page 305). Repeat the process with additional portions of the standard solution until the instrument remains in balance (within $\pm$ 0·02 pH unit) for two successive portions without a change in the position of the asymmetry potential knob. If the initial temperature of the electrodes differs appreciably from that of the solutions, several portions of solution should be used and the electrodes immersed deeply to assure that both electrodes and solution are at the required temperature. The temperature of electrodes, standard solutions, and wash water should be kept throughout as close as possible to that of the unknowns.

Wash the electrodes and sample container again and fill the latter with the second standard after forming a fresh liquid junction. Adjust the instrument to balance, and read the pH of this second solution without changing the position of the asymmetry potential knob. Repeat with additional portions of the second standard until successive readings agree within $\pm$0·02 pH unit. The assembly is considered to be operating satisfactorily if the reading obtained for the second standard matches the assigned pH of this standard within ± 0.05 unit. If the amplifier is turned off at all the instrument should always be re-standardized. A final check should be made at the conclusion of a series of measurements. The need for more intermediate standardization should be examined from time to time. Always endeavour to work with solutions at the ambient temperature.

pH of the Test Solution

The procedure depends upon the nature of the test solution. In experimental work when the solutions are reasonably well buffered it is advisable to have the test solution at the same temperature as that of the standard buffer; this may usually be best attained by working with all solutions at a reasonably constant ambient temperature. With sea water freshly drawn which is neither in equilibrium with the atmosphere nor at ambient temperature it may not be brought to ambient temperature and a correction must be applied.

(1) *Reasonably well buffered solutions.* Wash the electrode and sample container thoroughly. Fill the container with solution, form a fresh liquid junction and obtain a preliminary value for the pH. Replace the sample with other portions of the test solution until the pH readings of two successive portions agree to within $0.02\,p$H unit. If the quantity of test solution is limited the electrode may be washed with the solution and allowed to stand in the first sample until drift ceases.

(2) *Poorly buffered solutions—sea water.* Some workers use a specially made cell in which the sample is protected from the atmosphere; a weighing bottle with a stopper through which the electrodes pass and which has a filling tube reaching to the bottom of the bottle and an overflow tube may be used. Alternately special electrode assemblies can be purchased. Some workers rely on rapidity of estimation to eliminate errors due to contact with the atmosphere. When working with cold deep-water samples in hot weather a Dewar flask may be used; Bruneau, Jerlov and Koczy (6) did not find this necessary when using 50 ml. of water sample.

Rinse the vessel and make a preliminary pH estimation; replace if possible with a new sample (again to conserve the sample allow the electrode to soak). Two successive portions should not differ by more than $0.02\,p$H unit, although in very poorly buffered water drifts of 0.05–$0.10\,p$H unit may be obtained if the samples are exposed to the atmosphere.

In order to obtain the pH *in situ* correction must be applied for:

(a) the temperature *in situ*;
(b) the pressure *in situ*;
(c) the error of the automatic temperature correction.

Buch and Gripenberg (8), Buch and Nynäs (9) and Buch (7) give the following equation to correct for the effects:

$$pH \; in \; situ = pH_t + x(t - t') \mp \frac{\xi D}{1000} + \delta\pi_{t^\circ}(t' - t^\circ),$$

where t' =temperature during measurement, t° =temperature of the buffer standard, t =temperature *in situ*, D =depth in metres, x = function of chlorinity, pH, and t (*see* Table 23), $\delta\pi_t$ =function of pH, in respect of instrument, ξ =function of pH (*see* Table 22). The correction factor $\delta\pi_{t^\circ}$ should be determined for each instrument. It must be obtained by determining the pH of buffer solutions whose temperature coefficient of pH is known (*see* Table 24) over the temperature range to be encountered or by the use of a precision potentiometric device if available (*see* Bates, 5, p. 228); if there is automatic temperature correction in the instrument, or a manual adjustment for temperature changes, this factor should still be checked; some authors have found the error independent of pH.

REFERENCES

1. Anon., 1950. 'Standardization of pH measurements with the glass electrode.' *Letter Circular, LC-993.* National Bureau of Standards, dards, Washington, D.C.
2. Anon., 1950. 'pH Scale, British Standard 1647.' British Standards Institution, London.
3. Anon., 1952. 'Determination of the pH of aqueous solutions with the glass electrode.' ASTM Method E 70–52T, Philadelphia, Pa.
4. Anon., no date. 'Instructions for servicing Beckman pH meters.' Beckman Bulletins, 132 D and 230, Beckman Instruments Inc., South Pasadena, California.
5. Bates, R. G., 1954. *Electrometric pH Determinations.* John Wiley and Sons, Inc., New York, 331 pp.
6. Bruneau, L., Jerlov, N. G., and Koczy, F. F., 1953. 'Physical and chemical methods.' Reports of the Swedish Deep-Sea Expedition, 1947–8. Vol. 3, *Physics and Chemistry*, No. 4, 101–12, Appendix I–LV. Göteborgs Vetensk. Samh.
7. Buch, K., 1938. 'Versuche über photoelektrische pH-Bestimmung im Meerwasser.' *C.R. Lab. Carlsberg, Série Chimique*, 22, 109–17.
8. ——, and Gripenberg, S., 1932. 'Über den Einfluss des Wasserdruckes auf pH und das Kohlensäuregleichgewicht in grösseren Meerestiefen.' *J. Cons. int. Explor. Mer*, 7, 232–45.
9. ——, and Nynäs, O., 1939. 'Studien über neuere pH-Methodik mit besonderer Berücksichtigung des Meerwassers.' *Acta Acad. åbo.*, 12, No. 3, 41 pp.
10. Hitchcox, G. I., 1951. 'Critical survey of pH meters.' *Mfg. Chem.*, 22, 93–7.

6

INORGANIC NITROGEN: NITRATE

Range, 0–50 μg.-atom NO_3–N/l.

At. wt. N = 14·008.

Factor, g. N to g.-atom N = 0·07139.

Factor, g. N to g. NO_3 = 4·4267.

Factor, g. NO_3 to g. N = 0·2259.

For the estimation of nitrates in such quantities as are present in natural waters four methods must be considered, namely:

(i) Nitration of phenoldisulphonic acid or related compounds.
(ii) Reduction to ammonia or nitrite.
(iii) The production of colours with various reagents in concentrated sulphuric acid solution as a result of the oxidizing properties of nitric acid.
(iv) Polarographically.

The first of these methods cannot be used with sea water, since even quite small quantities of chloride interfere. The second method suffers from the disadvantages first, that ammonia may be produced from nitrogenous material other than nitrate under the vigorous reducing conditions employed and secondly, that it is not readily carried out on board ship. Mullin and Riley (19) have recently overcome the difficulties in a quantitative reduction to nitrite and their method is given. The method requires a little more manipulation than the others which it will probably replace. The third method is the one which has been largely used for sea water estimations. It suffers from the disadvantage that it is not specific, but since (probably owing to catalytic reactions involving nitric oxide) it is far more sensitive for nitrates than other oxidizing agents, the latter have negligible interference in sea-water analysis.

Two reagents, Harvey's reduced strychnine (10 and 11) and diphenylbenzidine (Atkins, 1), in strong sulphuric acid have been largely used. The former reagent has given considerable trouble, and although it appears somewhat more sensitive than diphenylbenzidine it is not clear why the latter has been so much neglected. Zwicker and Robinson (23) have demonstrated that Harvey's reagent is a mixture of reduction products of strychnine and that

113

pure strychnidine is a more satisfactory reagent. Rochford's (21) method eliminates most of the troubles encountered in preparing the Harvey reagent; this method is given, as well as Zwicker and Robinson's instructions for the preparation of pure strychnidine, although the necessary facilities for this may not always be readily available. The estimation of nitrates with either of these reagents and with the diphenylbenzidine reagent then follows.

THE REDUCED STRYCHNINE METHOD

Reagents

Reagent 1: Preparation of reduced strychnine (20, 21). The difficulties arise partly as a result of impurities in the reagents and partly from contamination and reoxidation by atmospheric gases during preparation. Many of the troubles are eliminated by preparing the reagent under an atmosphere of carbon dioxide.

If necessary purify concentrated sulphuric acid by fuming with a crystal of ammonium sulphate (2 and 7). Use only iron-free zinc and the highest grade hydrochloric acid. Wash 100 g. of pure granulated zinc or zinc foil with dilute HCl, and then with a dilute solution of mercuric chloride to amalgamate; follow by rinsing with distilled water. Dissolve 2 g. of strychnine sulphate in 25 ml. of distilled water and transfer this and the amalgamated zinc to the flask (A) (Fig. 30), which is heated gently on a water bath. Blow carbon dioxide through the flask and then add 150–200 ml. of concentrated hydrochloric acid in 25 ml. lots at 15-minute intervals from (G) whilst maintaining the slow flow of carbon dioxide. When the vigorous zinc-hydrochloric acid reaction is over, increase the flow of carbon dioxide. Over a period of 15–20 hours evaporate to a volume of 100–125 ml. under carbon dioxide. The reagent should be colourless. When the required volume has been reached, the carbon dioxide supply is connected to the flask (A) at (H), the two-way tap at (D) adjusted so that connection with (E) is established, and the liquid blown over into flask (B). Add 500 ml. of concentrated sulphuric acid with shaking; the hydrogen chloride evolved is swept out at (E) by the carbon dioxide. Allow the solution to stand for about a day until all the zinc sulphate has settled, and then decant off the supernatant reagent into a dark bottle. This stock reagent should stand a few days before use.

Harvey diluted his reagent with 1 litre of sulphuric acid and allowed to stand six weeks before use. Rochford (21) finds that the reagent prepared as described above deteriorates less if diluted with only 500 ml. of sulphuric acid and that it gives satisfactory results within several days of preparation: when extreme sensitivity is required the optimum dilution should be ascertained by testing with a standard nitrate solution. In general between three- and six-fold dilution gives little change in the sensitivity of the reagent.

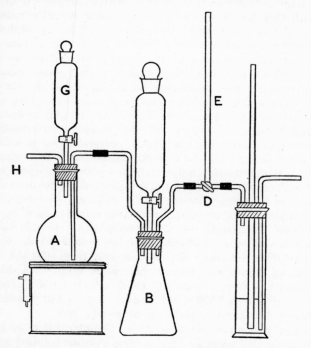

FIG. 30. Apparatus for the preparation of Harvey's Reagent.

Matida (18) has used a mercury amalgam reducing agent. Dissolve 4 g. of strychnine sulphate in 150 ml. of 18 N-H$_2$SO$_4$. Introduce 10 ml. of the solution, 10 ml. of water and 150 g. of zinc amalgam into a vessel through which carbon dioxide can be passed. Heat on a water bath for 3 minutes; shake and repeat heating several times during 15 minutes. Remove the amalgam whilst still passing carbon dioxide through the vessel. Add 120 ml. of concentrated sulphuric acid and mix. Use directly at this strength. The reagent is almost as sensitive as the strychnidine reagent (9).

Reagent 2: Preparation of strychnidine. This is prepared by the electrolytic reduction of strychnine on a mercury cathode according to the following instructions (22 and 23).

Dissolve about 10 g. of strychnine sulphate in 55 ml. of 64% sulphuric acid (sp. gr. 1·54). Cool and place in the cathode compartment of a reduction cell, containing 17·8 cm.[2] of mercury cathode, the porous anode compartment of which contains 60% by weight sulphuric acid and a strip platinum anode of 15 cm.[2] surface. Reduce for 35 hours at a temperature of 25°C. with a current of 0·75 ampere, and with 5 terminal volts and 3 cathode volts. After the reduction is completed, dilute the catholyte with 83 ml. of 0·01% sulphuric acid to give 28·5% sulphuric acid. Cool to room temperature or less, when most of the unreduced strychnine is precipitated as the acid sulphate which is filtered and washed with a small quantity of 28·5% sulphuric acid. Neutralize the excess acid in the filtrate with concentrated ammonia adding 100–200 g. of ice to cool the solution. Digest at 40–50°C. to remove excess ammonia and to dissolve the tetrahydrostrychnine. Filter off the residual strychnidine and purify with two extractions of 100 ml. portions of warm water.

To increase the yield the aqueous extracts may be concentrated, the crude tetrahydrostrychnine extracted with chloroform and then mixed with ten times its weight of phosphorus oxychloride under an atmosphere of carbon dioxide. After refluxing 45 minutes at 60–70°C. under reduced pressure, remove the excess reagent by vacuum distillation. Precipitate the strychnidine from the diluted brown syrup with ammonia, or as the hydriodide with hydriodic acid.

Recrystallize the crude strychnidine first from 100 ml. of 95% ethanol and then slowly two or three more times from thiophene-free benzene. This gives pure strychnidine, m.p. 256·6°C. (*in vacuo*).

For use dissolve 0·3200 g. in 1 litre concentrated sulphuric acid for nitrate concentrations up to 50 μg.-atom NO_3-N/l.

Standard potassium nitrate solution. Dissolve 1·0 g. of pure dry KNO_3 in distilled water or 35‰ sodium chloride solution and make up to 1 litre. This solution contains 9·84 mg.-atoms NO_3-N/l. Prepare further dilutions as required.

Procedure

Mix equal volumes of either reagent 1 or 2 and sea water by four rapid transfers in well-aged Pyrex test-tubes Allow to stand in dark 1 hour. Measure transmittancy using a Zeiss S-53, or Ilford blue filter No. 602, or at a wave-length of 530 mμ.[1]

With the Harvey reagent two drops of concentrated hydrochloric acid should be added to each sample.

Repeat with distilled water for blank.

Set up a calibration curve using standard potassium nitrate solutions in 35‰ sodium chloride solution or by nitrate additions to nitrate-free sea water.

---

[1] When a definite filter or working wave-length has been recommended for the measurement of transmittancies they will be quoted; alternative filters by other makers can be chosen from their catalogues.

Remarks

1. Between three- and six-fold dilution of the stock Harvey reagent gives little change in sensitivity. Matida's reagent should be used as prepared.

2. The optimum development time varies with reagent dilution; 1 hour is usually adequate for required sensitivity and keeps the blank low. The colour should be developed in the dark.

3. Conditions should be kept, as far as possible, the same in the preparation of the calibration curve and in all estimations.

4. Some workers object to any transfer or exposure to air after the reagent has been added; mixing is carried out by shaking.

5. Aging of the reagent should be checked from time to time with standard nitrate solution.

6. Sensitivity with strychnidine is $0 \cdot 5$–$1 \cdot 0$ μg.-atom NO_3-N/l.

7. A detailed study of the precision of Zwicker and Robinson's method has recently been published by Marvin (17). In these tests 1 ml. of sample was transferred to a 10 ml. test-tube and 2 ml. of distilled water added; this was followed by 3 ml. of strychnidine reagent, and the solutions mixed by transfer. Readings were taken on a photometer using 3 ml. micro-cells and a 525 mμ filter. It was found that the greatest single factor affecting the precision of the results is the variation in heat production during the mixing of sample and reagent. This mixing procedure should be carefully standardized. It is suggested that a set of standards should be included with every series of samples.

8. Nitrites interfere if present in excessive amounts and should be removed, for example in polluted waters. The interference is irregular.

THE DIPHENYLBENZIDINE METHOD (1, 3 and 4)

Reagent

Dissolve 20 mg. pure recrystallized (from boiling toluene) diphenyl-benzidine in 100 ml. N-free concentrated sulphuric acid.

Procedure

Transfer 7·5 ml. of the reagent to a test-tube (preferably silica) and add 2·5 ml. of the water sample, mixing rapidly. Allow to stand 20–24 hours. Measure the transmittancy using an orange filter (Ilford 607) or compare with standards in a colorimeter.

Set up a calibration curve by addition of nitrate solutions to nitrate-free sea water. Run a blank estimation. The calibration curve is not linear.

Remarks

1. The standards and unknown should be dealt with in an identical manner in view of the empirical nature of the method. The addition of water to sulphuric acid generates heat; care must be taken during this addition. Since it is essential to maintain the same conditions for every estimation, Black (4) therefore recommends adding the sea water at a known dropping rate from a pipette.

2. In the original method the acid was first mixed with the sample and followed by the reagent addition; the procedure given reduces any errors due to interaction of the liberated nitric acid with organic matter in the sea water because the reagent is present in the acid used.

3. The precision appears to be about $\pm 5\%$.

4. Difficulties are sometimes experienced when glass test-tubes are used perhaps due to the presence of manganese in white glass (not nitrate as suggested by Atkins, 1).

5. The colour intensity varies with the water-acid ratio; that given is optimal for maximum colour development. It is close to the mixture that gives maximal heat production.

6. The calibration is not linear: results must be compared with a curve.

7. Distilled water free from nitrate may be prepared by distillation from barium hydroxide in a clean atmosphere.

8. Plankton-rich samples should be centrifuged.

9. Nitrite interferes, and when present in large quantities tends to give irregular interference. In polluted water nitrites should be destroyed by the addition of sodium azide.

10. The colour is quite stable towards light.

11. There is a considerable salt effect and although a calibration curve may be set up in sodium chloride solutions it is better prepared in sea water with a low nitrate content.

REDUCTION TO NITRITE (19)

Since nitrite can be very readily estimated by the Griess-Ilosvay method (p. 126) a number of attempts have been made to reduce nitrate to nitrite and estimate it in this form (5 and 8). The conditions for a satisfactory quantitative and reproducible method have proved difficult to determine; under vigorous reducing conditions it is difficult to stop the reaction at the nitrite stage and mild reducing conditions give poor yields of nitrite. Mullin and Riley have overcome these difficulties and their method will probably replace those just described. These authors reduce the nitrate by means of hydrazine in alkaline solution (pH 9·6) in the presence of copper ions which act as a catalyst. The reaction is complete in 24 hours.

Reagents

All reagents and solutions must be made up with water freshly distilled from an all-glass still.

1. *Phenol-sodium phenate buffer*. Dissolve 9·40 g. of pure phenol in 200 ml. of water. Filter through a sintered glass filter (porosity 4) and dilute to 250 ml. Pipette 50 ml. of this stock phenol solution into a 100 ml. graduated flask, add 16 ml. of 1·00 N sodium hydroxide solution, dilute to volume, and mix thoroughly. Store the reagent in a dark glass bottle and reject when it becomes discoloured.

2. *Copper sulphate catalyst*. Prepare a solution containing 0·0393 g. of copper sulphate pentahydrate per 100 ml.

3. *Hydrazine sulphate solution*. Dissolve 1·20 g. of hydrazine sulphate in about 240 ml. of water. Dilute to 250 ml. and filter through a sintered glass filter (porosity 4).

4. *Hydrazine-copper reducing agent*. Mix 25 ml. of the stock hydrazine sulphate solution with 5 ml. of the copper sulphate catalyst and dilute to 50 ml. This reagent should be prepared daily.

5. *Sulphanilic acid*. To a solution of 0·30 g. of sulphanilic acid in about 80 ml. of water add 12·9 ml. of concentrated hydrochloric acid and dilute to 100 ml.

6. *α-Naphthylamine*. Dissolve 0·60 g. of recrystallized α-naphthylamine hydrochloride in about 80 ml. of water containing 1 ml. of concentrated hydrochloric acid. Dilute to 100 ml.

7. *Sodium acetate*, 2 M. 27·2 g. of hydrated sodium acetate/100 ml.

8. *Acetone*. Pure reagent grade.

9. *Standard nitrate solution*. (10 μg. NO_3-N/ml.). 0·0722 g. of reagent grade potassium nitrate/l. Dilute as required.

Treatment of Flasks

Clean all graduated flasks which are to be used for the determination of nitrate by filling them with concentrated sulphuric acid. After a few hours, empty them, and rinse first with water, then with dilute (0·1 N) sodium hydroxide, and finally wash well with distilled water.

Procedure

Place 40 ml. of the sea-water sample (freshly filtered, through a fine textured filter paper) in a 50 ml. graduated flask, and add 2 ml. of phenol-sodium phenate buffer while gently swirling the solution. Add 1 ml. of the hydrazine-copper reagent, mix thoroughly and set aside in the dark.

After 24 hours, add 2 ml. of acetone in order to complex any residual hydrazine and to retard the precipitation of the red azo-dye from nitrate-rich sea waters (containing 7–14 μg.-atom NO_3-N/l.). Allow the reaction to proceed for at least 2 minutes and then add 2 ml. of sulphanilic acid reagent with shaking. After not less than 5 minutes add 1 ml. of the naphthylamine reagent, shake, and then add 1 ml. of 2 M sodium acetate. Dilute to 50 ml. and mix thoroughly. After 15 minutes measure the optical density of the solution at 524 mμ, or with a suitable filter (Ilford 604) in a cell of appropriate length.

Reagent Blank for Sea Waters

Since it is frequently impossible to obtain sea water absolutely free from nitrate, it is necessary to determine the reagent blank in the following fashion. With 40 ml. of water freshly distilled from alkali, determine the optical density of the total reagent blank A as described above. Determine the optical density B of a similarly treated sample of the same distilled water, to which the α-naphthylamine reagent has not been added. The value for B is independent of whether sea water or distilled water is used. The reagent blank for sea water $= B + (A - B) \times$ salt error (Table I). This reagent blank should be determined daily. If the nitrate concentration of the water sample is high (above 5 μg.-atom NO_3-N/l.) then it suffices to employ the uncorrected distilled water blank as reagent blank.

Calibration

Calibrate the method by adding 1 ml. portions of suitably diluted standard nitrate solution to 40 ml. samples of sea water (low in nitrate), and develop the colour as described above. If suitable sea water is not available use instead 40 ml. of water freshly distilled from alkali, and correct the results using the salt-error factors given in Table I, p. 122.

Determination of Nitrate in Fresh Waters

The method described above may be used for the determination of nitrate in fresh waters. Since the nitrate concentrations of such water are often high (up to 700 μg.-atom NO_3-N/l.) it is necessary to take smaller samples (e.g. 5 ml. or less) and to dilute to 40 ml. with water distilled from alkali before carrying out the reduction. The reagent blank and calibration curve are determined using water distilled from alkali.

Calculations

In general it is not necessary to correct for nitrite interference in sea waters if it amounts to less than about 5 % of the nitrate present. In order to make the method of calculation clear a worked-out example is given. The following optical densities were recorded by Mullin and Riley using a 7·62 cm. cell at 524 mμ.

Calculation with Low Concentrations of Nitrite

Reduction procedure on 40 ml. of sea-water sample X ($Cl=18.7\%_0$)	0·455	...(1)
Similar determination on distilled water omitting α-naphthylamine	0·028	...(2)
Reduction procedure on alkali distilled water (40 ml.)	0·087	...(3)
Nitrate in reagents$=(3)-(2)=0·087-0·028$	$=0·059$	
Correcting for salt error (Table I) to chlorinity 18·7‰		
Sea-water blank due to nitrate in reagents $=0·059\times0·77$	$=0·045$	
Total sea-water blank$=0·045+0·028$	$=0·073$	...(4)
This total blank is constant throughout a series of determinations		
Optical density due to nitrate$=0·455-0·073$	$=0·382$	

Read off the nitrate concentration from the calibration curve. If the chlorinity of the water sample is appreciably different from 19‰, the observed optical density of the reduced sample should be divided by the salt-error factor (Table I) at the appropriate chlorinity, and the nitrate concentration read from the distilled water calibration curve.

Calculation in Presence of High Nitrite Concentrations

Considering a sea water rich in nitrite giving the same readings as in (1) and (2) above.

Sample X with reagents 5 and 6, (less reagent blank)	$=0·162$	...(5)
Calibration with 40 ml. of distilled water containing 1·7 μg.-atom NO_2-N/l. (less reagent blank)	$=0·456$	...(6)

Hence X contains 0·6 μg.-atom NO_2-N/l.

NO_2-N correction for the nitrite concentration is 0·39.

The nitrate equivalent of various quantities of nitrite must be determined in a separate series of experiments if waters rich in this anion are to be dealt with. The nitrite contribution to the absorption of the reduced solution$=0·39\times0·162=0·063$ using Mullin and Riley's factor. Optical density due to total reagent blank (equation 4) and nitrite in sea water after reduction$=0·073+0·063=0·136$; hence absorption due to nitrate$=0·455-0·136=0·319$. Read the nitrate concentration from the calibration curve.

Remarks

1. In the absence of added copper catalyst the reduction is erratic, in part due to variations in the copper content of the distilled water. The amount of copper required for maximum and reproducible yields is about 6 μg. $Cu^{++}/40$ ml., but the quantity is not critical.

2. The reduction is inhibited by traces of magnesium ions at high pH values. This interference is eliminated by buffering the solutions at pH 9·5.

3. The reduction is complete in both fresh and sea water in about 22 hours at 20°C. and no further change in the nitrite content takes place during a further 20 hours.

4. The temperature should lie between 18° and 30°C.; below the former a reduction in optical density takes place and above the latter precipitation of calcium and magnesium salts may occur and inhibit the reaction.

5. Salts reduce the efficiency of reduction; the salt error (ratio of optical density in sea water to that in distilled water for the same quantity of nitrate) is a linear function of chlorinity and to within 3% independent of nitrate concentration. Correction factors (F) are given in Table I.

TABLE I

Salt-error corrections

$Cl‰$	0	5·0	10·0	15·0	16·0	17·0	18·0	19·0	20·0
F	1·00	0·94	0·88	0·82	0·81	0·80	0·78	0·77	0·76

6. In general it is not necessary to correct for nitrite present. With high nitrite content a correction must be applied; a calibration curve for the nitrate equivalent of nitrite subjected to the reduction treatment must be determined from a separate series of experiments.

7. It is not advisable to work with concentrations much greater than 30 μg.-atom NO_3-N/l.

8. The standard deviation is quoted as $\pm 2\%$.

9. It is most important to filter all the samples through a close-textured paper before analysis, since even small amounts of suspended matter prevent the reduction from nitrate to nitrite.

10. Ammonium ions and urea interfere with the estimation, but the effect is only appreciable at concentrations twenty times that of the nitrate nitrogen; such conditions are never found in sea water.

11. If samples have to be stored (they are best analysed within 24 hours) they should be filtered and kept in glass bottles in the presence of not more than 2 μg./ml. of mercuric chloride. Polythene bottles must not be used and neither chloroform nor formaldehyde should be added as preservative.

NITRATE: POLAROGRAPHIC METHOD

In their investigation of the polarography of uranium, Kolthoff, Harris and Matsuyama (14) found that in acid solution there were two waves indicating reduction of U^{VI} to U^V and U^V to U^{III}, and that nitrate was reduced to nitrogen gas at potentials where the second wave occurred. They further demonstrated a linear relation between diffusion current and nitrate concentration when the uranyl ion content was above a minimum value which was a function of the nitrate content. This method has been used by Chow and Robinson (6) to determine nitrate in sea water using a standard polarograph. The method is not suitable for shipboard use. Little work has been done with this technique.

Apparatus

A Heyrovský micro-polarograph (Model X) was calibrated by the method of Kolthoff and Lingane (15). An H-shaped electrolytic cell (13 and 16) with a saturated calomel reference electrode as one arm connected by a KCl bridge was used. The capillary characteristic $m^{2/3} \cdot t^{1/6}$ (12) was $1\cdot30$ mg.$^{2/3}$ sec.$^{-1/2}$. The electrolytic cell was immersed in a thermostat adjusted to $20°\ \pm0\cdot1°C$.

Preservation of the Water Samples

The method cannot be used on board ship, and because rapid changes in nitrate content may take place on storing, preservation of samples is essential. They should *not* be stored in polythene bottles since, at the potential used, samples stored in this way give a rapidly increasing current which completely masks the nitrate wave. Chloroform, which is removed during deoxygenation, is a satisfactory preservative.

As soon as the sample is taken add 2 ml. of chloroform to each 300 ml.: store in a dark, cool place.

Reagents

1. *Uranyl acetate solution.* Dissolve $0\cdot8484$ g. uranyl acetate crystals, $UO_2(CH_3COO)_2 \cdot 2H_2O$ in distilled water and make up to 1 litre. This solution is $2\cdot00 \times 10^{-3}$ M with respect to the uranyl ion.

2. *Aluminium chloride-hydrochloric acid reagent.* Dissolve $32\cdot2$ g. $AlCl_3 \cdot 6H_2O$ crystals in distilled water, add $83\cdot3$ ml. of 12 N-HCl and make up to 1 litre. This reagent is 1 M with respect to the HCl and $0\cdot13$ M with respect to the $AlCl_3$.

3. *Standard nitrate solution.* Dissolve $0\cdot17$ g. sodium nitrate in distilled water and make up to 1 litre.

Procedure

Transfer 100 ml. of the sample into the electrolytic cell by pipette, add 5 ml. of the uranyl acetate solution followed by 1·5 ml. of the $AlCl_3$-HCl reagent. Remove the dissolved oxygen by washing with nitrogen gas and take the polarogram immediately. Measure the current at $-1·2$ V. vs. S.C.E. Run a calibration curve with known quantities of nitrate.

Remarks

1. In the presence of fluoride the nitrate wave is distorted, and the half-wave potential is shifted towards the negative side, probably due to interaction of the U^{III} ions with fluoride. The aluminium chloride complexes any fluoride and prevents interference.

2. Nitrite is reduced in the same manner as nitrate, but its current is only about three-fifths of that due to nitrate. Nitrite is usually less than 0·4 μg.-atom/l. and its effect may be ignored: if its concentration exceeds 10 μg.-atom/l. an appropriate correction should be applied.

3. The results in natural sea water are different from those in equivalent sodium chloride solutions as a result of the sulphate present in the former. The calibration curve should be run on artificial sea water, or, nitrate-free natural sea water and not on chloride solutions: for chlorinities between 14 and 19‰ a single calibration is adequate. Below 14‰ chlorinity it is suggested that new calibration curves should be set up using sea water from which the sulphate has been removed by the addition of a strontium salt.

4. The nitrate may be calculated from the equation

$$i = (1·17 \times 10^{-2})(m^{2/3}t^{1/6}) . C,$$

where i is the diffusion current due to nitrate in microamperes, $m^{2/3}t^{1/6}$ (12) is the capillary characteristic and C is the concentration in μg.-atom NO_3-N/l.

5. The hydrogen-ion concentration must be adjusted to lie between 0·005–0·02 M, i.e. 1·5 ml. M-HCl per 100 ml. sample, and this is effected by the mixed reagent.

6. The average deviation, over a range of chlorinities, and for nitrate additions between 10 and 40 μg.-atom NO_3-N/l. with a total concentration of 10–70 μg.-atom NO_3-N/l., was found by Chow and Robinson to be $\pm 0·20$ μg.-atom NO_3-N/l.

REFERENCES

1. Atkins, W. R. G., 1932. 'Nitrate in sea water and its estimation by means of diphenylbenzidine.' *J. Mar. biol. Ass. U.K.*, **18**, 167–92.
2. ——, 1932. 'Preparation of sulphuric acid free from nitric acid.' *Nature, Lond.*, **129**, 98.

3. Atkins, W. R. G., 1954. 'Note on the use of diphenylbenzidine for the estimation of nitrate in sea water.' *J. Cons. int. Explor. Mer*, **20**, 153–5.

4. Black, W. A. P., and Dewar, E. T., 1949. 'Correlation of some of the physical and chemical properties of the sea with the chemical constitution of the algae.' *J. Mar. biol. Ass. U.K.*, **28**, 673–99.

5. Bray, R. H., 1945. 'Nitrate tests for soil and plant tissues.' *Soil Sci.*, **60**, 219–21.

6. Chow, D. T.-W., and Robinson, R. J., 1953. 'Polarographic determination of nitrate in sea water.' *J. Mar. Res.*, **12**, 1–12.

7. Cooper, L. H. N., 1932. 'The determination of nitrate in the sea by reduced strychnine.' *J. Mar. biol. Ass. U.K.*, **18**, 161–6.

8. Føyn, E., 1951. 'Nitrogen determinations in sea water.' *Fiskeridirektoratets Skrifter* **9**, No. 14, 7 pp..

9. Fukai, R., 1955. 'Critical studies on the analytical methods for minor chemical constituents in sea water. Part 3. Remarks on the methods of estimation of nitrogen nitrate by means of reduced strychnine reagent.' *J. Oceanogr. Soc. Japan*, **11**, 19–23.

10. Harvey, H. W., 1926. 'Nitrate in the sea.' *J. Mar. biol. Ass. U.K.*, **14**, 71–88.

11. ——, 1930. 'Nitrate in the sea. II.' *J. Mar. biol. Ass. U.K.*, **15**, 183–90.

12. Ilkovic, D., 1934. 'Dependence of limiting currents on the diffusion constants on the rate of dropping and on the size of drops.' *Coll. Trav. chim. Tchecosl.*, **6**, 498–513.

13. Keilin, B., and Otvos, J. W., 1946. 'The polarographic analysis of nitrite and nitrite-nitrate mixtures.' *J. Amer. chem. Soc.*, **68**, 2665–8.

14. Kolthoff, I. M., Harris, W. E., and Matsuyama, G., 1944. 'A new method for the polarographic determination of nitrate.' *J. Amer. chem. Soc.*, **66**, 1782–6.

15. ——, and Lingane, J. J., 1946. *Polarography*. Interscience Publishers, New York, 228 pp.

16. Lingane, J. J., and Laitinen, H. A., 1939. 'Cell and dropping electrode for polarographic analysis.' *Industr. Engng. Chem. (Anal.)*, **11**, 504–5.

17. Marvin, K. T., 1955. 'Notes on the precision of a modified routine nitrate-nitrite analysis.' *J. Mar. Res.*, **14**, 79–87.

18. Matida, Y., 1951. 'New method of preparing reduced strychnine reagent for the nitrate determination in sea water.' *Bull. chem. Soc. Japan*, **24**, 254–7.

19. Mullin, J. B., and Riley, J. P., 1955. 'The spectrophotometric determination of nitrate in natural waters with particular reference to sea water.' *Analyt. chim. acta*, **12**, 464–80.

20. Riddell, W. A., 1936. 'The reduced strychnine method for determining nitrates in sea water.' *J. biol. Bd. Can.*, **2**, 1–11.

21. Rochford, D., 1947. 'The preparation and use of Harvey's reduced strychnine reagent in oceanographical chemistry.' *Bull. Counc. sci. industr. Res. Aust.*, No. 220, Report No. 13.

22. Zwicker, B. M. G., and Robinson, R. J., 1942. 'Electrolytic reduction of strychnine.' *J. Amer. chem. Soc.*, **64**, 790–3.

23. ——, ——, 1944. 'The photometric determination of nitrate in sea water with a strychnidine reagent.' *J. Mar. Res.*, **5**, 214–32.

7

INORGANIC NITROGEN: NITRITE

Range, 0–2·0 μg.-atom NO_2-N/l

At. wt. N=14·008.

Factor, g. N to g.-atom N=0·07139.

Factor, g. N to g. NO_2=3·2844.

Factor, g. NO_2 to g. N=0·3045.

All modern methods for the estimation of trace amounts of nitrite depend upon diazotization of an amino compound, followed by a coupling reaction to give an azo dye. Sulphanilic acid and α-naphthylamine are used most frequently; for extreme sensitivity sulphanilamide and N-(1 naphthyl) ethylenediamine hydrochloride may be used. Reported discrepancies in the method are due to variations in reagents and procedure (1, 2, 5, q.v. for further references). The method given below ensures optimal conditions, since the first stage diazotization is done at a low pH, and the coupling at a higher pH. A mixed diazotizing and coupling reagent should not be used (4).

Reagents

1. *Sulphanilic acid.* Dissolve 0·6 g. sulphanilic acid in 20% v/v hydrochloric acid, warming gently if necessary, and make up to 100 ml. with acid of this strength.

2. *α-Naphthylamine.* Dissolve 0·48 g. in 1·3% v/v hydrochloric acid and make up to 100 ml. with acid of this strength.

3. *Sodium acetate buffer.* Dissolve 272 g. crystalline sodium acetate, $CH_3COONa.3H_2O$, in distilled water and make up to 1 litre.

4. *Sodium nitrite.* Dry sodium nitrite at 110°C. for several hours. Dissolve 0·6900 g. in boiled-out distilled water and make up to 1 litre with same. Add 0·2 ml. of chloroform as preservative. 1 ml. of this solution contains 10 μg.-atom NO_2-N. Dilute as required.

If silver nitrite is to be used as the standard (*see* p. 127) dissolve 0·10979 g. of the dry solid in about 10 ml. of hot distilled water, add 0·109 g. of sodium chloride, shake until the silver chloride flocculates and dilute to 1 litre. Draw off 10 ml. of the clear solution and dilute to 1 litre. This final solution contains 7·1 μg.-atom NO_2-N/l.

Procedure

To 100 ml. of sea water add 2 ml. of sulphanilic acid reagent. Mix well and after standing 5 minutes add 2 ml. of α-naphthylamine reagent followed by 2 ml. acetate buffer. After standing 30 minutes measure transmittancy against distilled water with a green filter (Ilford 604), or at 524 mμ.

Remarks

1. The method given ensures maximum sensitivity and minimum time for the development of maximum colour which is stable for at least 12 hours in the dark.

2. Hydrochloric acid is preferable to acetic acid; the reagents dissolve more easily and the latter has no advantage.

3. Solutions very quickly become poisoned with nitrite in a laboratory as a result of smoke and dust. Precautions should be taken against this during manipulation.

4. Use of boiled-out water for the diluted stock helps to prevent deterioration of these dilute standards.

5. There is no salt error and the standards for the calibration curve may be made up in distilled water and the absorbancy index calculated from these results. The rate of colour development is, however, greater in sea water; the time recommended is adequate for both solutions.

6. Increase in temperature within the limits usually encountered has no significant effect on the maximum colour although it affects the rate of development.

7. The stock solution should be stored in the dark.

8. The samples should be treated as soon as possible after collection.

9. Some Japanese workers (3) prefer to use a solid reagent, which is considered simpler, more convenient and more stable.

Grind 1 g. α-naphthylamine, 10 g. sulphanilic acid and 89 g. tartaric acid together with pestle and mortar. For use add 0·3 g. reagent to 50 ml. sea water.

10. The use of silver nitrite has been recommended as a standard. To prepare the solid, add to a cold solution of about 2·0 g. of sodium nitrite dissolved in 50 ml. of water a solution of silver nitrate so long as a precipitate forms. Decant off the liquid and thoroughly wash the precipitate with cold water. Recrystallize from boiling water and dry in the dark *in vacuo* at room temperature. Preserve in dark bottles in a cupboard. Although not considered reliable by some workers, sodium nitrite is frequently assayed by titration with potassium permanganate. A good quality dry sodium nitrite may be 99% pure. The following method of assay is used.

Nitrites are oxidized in acid solution to nitrates by potassium permanganate, but acidification of a nitrite solution prior to titration would lead to loss of volatile oxides. Weigh out accurately about 1 g. of the nitrite and make up to 250 ml. Prepare a 0·1 N solution of potassium permanganate and a 0·1 N solution of ferrous ammonium sulphate. Transfer 25 ml. of the standardized permanganate to a beaker, add 300 ml. of 0·75 $N-H_2SO_4$, warm to 40°C.

Add 10 ml. of the nitrite solution slowly with the tip of the pipette just under the surface of the liquid. Allow to stand 5 minutes at 40°C. Titrate the excess of permanganate with the ferrous ammonium sulphate. The permanganate should be standardized with the ferrous ammonium sulphate; 1 ml. 0·1 $N-KMnO_4$ is equivalent to 0·00345 g. sodium nitrite.

REFERENCES

1. Barnes, H., 1954. 'The estimation of nitrites.' *Mem. Ist. Ital. Idrobiol.*, **8**, 73–99.
2. ——, and Folkard, A. R., 1951. 'The determination of nitrites.' *Analyst*, **76**, 599–603.
3. Matida, Y., 1948. 'A study on the colorimetric determination of nitrite with the Griess-Romijn reagent.' *J. chem. Soc. Japan*, **69**, 176–8.
4. Rider, B. F., with Mellon, M. G., 1946. 'Colorimetric determination of nitrites.' *Industr. Engng. Chem. (Anal.)*, **18**, 96–9.
5. Robinson, R. J., and Thompson, T. G., 1948. 'The determination of nitrites in sea water.' *J. Mar. Res.*, **7**, 42–8.

INORGANIC NITROGEN: AMMONIA

Range, 0–3·5 μg.-atom NH_3-N/l.

At. wt. N=14·008.

Factor, g. N to g.-atom N=0·07139.

Factor, g. N to g. NH_3=1·2159.

Factor, g. NH_3 to g. N=0·8225.

After making a sample alkaline, the ammonia may be distilled off, absorbed, and then titrated, but there is always the danger that combined nitrogen may be liberated as ammonia by the breakdown of nitrogenous substances; furthermore, the method is not readily carried out on board ship. The presence of calcium and magnesium in sea water leads to turbidities when an alkaline Nessler reagent is added. Witting and later Buch (3) avoided this difficulty by precipitating these ions with barium chloride and sodium hydroxide. No loss of ammonia results from this procedure, and if Treadwell's Nessler reagent is used on the resultant calcium- and magnesium-free solutions very satisfactory results are obtained because this reagent does not have a non-sensitive range in *sea water*.

Wattenberg (11) introduced the use of Rochelle salt to complex the calcium and magnesium, and so allow direct Nesslerization. This method appears to be a little capricious: turbidities have been reported (2) and Cooper (5) emphasises the difficulties. Further, Føyn (7) has shown that for the prevention of turbidity there is an optimum content of the Rochelle salt and that this is a function of the salinity; the reported discrepancies are probably related to this fact. In view of the foregoing, the Witting-Buch as well as Cooper's modification of Wattenberg's method will be given.

WITTING-BUCH METHOD (12)

Although more time-consuming, this method is free from many of the difficulties of the Wattenberg method: Robinson and Wirth (10, 12) substitute Treadwell's Nessler reagent for Rubens reagent which was used by Wattenberg, because this eliminates the non-sensitive range at low ammonia concentrations.

Reagents

1. *Ammonium sulphate solution.* A stock standard solution containing 0·4716 g./l. 1 ml. of this solution made up to 100 ml. with NH_3-free water contains 71 μg.-atom NH_3-N per litre. Dilute as required. To obtain ammonia-free water the simplest method is to shake distilled water with Folin's permutit, or a modern exchange material such as Amberlite IR 120H or Zeo-Carb 215. This water should be used to make up all reagents and standard solutions.

2. *Treadwell's Nessler solution.* Dissolve 115 g. of mercuric iodide and 80 g. of potassium iodide in water, mix and make up to 500 ml. Add 500 ml. of 6 N sodium hydroxide.

3. *Barium chloride solution.* Dissolve 200 g. of $BaCl_2 . 2H_2O$ in 1 litre of distilled water; evaporate to free from ammonia and then dilute to the original volume with ammonia-free distilled water.

4. *Sodium hydroxide-sodium carbonate solution.* Dissolve 200 g. of NaOH and 69 g. of $NaHCO_3$ in water, mix, free from ammonia by partial evaporation and make up to 1 litre.

Procedure

To 250 ml. of the sample add 10 ml. of the barium chloride solution and 20 ml. of the alkali reagent. Allow to stand three days. Syphon off the supernatant.

Add 2 ml. of the Nessler reagent to 100 ml. of the clarified sample. Allow to stand 30 minutes. Measure the transmittancy using a violet filter (Ilford 601, Zeiss S-43) or working at about 430 mμ.

Remarks

1. If the chlorinity is less than 17‰ smaller quantities of the precipitating reagents should be used since excess reagents tend to give turbidities.

Cl 16·9–14·0‰, use 8 ml. $BaCl_2$+16 ml. alkali,

Cl 13·9–11·0‰, use 6·5 ml. $BaCl_2$+13 ml. alkali,

Cl less than 11·0‰, use 5 ml. $BaCl_2$+10 ml. alkali.

2. An accuracy of $\pm$0·07 μg.-atom NH_3-N/l. may be obtained over the range 0–3·6 μg.-atom NH_3-N/l.

3. Calibration curves should be prepared by adding known amounts of an ammonium salt to ammonia-free sea water; the latter is best prepared by boiling after precipitation with barium chloride and alkali. In the range 17·0–20·0‰ *Cl* there is no salt effect.

THE WATTENBERG METHOD (5, 11)

Reagents

1. *Nessler reagent.* Dissolve 5·5 g. potassium iodide in water and add 10 g. mercuric iodide, followed by 20 g. of sodium hydroxide; make up to 100 ml.

2. *Rochelle salt.* A 30% w/v solution of sodium potassium tartrate in distilled water.

3. *Sodium hydroxide.* A 20% w/v solution in distilled water, boiled out to remove ammonia.

4. *Ammonium sulphate solution. See* p. 130.

Procedure

Transfer 10 ml. of the 20% sodium hydroxide solution to a beaker and add 1·0 ml. of solution of Rochelle salt. Add 4·0 ml. of the latter to 100 ml. sample of sea water contained in a flask. Slowly pour the sea water into the beaker containing the sodium hydroxide whilst swirling. Return to the flask. Add 1·5 ml. of the Nessler reagent. Carry through the procedure as fast as possible. Allow the solution to stand 15 minutes. Determine the transmittancy, using a violet filter.

Remarks

1. The separate additions of Rochelle salt as recommended above appear to assist in the prevention of the formation of turbidities.

2. Beer's law is not obeyed over wide ranges of ammonia content and a calibration curve must be prepared by addition of the reagents to ammonia-free sea water.

AMMONIA: (MICRO) DISTILLATION, KROGH (8)

Krogh (8) has developed a distillation method, in which 0·05–2 μg. of ammonia can be dealt with by distillation in a partial vacuum. In this method the possibility of the production of ammonia by the action of strong alkali (used in the Nessler method) on nitrogenous compounds present in the sea water is avoided. The ammonia is collected in dilute acid and titrated by Teorell's hypobromite method.

Reagents

1. *Ammonia-free distilled water.* Distil water, with an efficient trap on the still head from a flask containing about 1·5 g. $KMnO_4$ and 0·1 ml. concentrated sulphuric acid per litre of water. Use only the middle portion of the distillate, which should be collected whilst

blowing a stream of NH_3-free air or CO_2 through the collecting bottle.

2. *Sodium hydroxide.* About 1% w/v solution of NaOH in distilled water.

3. *Hydrobromic acid.* About 0·01 N. Add 0·2 ml. of 25% HBr to 133 ml. of NH_3-free water. Protect from any contamination.

4. *Hydrobromic acid.* A solution (4%) containing 30 ml. of 25% HBr in 200 ml. NH_3-free distilled water.

5. *Sodium hypobromite.* About 0·001 N. Prepare a stock solution (0·1 N) by dissolving 1·25 ml. of liquid bromine in a solution of 2·5 g. NaOH in water; make up to 500 ml. For use, dilute this solution 1 part to 100 with distilled water. This solution should contain sufficient alkali to give a pH 8·5–9·0 when 1 ml. of it is added to 1 ml. of the 0·01 N-HBr: this requires the addition to it of about 5 ml. of 2 N-Na_2CO_3 per 500 ml. The strength of the stock remains constant if stored in the refrigerator; the dilute solution which should be kept in a brown bottle must be checked at intervals.

6. *Naphthyl red solution.* About 0·0005 N. Mix 30 ml. of glacial acetic acid, 3·75 ml. of 89% H_3PO_4, 1·9 ml. 25% HBr, 10·5 ml. of a freshly prepared 0·1% solution of naphthyl red in that order and make up to 500 ml. with water.

In time a brown precipitate may form; it should be filtered off before use.

7. *Ammonium sulphate solution.* See p. 130.

Apparatus

Instead of using steam to blow off the ammonia as in the normal method (*see* p. 147) distillation under reduced pressure is employed. The Pyrex 50 ml. distillation flask (A, Fig. 31) is provided with a standard ground joint, which is lubricated with slightly alkaline glycerine; several flasks should be available for rapid serial determinations. The connecting piece (B) must also be Pyrex, but the rest of the apparatus may be ordinary soda glass. The final 2–3 cm. of the condenser tube (C) should be capillary tubing of 0·5–0·6 mm. diameter and constricted at the tip to about 0·1 mm. The collecting bottle (D), which has a ground-glass stopper, is kept in an enclosed tube connected by a three-way tap to the vacuum, the bottle itself resting on the stopper of this tube and being adjusted by means of a glass rod (G). A metal ring (H) is sealed on to the inside of the bottle with cement to prevent the stopper from being sucked in by the vacuum. The stopper and glass rod are kept well lubricated with alkaline glycerine. Ammonia-free air is admitted to the apparatus through the sulphuric acid bottles (K) and (L). The tube (M), between 60 and 100 cm. in length and about 0·1 mm. bore, is permanently open and should provide just enough air to drive over the ammonia when the vacuum is on. The tube (N) is wider. The tap (O) is opened only when the distillation is finished and the pressure raised to that of the atmosphere.

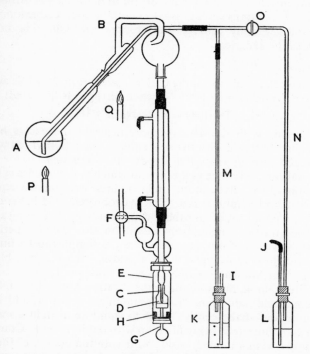

FIG. 31. Micro-ammonia Distillation. (Redrawn from Krogh, A., *Biol. Bull.*, 1934.)

Procedure

It is advisable to begin with one or more blanks to get rid of traces of ammonia which collect even in the closed apparatus. Charge the collecting bottle with 1 ml. 0·01 N hydrobromic acid and adjust its position so that the tip of the tube (C) just dips into the fluid with the vacuum (J) on. Put about 20 ml. ammonia-free water into the distillation flask and add one drop of 1% caustic soda solution (or enough to give pH 9–11). Start the evacuation as soon as the distillation flask is in place. Set the burners (P) and (Q) in position, and regulate so that the distillation proceeds at about 1 ml. per minute. (The burner (Q) prevents condensation in (B).) As distillation proceeds, lower the collecting bottle gradually in order to minimize splashing; before it is finished the tube (C) should be clear of the fluid. After distillation of about 5 ml., remove the burners, turn the tap (F), thus shutting off the apparatus from the pump without opening it to the atmosphere, and open the tap (O), admitting a fairly rapid current of air. (It is important to have the gas turned off between determinations since it usually contains appreciable amounts of ammonia.) Finally remove and stopper the collecting bottle. Repeat with the sample.

The Titration

To the ammonia (absorbed in the 0·01 N hydrobromic acid) is added the alkaline hypobromite (0·001 N) when nitrogen is liberated:

$$2NH_3 + 3NaBrO = N_2 + 3NaBr + 3H_2O.$$

After acidifying with the 4% hydrobromic acid the excess hypobromite is back-titrated with the acid solution of naphthyl red which is decolorized so long as sodium hypobromite remains.

The hypobromite is kept in a bottle in which is mounted a syringe pipette adjusted to deliver about 1 ml.—namely the quantity equivalent to 1·8–2·0 ml. naphthyl red. The hydrobromic acid is kept in a small bottle with a ground-in rubber-capped pipette delivering about 0·2 ml. The titration is made from a 2 ml. burette. The temperature should be kept as uniform as possible or the samples to be titrated may be brought to about the same temperature. Two to four blanks and two to four known ammonias may be done per day.

For a direct blank, measure off in the titrating bottle 1 ml. 0·01 N hydrobromic acid, add about 5 ml. ammonia-free water, add 1 ml. hypobromite and shake gently; allow to stand about half a minute while the 2 ml. burette is being filled up with naphthyl red. Constant timing should be maintained. Add to the solution 0·2 ml. of the 4% hydrobromic acid, shake and titrate from the burette to a perceptible rose colour, comparing with water to which sufficient naphthyl red has been added; the titration should take about one minute.

For the ammonia equivalent of the naphthyl red, add 1–2 ml. of the diluted standard ammonium sulphate solution to 1 ml. 0·01 N hydrobromic acid in the titration bottle, add 5–6 ml. ammonia-free water and proceed as above.

For the sample add 0·2 ml. of the 4% hydrobromic acid and proceed as before. The direct blank and the direct ammonia-value should be compared with those obtained in a distillation.

Remarks

1. The method may be used for estimating the ammonia in air by passing a known quantity of air through the 0·01 N hydrobromic acid contained in the bottle. Titration is carried out as before.

2. Accuracy is $\pm 2 \mu g$. NH_3-N/l., i.e. $\pm 0.04 \mu g$. in the titration.

3. If there is insufficient hypobromite to give a hypobromite-ammonia ratio of 3/2 M then the reaction does not proceed to nitrogen and the titration is inaccurate. Buljan (4) has pointed out that this may be obviated by using potassium-indigo-disulphonate (0.063 g. in 100 ml. of water) and omitting the addition of the 4% hydrobromic acid. The amount of dye needed is less but the end-point is said to be clearer and the reaction goes to completion. There is then no need to repeat the titration if excessively large quantities of ammonia are encountered. Further, there is no absorption on the walls of the titration vessel of the oxidation products of the dye which tend to cause errors when successive titrations are done with naphthyl red.

4. Dr Ketchum reports that an electrically controlled water-bath around the generator and an electrical heating wire round the trap are much preferable to Bunsen burners.

5. Riley (9) has used a similar distillation technique, modifying Krogh's apparatus and estimating the ammonia in the distillate by means of the phenol-hypochlorite reaction (*see* p. 138). The apparatus is shown in Fig. 32. It is all-glass and electrically heated. The evacuation is by means of a filter pump to a pressure of 4–5 cm. mercury (measured on the manometer M). Distillation is carried out in the tube (D), which is heated to 60°C. by means of the electrically heated water bath (G). A gentle stream of acid-washed air is admitted to (D) through the capillary (C) and its flow controlled by a capillary leak. After condensation the distillate passes down the capillary (B) which dips under the surface of 1 ml. of about 0.01 N hydrochloric acid contained in the receiver (R); the latter may be raised or lowered by means of the coarse-pitched screw (S), working through a vacuum-tight gland packed with polythene. The tap (T) serves either to connect the apparatus to the filter pump, or to admit acid-washed air to the distillation train, thereby blowing the undistilled residue over into the trap (E) from which it can be drained away. To prevent atmospheric contamination, U-tubes containing glass beads and 2 N sulphuric acid are fitted to all tubes leading to the apparatus.

Before use, steam out the apparatus. Place 1 ml. of hydrochloric acid in the receiver (R) and raise it until the tip of the capillary is submerged. Turn the tap (T) to evacuate the apparatus.

Introduce the sample of 50 ml. of sea water into the distillation tube (D) by means of the funnel (F), and rinse the funnel into (D) with 10 ml. of a metaborate buffer (2.55 g. of sodium metaborate plus 100 ml. 0.1 N sodium hydroxide per 500 ml.). Allow the distillation to proceed at a pressure of 4–5 cm. of mercury (boiling at about 45°C.). After 10 minutes lower the receiver (R) until the capillary is

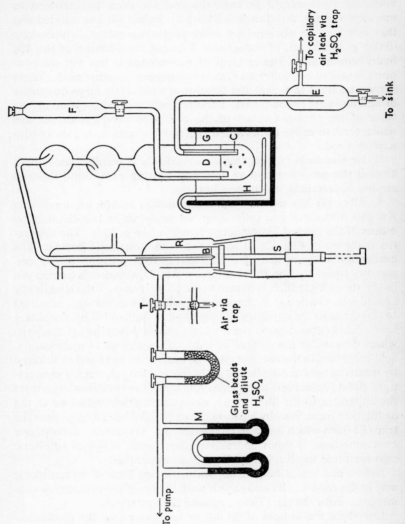

Fig. 22. Micro arsenic Distillation. (Redrawn from Riley J.P. *Analyt. chim. acta* 1953.)

well clear of the surface of the distillate, and continue distillation for a few minutes to wash out the capillary. Turn the tap (T) to release the vacuum in the apparatus. Remove the receiver (R) and transfer the contents to a 25 ml. graduated flask. Determine the reagent blank by distilling 10 ml. of borate buffer.

The colour is developed as directed on p. 139. Add 4 ml. of the sodium phenate reagent; shake and then add 2 ml. of the hypochlorite solution, followed by 1 ml. of the manganese sulphate solution. Dilute to 25 ml. with ammonia-free water and mix well. Heat in a water bath at 70°C. for 45 minutes, cool, and after at least 10 minutes measure the optical density at 625 mμ. Calibrate with ammonium sulphate solutions.

Beer's law is obeyed up to 0·14 mg.-atom NH_4-N/l. but the method gives reproducible results up to 0·42 mg.-atom NH_4-N/l., although the relative sensitivity is less. It is considered by Riley to be preferable to Nessler's technique. The overall coefficient of variation is 0·7%.

AMMONIA: NESSLER REAGENT
(FRESH WATER)

The direct estimation of ammonia in sea water by the Nessler reagent has already been dealt with. Some of the difficulties referred to do not apply in distilled water solutions of ammonia, and the following method may be used for estimating ammonia in a distillate (e.g. from Kjeldahl digestions or albuminoid nitrogen estimations).

Reagents

1. *Ammonia-free water (see* p. 130). All reagents should be made up with ammonia-free water.

2. *Standard ammonium sulphate (see* p. 130).

3. *Nessler reagent.* Dissolve 50 g. of KI in 35 ml. cold ammonia-free water. Add a saturated solution of $HgCl_2$ in ammonia-free water until a slight red precipitate persists (about 415 ml.), and then add 400 ml. of 9 N-NaOH. Dilute to 1 litre and allow to settle for a few days. Decant the clear supernatant liquid.

Procedure

Treat 50 ml. of the sample with 2 ml. of reagent and allow to stand for 15 minutes. The colour may be developed more quickly by using 5 ml. reagent. Compare with standards or measure transmittancy using a violet filter (Ilford 601, Zeiss S-43) or at a wave-length of about 430 mμ.

TOTAL INORGANIC NITROGEN (SEA WATER)

We may conclude this section by describing a method (J. P. Riley, personal communication) for estimating all forms of inorganic nitrogen by reduction to ammonia with Raney nickel. The final estimation of the ammonia is made using its colour reaction with phenol and sodium hypochlorite in alkaline solution.

Reagents

1. *Raney nickel.* Weigh out about 7 g. of powdered nickel-aluminium alloy (50/50) and gradually add it to a solution of 15 g. of sodium hydroxide in 70 ml. of distilled water contained in a 250 ml. beaker. When the addition is complete, heat the covered beaker in an oil bath at 120° for 30 minutes. Wash the nickel with hot water by decantation until the washings are neutral to phenolphthalein. Preserve under water, and do not allow to become dry.

2. *Ethylenediamine-tetra-acetic acid.* 4% w/v solution. Dissolve 4 g. of ethylenediamine-tetra-acetic acid (disodium salt) in 100 ml. of ammonia-free distilled water.

3. *Sodium hydroxide.* 1 N. Dissolve 4 g. of reagent grade sodium hydroxide in ammonia-free distilled water and dilute to 100 ml.

4. *Sodium phenate reagent.* Dissolve 5·4 g. of pure pellet sodium hydroxide in about 20 ml. of water. Boil for about half a minute and then cool. Weigh out 12·5 g. of pure phenol into a 100 ml. graduated flask, and add to it 60 ml. of water. Add the cold sodium hydroxide solution to the phenol and mix while cooling under the tap. Make up to 100 ml. with ammonia-free water. The reagent, which should be colourless, is preserved in a dark glass bottle in the refrigerator until required, but should be made freshly at least every other day.

5. *Manganese sulphate reagent.* The stock solution of manganese sulphate (0·008 M) is prepared by dissolving 0·446 g. of reagent grade manganese sulphate in 250 ml. of water. The reagent solution, which is 0·00024 M, is prepared by diluting 3 ml. of the stock solution to 100 ml.

6. *Sodium hypochlorite reagent.* The reagent solution is prepared by dilution of commercial sodium hypochlorite solution, and should contain 0·9 g. of available chlorine per 100 ml. Its strength should be periodically checked iodimetrically.

7. *Hydrochloric acid.* 0·01 N. Prepare by diluting 1 ml. of concentrated hydrochloric acid to 1 litre.

8. *Standard nitrate solution* (10 μg. NO_3-N/ml.). Dissolve 0·0722 g. of reagent grade potassium nitrate in water and dilute to 1 litre.

Treatment of Flasks

Clean all Cavett and graduated flasks which are to be used for the determination by filling them with concentrated sulphuric acid. After a few hours empty them, and rinse first with water, then with dilute (0·1 N) sodium hydroxide, and finally wash well with distilled water and allow them to drain. Thoroughly lubricate the ground surfaces of both the flasks and stoppers with a mixture of equal parts of paraffin wax (congealing point about 49° C.) and medicinal paraffin.

Procedure

Place 50 ml. of the sea-water sample in a Cavett flask, add approximately 0·3 g. of Raney nickel and 1 ml. of the 4% ethylenediamine-tetra-acetic acid reagent. Into the cup of the Cavett flask stopper, pipette 1 ml. of 0·01 N hydrochloric acid. Cap the flask with its stopper and place it in an oven at 70° C. After about 10 minutes pipette 1 ml. of 1 N sodium hydroxide into the flask, restopper it immediately and mix the solutions gently. Replace the flask in the oven, and agitate it occasionally to prevent the formation of a film of precipitate on the surface of the liquid.

After 20 hours transfer the hydrochloric acid solution from the cup to a 10 ml. graduated flask by means of a suction pipette. Wash the cup well with ammonia-free distilled water. Add 2 ml. of sodium phenate reagent, followed by 1 ml. of sodium hypochlorite reagent and 0·5 ml. of manganese sulphate reagent. Dilute to 10 ml. with ammonia-free water. Mix well. Press home the glass stopper of the flask tightly. Heat the flask in the water bath at 70° C. for 45 minutes, cool, and after at least 10 minutes measure the optical density of the solution at 625 mμ or with an Ilford filter 607. Run a blank determination using freshly distilled water instead of sea water. Calibrate the method using known volumes of suitably diluted standard potassium nitrate solution; 98 to 100% recoveries of NH_4-N should be obtained.

Remarks

1. Since Raney nickel residues tend to be pyrophoric they should be rinsed down the drain with plenty of water and on no account should they be put in the ordinary laboratory refuse bins.

2. The method can be used for the estimation of ammonia if the diffusion is carried out in the presence of 10 ml. metaborate buffer only.

3. Crowther and Large (6) have found considerable variation between successive calibration curves when using the Riley method for the estimation of ammonia by the sodium phenate-sodium

hypochlorite reaction. They found it advisable to make the sodium phenate reagent as required by mixing an alcoholic solution of phenol and an aqueous solution of sodium hydroxide. They also report an increased sensitivity in the presence of various organic solvents amongst which acetone was selected as the best; further in the presence of acetone they state that the addition of manganese sulphate as a catalyst is unnecessary. Their recommended procedure is as follows.

Dissolve 62·5 g. analytical grade phenol in industrial methylated spirit, add 18·5 ml. of acetone and dilute to 100 ml. with industrial methylated spirit. Store the solution in the refrigerator. Dissolve 27 g. of sodium hydroxide in distilled water and dilute to 100 ml. For use mix 20 ml. of each reagent and dilute to 100 ml. with distilled water.

Dilute the test solution to 10 ml. with distilled water and add 4 ml. of sodium phenate reagent. After mixing add 3 ml. of sodium hypochlorite solution (0·9% available chlorine). Mix, dilute to 25 ml. with distilled water. Allow to stand 20 minutes at room temperature. Measure the transmittancy. Carry out a blank using distilled water.

REFERENCES

1. American Public Health Association and others, 1955. *Standard Methods for the Examination of Water, Sewage and Industrial Wastes*. Amer. Publ. Health Ass. Inc., New York, 10th Ed., 1955, 522 pp.
   [Note: there are a vast number of 'Nessler' reagents adapted to special purposes: the one given is satisfactory for distillates.]
2. Braarud, T., and Føyn, B., 1931. 'Beiträge zur Kenntnis des Stoffwechsels im Meere.' *Avhandliger Norsks Videnskap-Akademi i Oslo. Matern-Naturvid.* Klasse, No. 14, 14 pp.
3. Buch, K., 1923. 'Methodisches über dei Bestimmung von Stickstoffverbindung im Wasser.' *Merentutkimuslait. Julk.* (*Havsforskn. Inst. Skr., Helsingf.*), N : o 18, 22 pp.
4. Buljan, M., 1951. 'A modification of Teorell's method for determining small quantities of ammonia.' *Arhiv za Kemiju*, **23**, 119–22.
5. Cooper, L. H. N., 1933. 'Chemical constituents of biological importance in the English Channel, November 1930 to January 1932. Part I. Phosphate, silicate, nitrate, ammonia.' *J. Mar. biol. Ass. U.K.*, **18**, 677–725.
6. Crowther, A. B., and Large, R. S., 1956. 'Improved conditions for the sodium phenoxide-sodium hypochlorite method for the determination of ammonia.' *Analyst*, **81**, 64–5.
7. Føyn, E., 1949. 'Ammonia determination on sea water.' *J. Cons. int. Explor. Mer*, **16**, 175–8.
8. Krogh, A., 1934. 'A method for the determination of ammonia in water and air.' *Biol. Bull., Woods Hole*, **67**, 126–31.

9. Riley, J. P., 1953. 'The spectrophotometric determination of ammonia in natural waters with particular reference to sea water.' *Analyt. chim. acta*, **9**, 575–89.

10. Robinson, R. J., and Wirth, H. E., 1934. 'Free ammonia, albuminoid nitrogen and organic nitrogen in the waters of the Pacific Ocean off the Coasts of Washington and Vancouver Island.' *J. Cons. int. Explor. Mer*, **9**, 187–95.

11. Wattenberg, H., 1929. 'A simple method for the direct estimation of ammonia in sea water by the use of Nessler's reagent.' *Rapp. Cons. Explor. Mer*, **53**, 108–14.

12. Wirth, H. E., and Robinson, R. J., 1933. 'Photometric investigation of Nessler reaction and Witting method for determination of ammonia in sea water.' *Industr. Engng. Chem. (Anal.)*, **5**, 293–6.

9

ORGANIC NITROGEN IN SEA WATER AND PLANKTON

At. wt. N=14·008.

Factor, g. N to g.-atom N=0·07139.

The Kjeldahl method (*see* p. 146) takes large quantities of water: Krogh and Keys (7) have developed a technique in which only a few ml. of sea water are required. This has been used by von Brand and Rakestraw (3, 4, 5). Modifications of the standard Kjeldahl method for very small quantities of nitrogen were not found possible because even with extreme precautions in the purification of sulphuric acid, the amounts of nitrogen (0·5–2·0 μg./ml.) given off on treating it with caustic soda were high and variable. A modified Will-Warrentrapp method in which the material is heated to about 500° C. with alkali in an atmosphere of hydrogen was therefore developed. The combustion must be carried out in a silver tube; the ammonia is taken up in 0·01 N hydrobromic acid and dealt with exactly as described in the previous section (p. 134).

Apparatus (Fig. 33)

Cylinder hydrogen is purified by passing it first through sulphuric acid to remove any traces of ammonia (and to indicate the rate of flow, which should be maintained at 10–20 ml. per minute) and then through a quartz tube containing metallic copper heated to dull red heat to remove traces of oxygen. If the copper contains traces of arsenic and antimony this method is invalidated, and a safer procedure is to pass the gas through sulphuric acid, pyrogallic acid, sulphuric acid again, and then over platinum foil heated to a red heat in a quartz tube. The glass connecting piece (C) leads on the one hand to the entry for the solution (D) and on the other into the bent silver combustion tube (E). The latter is surrounded in part with a brass water jacket (F) by which the silver tube is held in position.

Procedure

Place a pellet of caustic soda in the combustion tube, connect up at (C) and wash the system out with hydrogen. Run the water sample of 5 ml. in through (D). The narrow tip of the capillary tube just dips into 1 ml. of 0·01 N hydrobromic acid contained in a collecting bottle similar to that described previously (*see* p. 132).

Heat the combustion tube gently to boil off the water and ignite to a dull red heat as observed in a darkened room. Cool, add 2 ml. ammonia-free water and again heat; this re-heating with water is necessary to remove ammonia occluded in the residual salts. Finally heat the whole tube by moving the flame so that every trace of water is transferred into the collecting bottle. Two estimations may be made without opening the combustion tube but the residual salts must then be washed out.

The titration is performed as previously described (*see* p. 134).

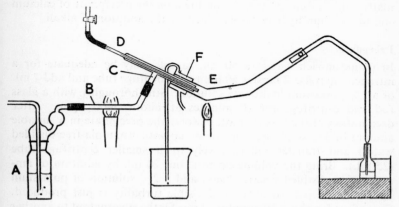

FIG. 33. Apparatus for the determination of dissolved organic nitrogen in sea water. (Redrawn from Krogh, A., and Keys, A., *Biol. Bull.*, 1934.)

Remarks

1. One of the greatest difficulties is the preparation of 'ammonia-free water' (for preparation, *see* p. 130). Blanks must be run with every batch of analyses using the same amounts of wash water and, also, with every new batch of ammonia-free water which should be tested at fairly frequent intervals. 1 ml. of water may contain 0·03 μg. N.

2. Nitrates do not interfere.

3. Amounts of nitrogen between 0·5 and 2·5 μg. N may be determined; increased quantities can be estimated by doubling the strength of the reagents used.

4. The accuracy of the method has been considered by von Brand and Rakestraw (5). They give a series of figures from which it is possible to calculate a standard deviation. In the first set, such as they state may be obtained without any difficulty, the standard

deviation was ± 22 μg. on 229 μg. of nitrogen (in 5 ml. of sea water), i.e. almost $\pm 10\%$ standard deviation. In a second series, requiring more care and practice, with a mean value of 189 μg. N, the standard deviation was ± 8.3 μg. N or $\pm 4.4\%$.

5. Samples for analyses should be filtered and stored on ice.

APPLICATION TO PLANKTON SAMPLES

The above method has been used by von Brand (3, 4) for estimating the particulate nitrogenous matter in a sample of sea water.

It is first necessary to concentrate the plankton and particulate matter; this is done by carrying it down on the precipitate of calcium and magnesium hydroxides obtained by the addition of alkali.

Procedure

In plankton-rich waters a 50 ml. sample may be adequate for a nitrogen analysis. Transfer 50 ml. to a centrifuge tube and add 1 ml. of a 2% potassium hydroxide solution. Stir thoroughly with a glass rod and centrifuge for 10 minutes at about 3400 r.p.m. After decantation of the supernatant, dissolve the precipitate in a suitable amount of 3% sulphuric acid (made up with ammonia-free distilled water) and transfer quantitatively to a smaller centrifuge tube (25 ml.). Bring the volume up to about 20 ml. by addition of ammonia-free distilled water. Again add a 2% solution of potassium hydroxide drop by drop until a visible turbidity is just produced. Centrifuge for about 10 minutes. Transfer the supernatant to another centrifuge tube and, by addition of a suitable amount of a 2% solution of potassium hydroxide and centrifugation, obtain a control precipitate similar to that of the sample; this procedure is necessary, since a precipitate of hydroxides in sea water always appears to contain a certain amount of nitrogen which must not be neglected. A blank is, therefore, run on the control precipitate. It is advisable to make both precipitates as small as possible and as nearly as possible the same size (about 0.1 ml.). To each of both tubes are now added 1.9 ml. of ammonia-free distilled water. The total amount of fluid should then be very nearly 2 ml. The precipitates are thoroughly mixed with the water by means of a glass rod, and an aliquot transferred to the ignition tube exactly as described for a sample of water.

Remarks

1. The final volume of the suspension to be analysed is 2 ml.; duplicate 1 ml. samples are taken for analysis. It is not necessary as with water samples to burn an extra 2 ml. of water in order to remove

occluded ammonia, since there are fewer salts present; furthermore, eight to ten analyses may be made without opening up and washing the silver tube.

2. If the particulate matter of the water is very small a larger water sample may be required. In this case the following procedure should be adopted.

Pour 1 litre of the water sample into a graduated litre cylinder; add 5–10 ml. of a 5% caustic potash solution and stir thoroughly with a clean glass rod; cover with a clean watch glass and stand for 12 hours, during which time the cylinder should not be disturbed. The level of the precipitate will be between the 50 and 100 ml. mark. Syphon off the supernatant not allowing the syphon to go below the 200 ml. mark and, when the level of the water has fallen to 220–230 ml., remove the syphon carefully and stir up the precipitate. Add a few ml. of 5% hydrochloric acid so that the liquid is still just turbid, and transfer to a 250 ml. centrifuge tube; centrifuge at high speed for 5–10 minutes. Pour off the supernatant, and dissolve the residue by the dropwise addition of 5% hydrochloric acid, whilst stirring with a glass rod. Transfer to a 50-ml. centifruge tube and again add enough caustic potash solution to make distinctly cloudy. Centrifuge. Transfer the supernatant to a second centrifuge tube, add caustic potash solution and again centrifuge to obtain a control precipitate. Suspend both sample and control precipitates in about 2 ml. of ammonia-free water, and take aliquots for analysis as before.

3. Scrupulous care should be taken in cleaning the apparatus.

4. The method may be used for plankton cultures.

5. The method does not distinguish between living and other organic particulate matter present in the sample. Only if the number of organisms and their nitrogen content is known from separate estimations on cultures can an estimate be made of the separate fractions.

TOTAL ORGANIC NITROGEN, SEA WATER (KJELDAHL)

As already stated when small volumes of sea water are used the Kjeldahl method has been found inapplicable because of variable quantities of nitrogen given off from the acid (*see* p. 131). However, the method has been used with 250 ml. samples of sea water (9).

Reagents

As for ammonia estimation and in addition concentrated nitrogen-free sulphuric acid.

Procedure (*see also* pp. 148–50).

Transfer 250 ml. of sea water to a Kjeldahl flask and add 9 ml. of concentrated sulphuric acid. Evaporate cautiously and heat until copious fumes of sulphur trioxide are evolved. When solids begin to separate the Kjeldahl flask should be swirled to reduce bumping. Cool and determine the ammonia as is described below (total organic nitrogen). Repeat on ammonia-free water, for reagent blank. Estimate the ammonia in the distillate. A correction for the free ammonia in the sea water must be applied; this is best determined directly on a separate sample.

ALBUMINOID NITROGEN

Range, 0–0·3 mg.-atom N/l.

Very few estimations have been made of albuminoid nitrogen (9): the nitrogen is liberated from albuminoid material in the form of ammonia on distillation with an alkaline potassium permanganate solution. The ammonia released in this way depends upon the quantity of albuminoid material present and upon the length and speed of the distillation. The method must be carefully standardized and even then the results are somewhat arbitrary.

Reagent

Alkaline potassium permanganate. Dissolve 8 g. of potassium permanganate in 500 ml. distilled water and add 400 ml. of clarified 36% NaOH solution; make up to about 1·25 litres: concentrate to 1 litre when the solution should go green.

Procedure

Add 25 ml. of the alkaline permanganate solution to 250 ml. of sea water. Distil through a block tin or silica condenser until 150 ml. of distillate have collected. Determine the ammonia in an appropriate aliquot of the distillate by Nessler (*see* p. 137). Correct for ammonia present in sea water. It is better to do this by a separate estimation rather than by boiling off the ammonia in a preliminary estimation.

TOTAL ORGANIC NITROGEN, SEMI-MICRO (PLANKTON, TISSUES, MUDS)

The Kjeldahl method may be used when moderate quantities of material are available. There have been very many minor modifications; the technique given below has been found to be satisfactory for biological materials. The material is decomposed by digestion with sulphuric acid in the presence of a catalyst when the nitrogen is converted into ammonia which, after making the digest alkaline, is distilled off into a solution of boric acid and titrated with standard acid.

Apparatus

Digestion flasks. The flasks normally used for the digestion are of hard glass or Pyrex and pistol-shaped, with 30–70 ml. bulbs and long necks. When only very small quantities of material are to be dealt with Pyrex or hard-glass test-tubes may be used.

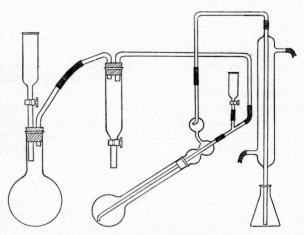

Fig. 34. Typical Kjeldahl Distillation Apparatus.

Digestion stand. A number of analyses are usually run simultaneously in which case the digestion flasks are supported and heated on a digestion stand which has a number of micro-burners under separate control but fed from a common supply (*see* maker's catalogue).

Distillation apparatus. The modern form of distillation apparatus (Fig. 34) enables serial analyses to be made without taking the assembly to pieces. Essentially it consists of a flask in which steam is generated, a steam trap, and the distillation flask. The last is fitted with a ground-glass joint which carries the steam inlet tube, a splash head, and a small tap funnel for introducing the diluted digest and alkali into the distillation flask. It is connected to a Liebig condenser with a 10-inch jacket. In order to obviate errors arising from the solution of alkali by the steam from either Pyrex or ordinary soft glass the connection to the splash head and the inner tube of the condenser are formed from a single continuous tube of transparent silica.

(Although for simplicity the apparatus is shown arranged in a line, the parts are most conveniently mounted round a central retort stand.)

Reagents

1. *Sulphuric acid.* Concentrated acid, reagent grade.

2. *Sodium hydroxide-sodium thiosulphate solution.* A solution containing 40 g. of pure sodium hydroxide (and 5 g. sodium thiosulphate $Na_2S_2O_3 \cdot 5H_2O$ if mercury is included in catalyst mixture) per 100 ml. distilled water.

3. *Catalyst mixture.* Grind together 32 g. of potassium sulphate, 5 g. of mercuric sulphate (or 5 g. copper sulphate) and 1 g. of powdered selenium (omitted by some workers).

4. *Boric acid solution.* A saturated solution of boric acid in distilled water; the solution contains approximately 4 % of boric acid.

5. *Standard hydrochloric acid solution.* 0·02 N.

6. *Mixed methyl red-methylene blue indicator.* Dissolve separately 0·1250 g. of methyl red and 0·0830 g. of methylene blue each in 50 ml. of absolute alcohol; for use mix equal volumes of the two indicators. The mixed indicator should be renewed weekly.

Procedure

Transfer to a dry digestion flask a weighed quantity of the material to be analysed which should have been previously dried thoroughly in an oven. Add approximately 0·5 g. of catalyst mixture and 2–4 ml. of concentrated sulphuric acid. Place the flask on the digestion stand over the micro-burner and gradually raise the temperature to boiling; continue boiling for 15 minutes; cool.

If it has not been in use for some time, steam out the distillation apparatus for about 30 minutes while digestion is proceeding, during which time the taps on the steam trap and the filling funnel, as well as the screw-clamp on the rubber tubing connection to the distillation apparatus, should be left open. Remove the burner from the steam generator and allow the liquid which has collected in the distillation flask to be sucked back into the trap, which is then emptied. This is the procedure for emptying the flask after each distillation. The liquid is blown out of the trap by steam pressure. Close the screw-clamp on the connection to the distillation flask. Put 10 ml. of the saturated boric acid solution into the receiver to a depth of a few millimetres so that when the condenser tip is inserted into the flask its orifice is submerged to a depth of about 1 mm.

After cooling and diluting with about 10 ml. of distilled water, transfer the digest and washings from the Kjeldahl flask through the tap funnel to the distillation flask. Add 10 ml. of the strong alkali (with thiosulphate if a mercury catalyst has been used) through the funnel. Rinse down the funnel with distilled water and close the tap, leaving a little water in the funnel to act as a seal. The volume of liquid in the distillation flask should be kept less than half the capacity of the latter so that frothing and priming does not force liquid over into the receiver. Close the tap on the steam trap and open the screw clip so that steam passes into the distillation flask. To prevent excessive condensation the liquid in the distillation flask is heated gently with a micro-burner. The distillation is continued for 5 minutes at a rate of about 4 ml. of distillate per minute from the time that steam first enters the condenser. The contents of the receiver must remain cold during the distillation. After driving over all the ammonia in this way, lower the receiving flask a little and continue distillation for 1 minute to wash the outlet. Wash the end of the condenser into the receiver with distilled water from a wash bottle.

Remove the receiver and take away the burners from both the steam generator and distillation flask; the contents of the distillation flask are then sucked over into the steam trap, from which they may be run off; the apparatus is then ready for the next distillation without any washing.

Add a few drops of the mixed indicator and titrate the contents of the receiver with the standard 0·02 N solution of hydrochloric acid to a violet colour using a 25 or 50 ml. burette. Repeat the procedure for a blank using pure sucrose as the organic substance. A comparison flask containing acidified boric acid and indicator helps to ascertain the end-point.

Calculation

Subtract the blank titration from sample titration, thus obtaining the number of ml. of 0·02 N hydrochloric acid required to neutralize the ammonia.

1 ml. of 0·02 N-HCl is equivalent to 0·28 mg. NH_3-N.

Remarks

1. The amount of acid, catalyst and strength of the hydrochloric acid used in the titration may be varied according to amount of organic matter and its nitrogen content.

2. The sample may be conveniently weighed out on cigarette paper and the whole transferred to the digestion flask.

3. Standard hydrochloric acid may be conveniently prepared from ampoules of standard acid now readily available. Otherwise, standardize a solution containing 2·5 ml. concentrated acid per litre with borax using the mixed indicator given above.

4. Boric acid frequently contains sodium borate as an impurity, in which case the latter may be removed by washing with distilled water.

5. The method may be readily modified for much smaller quantities of nitrogen by estimating the ammonia in the distillate by means of the Nessler or other reaction (*see* pp. 137, 138).

6. Distilled water may be freed from ammonia by standing over an exchange resin. If it is suspected that the water used in the steam generator is heavily contaminated with ammonia, a few drops of sulphuric acid and a crystal of ferrous sulphate are added.

REFERENCES

1. Belcher, R., and Godbert, A. L., 1945. *Semi-micro Quantitative Organic Analysis.* Longmans, Green & Co., London, 1947 Impression, 168 pp.
2. Bradstreet, R. B., 1940. 'A review of the Kjeldahl determination of organic nitrogen.' *Chem. Reviews,* **27**, 331–50.
3. von Brand, T., 1935. 'Methods for the determination of nitrogen and carbon in small amounts of plankton.' *Biol. Bull., Woods Hole,* **69**, 221–32.
4. ——, 1938. 'Quantitative determination of the nitrogen in the particulate matter of the sea.' *J. Cons. int. Explor. Mer,* **12**, 187–96.
5. ——, and Rakestraw, N. W., 1941. 'The determination of dissolved organic nitrogen in sea water.' *J. Mar. Res.,* **67**, 76–80.
6. Harvey, H. W., 1951. 'Micro-determination of nitrogen in organic matter without distillation.' *Analyst,* **76**, 657–60.
7. Krogh, A., and Keys, A., 1934. 'Methods for the determination of dissolved organic carbon and nitrogen in sea water.' *Biol. Bull., Woods Hole,* **67**, 132–44.
8. Miller, G. L., and Miller, E. E., 1948. 'Determination of nitrogen in biological materials.' *Analyt. Chem.,* **20**, 481–7.
9. Robinson, R. J., and Wirth, H. E., 1934. 'Free ammonia, albuminoid nitrogen and organic nitrogen in the waters of Puget Sound Area during the summers of 1931 and 1932.' *J. Cons. int. Explor. Mer,* **9**, 15–27, (q.v. for further references).

10

INORGANIC PHOSPHORUS: PHOSPHATE

Range, 0–2·0 (rarely 3·0) μg.-atom PO_4-P/l.

At. wt. P=30·98.

Factor, g. P to g.-atom P=0·03228.

Factor, g. P to g. PO_4=3·0659.

Factor, g. PO_4 to g. P=0·3262.

All sensitive methods for the estimation of orthophosphate currently in use depend upon the formation of phospho-molybdenum complexes and their reduction to molybdenum blue. Within wide limits of reagent strength and acidity many reducing agents will give this reaction, but for the amounts of phosphate present in sea water, it is essential, when working at room temperatures, to use a strong reducing agent such as stannous chloride. A correct physico-chemical formulation of the reaction is still not available. It is very sensitive to changes in the reagent concentrations particularly when using a strong reducing agent and it is essential, therefore, in analytical work, to adhere strictly to empirically determined optimum conditions. These are chosen such that, while interference from silicate is minimized, maximum sensitivity is obtained with the colour intensity reasonably stable and, within wide limits, a linear function of the phosphate concentration. The variables affecting the reaction may be summarized (*see* 4, 7, 9, 10, 11, 12, 16, 18).

1. *Variations in acidity and molybdate concentrations.* These are inter-dependent: at low acidities a blue colour is developed with low molybdate concentrations but a moderate increase in the latter gives rise to unstable blue colours even in the absence of phosphate. At high acidities, a higher concentration of molybdate is required to give a colour with phosphate; not until the concentration of the former is relatively high are blue colours then obtained in the absence of phosphate. Even small changes in the concentration of these reagents significantly affect the intensity of the blue colour; for example, a 1 % increase in the acidity (at the molybdate concentration recommended below) decreases the colour by 0·5%. It is essential, therefore, to maintain both constant acid and molybdate content at a point in the range where blue colour is only developed in the presence of phosphate. Different workers have utilized various parts

of this range (1, 4, 9, 10, 11, 12, 15, 18): the concentrations suggested below, namely 0·05% ammonium molybdate and 0·28 N sulphuric acid in the test solution, give satisfactory results.

The following observations relate to such conditions.

2. *Equilibrium between acid-molybdate and sea water.* The blue colour is intensified when the reducing agent is added immediately after the acid-molybdate: three minutes should be allowed for the attainment of equilibrium before adding the stannous chloride.

3. *The effect of temperature.* As the temperature is raised the velocities of the reactions involved in the production of the blue colour increase, so that for a given phosphate content maximum colour develops more rapidly and remains stable for a shorter time: furthermore, the intensity of the maximum is greater.

4. *The stannous chloride concentration.* With a given phosphate content maximum colour intensity rises rapidly with increasing concentration of stannous ions, until approximately 12 times more stannous chloride than PO_4-P is present; thereafter, the increase in colour is relatively small. Within the range 0·3–1·0 mg. Sn^{++} and up to 0·15 μg.-atom PO_4-P per 100 ml. of solution, the increase in colour is approximately 1% for each additional 0·14 mg. Sn^{++}. High Sn^{++} concentrations increase both the rate at which the maximum colour is reached and its stability. Extra additions of stannous chloride after the blue colour has developed further increase its intensity and stability. As the concentration of stannous ions is raised, however, there is a greater tendency for the production of green tints, and although it has been stated (19) that these do not interfere with the estimation when working at 700 mμ with a spectrophotometer, they must be avoided when other methods of comparison are used.

5. *The presence of suspended and organic matter.* Small quantities of either do not grossly affect the results if allowance is made for any resultant turbidity; large quantities should be avoided. Heavy contamination with dissolved organic matter may seriously interfere with the production of the typical blue colour.

6. *The effect of salt content.* Small changes in salt content such as are normally encountered in marine work do not seriously affect the results but the influence of all the variables considered above is significantly different in distilled water: this has an important bearing on the preparation of calibration curves (*see* 6 and 11, *also* pp. 80–3 and 154. The salt error should always be determined.

7. *The effect of arsenate.* Arsenate gives the same colour reaction as phosphate under these conditions and it will therefore be returned as phosphate.

8. *The presence of particulate phosphate.* Any particulate phosphate which is either soluble or readily hydrolyzed in the acid

solution resulting from addition of the reagent will be returned as inorganic phosphate.

9. *Storage of ammonium molybdate solutions.* When aqueous solutions of ammonium molybdate which have been stored in glass bottles are used for phosphate estimations high blank values are obtained (9). The presence of acid reduces the changes which give rise to this phenomenon. The acid-molybdate solution, whilst it need not be freshly prepared, should be renewed at moderately frequent intervals. When kept in polythene bottles the reagent is stable for several months (Dr J. P. Riley, personal communication).

Reagents

1. *Acid ammonium molybdate.* 25 g./l. in 14 N-H_2SO_4. Prepare approximately 18 N-H_2SO_4 by cautiously adding 250 ml. concentrated acid to 250 ml. distilled water, cooling and making up to 500 ml. Dissolve 10 g. pure ammonium molybdate $(NH_4)_6Mo_7O_{24}$.$4H_2O$ (clear crystals) in 100 ml. distilled water; if necessary filter, and add to 300 ml. of the 18 N acid. Store in an amber bottle.

2. *Stannous chloride.* Stock: dissolve 4·3 g. $SnCl_2$.$2H_2O$ (clear crystals) in 20 ml. 50% v/v HCl and dilute to 100 ml. with cold, boiled-out distilled water. The solution should be kept over a piece of mossy tin.

For use: dilute 5 ml. of stock to 25 ml. with 5% HCl prepared with boiled-out distilled water. This solution oxidizes rapidly on exposure to air and for each batch of analyses should be freshly prepared before use. It is preferable to make the diluted reagent up daily but it may be stored for short periods under paraffin oil.

Experience on the keeping qualities of stannous chloride solutions varies; some workers prefer to make up fresh batches very frequently. Dr Rakestraw reports that when kept in his reagent dispenser (*see* 19) over a little metallic tin and under paraffin oil it may be used for many days.

3. *Standard solution of phosphate.* Dissolve 0·3400 g. pure anhydrous potassium dihydrogen phosphate (KH_2PO_4) in distilled water and make up to 1 litre. Add 0·2 ml. chloroform as a preservative. 1 ml. of this solution contains 2·5 μg.-atom PO_4-P. Further dilutions are prepared as required.

Procedure

If heavily contaminated with plankton, filter or centrifuge the sample; to 100 ml. contained in a 250 ml. flask add 2 ml. of acid-molybdate reagent. Mix thoroughly, then measure the transmittancy against distilled water for the turbidity blank and note the temperature. After 3 minutes add 0·2 ml. of the dilute stannous chloride solution whilst swirling the liquid. Transfer to the photometer cell and measure the transmittancy, after maximum colour development, using a red filter (Ilford 608) or, if a spectrophotometer is used, at 705 mμ. The relation between the time of maximum colour development and temperature is as follows (9):

10°C.   16–27 minutes after Sn^{++} addition,

15°C.   12–16 minutes after Sn^{++} addition,

20°C.   7–12 minutes after Sn^{++} addition.

Repeat using 100 ml. distilled water for reagent blanks, again reading at maximum colour development according to following table:

10°C.   37–110 minutes,

15°C.   15–45 minutes,

20°C.   10–30 minutes.

Remarks

1. When using an absorptiometer a red filter (Ilford 608, Corning 2408 or Zeiss S 72) is recommended. With a spectrophotometer, a wave-length of 625 mμ is usually recommended, although Wooster and Rakestraw (19) have worked at 700 mμ, at which wave-length they state that the green colours evident visually when using high concentrations of Sn^{++} ion are without effect on the results. Other work has shown that the peak absorbancy depends upon the reaction conditions. The wave-length of maximum absorption in the method given is 705 mμ (Dr J. P. Riley).

2. The precision of the method in the laboratory is $\pm 5\%$ (coefficient of variation).

3. When working with batches of samples the reagents are conveniently delivered by automatic dispensers.

4. After a number of estimations vessels and optical cells become fouled with a coating of molybdenum blue and should be cleaned. When fresh, rubbing with wet cotton wool and much flushing with water will remove the deposit. Dr Rakestraw recommends a quick rinse with dilute hydrofluoric acid followed by flushing with water.

5. Sensitivity may be increased by increasing the Sn^{++} concentration to 2·1 mg. Sn^{++}/100 ml. (19); this should only be done when working with a spectrophotometer at 705 mμ (*see* above). Care should be taken that under these conditions colloidal or precipitated tin compounds are not formed.

6. Old solutions of stannous chloride invariably contain stannic tin which may give spuriously high reagent blanks in distilled water as a result of the presence of colloidal stannic tin; Armstrong (2) suggests a stannous chloride reagent containing 5% hydrochloric acid to obviate this error.

7. Dr J. P. Riley points out that he has recently found that the use of metol at 100°C. to replace the stannous chloride as reducing agent gives a 20% greater sensitivity (see Ref. p. 270).

8. Saeki (17) has stressed the fact that large quantities of nitrite, greater than 3·5 μg.-atom NO_2-N/l. interfere with the phosphate estimation; this should be borne in mind when dealing with highly polluted coastal waters.

9. Murphy and Riley (Ref. p. 270) have recently made a critical examination of the various methods recommended for the storage of samples prior to analysis for phosphate. They recommended filtration of the water, addition of 1 ml. of chloroform per 150 ml. of sample and storage in the dark at as low a temperature as possible; under these conditions no changes were observed after 1 month. Phosphorus changes in stored sea water may be the result of either bacterial action or the presence of enzymes in diatoms or the water (13, 17). They point out that the fluoride ion (recommended as a preservative by Ibañez) inhibits the formation of molybdenum blue. Although the preservative is moderately effective, the sensitivity of the estimation is reduced and the method must be calibrated in the presence of an equivalent amount of fluoride. 'Baiting' with aluminium hydroxide or thorium carbonate lead to high and variable results (see p. 159). They also point out that polythene rapidly adsorbs phosphorus from dilute solutions of phosphate in sea water, and, although excellent for storage of samples for silicate or trace metal analysis, should on no account be used for samples on which phosphates are to be determined.

SMALL QUANTITIES OF INORGANIC PHOSPHATE

Two methods have recently been suggested for determining inorganic phosphate when present in extremely low concentrations.

In the first (8) ascorbic acid is used as the reducing agent and it is stated that concentrations as low as 0·016 μg.-atom PO_4-P/l. may be determined. However, the transmission measurements were made at 820 mμ, i.e. outside the visible region. Up to 1·5 μg.-atom PO_4-P/l. the method requires 4 hours for full colour development.

In the second method (12) the technique of Berenblum and Chain (3) is adopted in which the phospho-molybdic complex is extracted with iso-butanol, thereby affecting a major concentration; the complex is reduced with stannous chloride whilst in the organic solvent. The authors point out that the day-to-day reproducibility is not good, but with adequate batch controls consider the method satisfactory.

REFERENCES

1. Atkins, W. R. G., 1923. 'The phosphate content of sea water in relationship to the growth of the algal plankton.' *J. Mar. biol. Ass. U.K.*, **13**, 119–50.
2. Armstrong, F. A. J., 1949. 'A source of error in the absorptiometric determination of inorganic and total phosphorus in sea water.' *J. Mar. biol. Ass. U.K.*, **28**, 701–5.
3. Berenblum, I., and Chain, E., 1938. 'Studies on the colorimetric determination of phosphorus.' *Biochem. J.*, **32**, 286–94.
4. Buch, K., 1929. 'Über die Bestimmungen von Stickstoffverbindungen und Phosphaten im Meerwasser.' *Rapp. Cons. Explor. Mer*, **53**, 36–52.
5. Cooper, L. H. N., 1934. 'The determination of phosphorus and nitrogen in plankton.' *J. Mar. biol. Ass. U.K.*, **19**, 755–9.
6. ——, 1938. 'Salt error in determination of phosphate in sea water.' *J. Mar. biol. Ass. U.K.*, **23**, 171–8.
7. Fukai, R., 1954. 'Critical studies on the analytical methods for minor chemical constituents in sea water. Part I. On the estimation of phosphate-phosphorus.' *J. Oceanogr. Soc. Japan*, **9**, 112–20.
8. Greenfield, L. J., and Kalber, F. A., 1954. 'Inorganic phosphate measurement in sea water.' *Bull. Mar. Sci. Gulf and Caribbean*, **4**, 323–35.
9. Harvey, H. W., 1948. 'The estimation of phosphate and of total phosphorus in sea waters.' *J. Mar. biol. Ass. U.K.*, **27**, 337–59.
10. Kalle, K., 1934. 'Meereskundliche chemische Untersuchungen mit Hilfe des Zeisschen Pulfrich-Photometers. Mitteilung III. Methodische Untersuchung der Phosphatgehaltbestimmung.' *Ann. Hydrogr., Berl.*, **62**, 65–74, 95–102.
11. ——, 1935. 'Mitteilung IV. Der Einfluss chemischer Stoffe auf die Phosphatgehaltbestimmung.' *Ann. Hydrogr., Berl.*, **63**, 58–65.
12. ——, 1935. 'Mitteilung V. Die Bestimmung des Gesamt-Phosphorgehaltes, des Plankton-Phosphorgehaltes (lebende Substanz) und Trübungsmessungen.' *Ann. Hydrogr., Berl.*, **63**, 195–204.
13. Matsue, Y., 1949. *Report of the Research Association of Fisheries.* No. 2.
14. Proctor, C. M., and Wood, D. W., 1954. 'Determination of inorganic phosphate in sea water by an iso-butanol extraction procedure.' *J. Mar. Res.*, **13**, 122–32.
15. Robinson, R. J., and Thompson, T. G., 1948. 'The determination of phosphates in sea water.' *J. Mar. Res.*, **7**, 33–41.
16. ——, and Wirth, H. E., 1935. 'Photometric investigation of the ceruleomolybdate determination of phosphate in waters.' *Industr. Engng. Chem. (Anal.)*, **7**, 147–50.
17. Saeki, A., 1952. 'Some substances in sea water which disturb the colorimetric determination of phosphate.' *J. Oceanogr. Soc. Japan*, **8**, 73–8.
18. Tischer, J., 1934. 'Über die Bestimmung der Phosphorsäure mittels der Phosphor-Molybdänblau-Methode und der Anwendung auf Pflanzenaschen.' *Zeit. Pflanz. Düng. u. Bodenkunde, Teil A*, **33**, 192–242.
19. Wooster, W. S., and Rakestraw, N. W., 1951. 'The estimation of dissolved phosphate in sea water.' *J. Mar. Res.*, **10**, 91–100.

11

ORGANIC PHOSPHORUS IN SEA WATER AND PLANKTON

Range, 0–0·6 μg.-atom P/l.

At. wt. P=30·98.

Factor, g. P to g.-atom P=0·03228.

The organic phosphorus content of sea water may be divided into particulate (living or otherwise) and soluble fractions, each of which it may be required to estimate separately. The total phosphorus in the sample may be determined and the total organic phosphorus obtained by subtraction of the inorganic phosphorus estimated on a separate sample; the particulate fraction may be determined either directly after its separation by filtration, or by subtraction of the total phosphorus as determined after filtration from that determined without filtration.

The problems centre round three questions:

1. The mode of release of phosphorus from the organic material to give orthophosphate, the form in which it is estimated.

2. The prevention of interference caused by arsenic; after oxidative treatment of the sample all the arsenic, unless subsequently reduced, is in the form of arsenate and is returned, therefore, as phosphate in the subsequent estimation.

3. The reliability of the reagent blanks.

In early work (3, 8, 10, 12, 14) a standard wet digestion with sulphuric acid was used to oxidize the organic matter but the method is somewhat tedious, time-consuming and not easily carried out on board ship. Furthermore, the reagent blanks are usually high and rather variable. The last-mentioned difficulty has been obviated in perchloric acid digestions (6, see Kuney, 11 for precautions). Harvey (7) has developed a much simpler and more convenient technique in which the sample is hydrolysed by acid treatment in an autoclave, and this has been extensively used after a critical examination by Ketchum, Corwin and Keen (9). The method has also been tested against a perchloric acid digestion and found to give almost complete recovery of organic phosphorus (1, 2, 9). It may therefore be confidently recommended. Part of the acid required for the colour reaction is introduced before autoclaving and no neutralization of the solution is required. Interference from arsenic is eliminated by the presence of sodium sulphite during autoclaving. Dr J. P. Riley has pointed out that he has found digestion with fuming nitric and perchloric acids to be the only satisfactory method for substances such as lecithins and cephalins.

If more refractory samples are encountered then recourse must be had to oxidative digestion techniques to which reference has been made.

Reagents

1. *Sulphuric acid.* 50% by volume.
2. *Sodium sulphite.* A saturated solution.
3. *Acid-ammonium molybdate solution.* 6·6 g. of the pure solid are dissolved in 400 ml. of distilled water and 6 ml. sulphuric acid added. The solution is stored in a waxed or polythene bottle and should be kept 48 hours before use.
4. *Stannous chloride.* As for inorganic phosphate (*see* p. 153).
5. *Thorium carbonate.* A dilute suspension in distilled water.

Procedure

To 67 ml. of sea water contained in a 100 ml. *silica* flask add 1 ml. of 50% sulphuric acid and 0·2 ml. of the saturated sodium sulphite solution. Autoclave for 5–6 hours at a pressure between 30 and 40 lb./sq. in. (2·1–2·8 kg./sq. cm.). Cool, and after adjusting the volume to 68 ml., add 2 ml. of the acid-molybdate solution. Note the temperature. Measure the transmittancy at 705 mμ or with a red filter (Ilford 608) against distilled water. Add 0·15 ml. of stannous chloride reagent, again transfer to the cell and measure the transmittancy against distilled water at the maximum colour development. Repeat the whole procedure for blank using distilled water. The calculated values are subject to a correction of -2% since there is an increase in the blue colour due to reduction of the acidity as a result of reaction between acid and sulphite. Note salt errors, pp. 152–4.

Remarks

1. The precision of the method is $\pm 5\%$ (coefficient of variation).
2. With reagent grade chemicals not specially purified the blank is approximately 0·2 μg.-atom P/l.
3. The organic phosphorus is frequently given by a small difference between two relatively large values, total and inorganic; unless this difference exceeds 10% of the concentration it cannot be regarded as significant.
4. Arsenic, whilst not interfering in the total phosphorus estimation, is included in that of the inorganic phosphate, so that the organic phosphorus obtained by subtraction is biased with the whole of the arsenic error. The most recent values for arsenic (14) of

0·025–0·047 μg.-atom As/l. are smaller than the values obtained by Gorgy, Rakestraw and Fox (5), namely 0·2–0·5 μg.-atom As/l. and the errors from this source are probably smaller than was originally thought (3, 8, 13).

5. On storage the apparent total phosphorus of a sample tends to decrease as a result of the activities of periphytic bacteria. If the samples are not to be analysed directly after collection, the sample bottle may be 'baited' with a few millilitres of the thorium carbonate suspension, thus providing a large surface area. On addition of acid prior to autoclaving this precipitate is dissolved and the small quantity of thorium sulphate does not affect the estimation. Ketchum *et al.* (9) prefer to scrub the sample bottle with 1 ml. of concentrated hydrochloric acid before transferring to the reaction flask (*see also* p. 155).

6. Samples may be stored up to two years without measurable loss in total phosphorus.

7. With a large series, temperature corrections may be avoided by working at ambient room temperature which may be adequately regulated.

8. The volume of the sample may be changed if equivalent changes are made in reagent additions.

9. Dr Ketchum reports that he has successfully used the Harvey hydrolysis technique for total phosphorus on plankton filtered off on a precipitate of barium sulphate deposited on a sinter glass filter. After digestion the barium sulphate is removed by filtration and the estimation carried out as for sea water. There is no salt error and distilled water calibration curves should be used.

ORGANIC PHOSPHORUS
(PLANKTON, TISSUES AND MUD)

When moderate amounts of such material with relatively high phosphorus content are available, alternative conditions for developing the blue colour, that are less sensitive to minor changes in the variables, may be employed.

H. Barnes has used the Fiske-Subbarow reagent (4) following a sulphuric acid-hydrogen peroxide digestion which may be conveniently carried out either in a hard glass or fused silica test-tube. The following procedure has been found satisfactory for milligram quantities of many types of material.

Reagents

1. *Sulphuric acid.* Concentrated and 10 N, the latter being prepared by carefully adding 278 ml. of concentrated acid to distilled water and making up to 1 litre.

2. *Hydrogen peroxide.* 100 vols. Micro-analytical (M.A.R.) reagent of the British Drug Houses or similar. This product has been found very satisfactory. Hydrogen peroxide should always, however, be tested for its phosphate content; some products are highly contaminated.

3. *Sodium hydroxide.* Approximately 10 N and N; that is 40% w/v and 4% w/v solutions, respectively.

4. *Ammonium molybdate.* Dissolve 2·5 g. clear crystals in distilled water and make up to 100 ml. Filter if necessary. Store in an amber bottle.

5. *Fiske-Subbarow reagent.* Grind 0·5 g. sodium-1-naphthol sulphonate with 15% w/v sodium metabisulphite solution and make up to 195 ml. with the same. Add 5 ml. 20% w/v sodium sulphite solution and dissolve by gently heating. Filter if necessary.

Procedure

Transfer the sample into a hard glass or silica test-tube; add 0·5 ml. of concentrated sulphuric acid. Warm gently to charring with a micro-burner using a small flame; if necessary add more acid to liquefy. Heat to fuming until a satisfactory digest is obtained; avoid excessive heating and do not heat at liquid meniscus. Cool and add 0·1 ml. hydrogen peroxide. Heat quickly to oxidize. If the liquid goes yellow after the effervescence has ceased, fume again, cool, add a further small quantity of hydrogen peroxide and repeat. When a colourless digest is obtained, heat for several minutes to destroy excess of hydrogen peroxide; dilute with 2 ml. distilled water and boil vigorously for 5 minutes. Cool, and if necessary centrifuge, to remove any insoluble matter. Neutralize the supernatant to litmus with caustic soda and transfer the neutral sample to a 10 ml. standard flask, making up to about 6 ml. with distilled water. Add successively 0·4 ml. of the 10 N sulphuric acid reagent, 0·8 ml. ammonium molybdate solution and 0·4 ml. of the Fiske-Subbarow reagent, mixing thoroughly between each addition; make up to 10 ml. Allow to stand 10 minutes, transfer to optical cell and determine the transmittancy against distilled water with red filter or at 625 mμ. Repeat procedure with distilled water adding all reagents for blank.

Remarks

1. The amount of acid required for digestion depends upon the organic matter content of the sample: it should be kept as low as possible, consistent with adequate sampling of the material and the phosphorus content. A few crystals of copper sulphate may be added.

2. It is essential to cool thoroughly before the addition of hydrogen peroxide, since otherwise most of it is decomposed on the surface of the hot acid.

3. Excessive heating, particularly at the liquid meniscus, tends to cause loss of phosphorus.

4. Any oxalic or other organic acids produced in the oxidative digestion tend to interfere with the development of the blue colour; with samples high in organic matter the diluted digest may be warmed with a slight excess of 1 % potassium permanganate and excess of the latter removed with 0·5 % hydroxylamine hydrochloride solution.

5. Iron (ferric) tends to interfere with the development of the blue colour. With small quantities no interference is experienced in the presence of sulphite which reduces it to the ferrous state. If necessary a small addition of sulphite may be made prior to the addition of the Fiske-Subbarow reagent, which in this case should be slowly added drop-wise with swirling.

6. Occasionally a turbidity will develop in the blue solution: in this case the solution should be centrifuged before the transmittancy is determined.

7. The time required for the blue colour to reach its maximum varies with different batches of the Fiske-Subbarow reagent, and with a given reagent tends to increase with age. After a few days the 'aging' is slow and the use of a very freshly prepared reagent is not therefore recommended.

REFERENCES

1. Armstrong, F. A. J., 1954. 'Phosphorus and silicon in sea water off Plymouth during the years 1950 to 1953.' *J. Mar. biol. Ass. U.K.*, **33**, 381–92.

2. ——, and Harvey, H. W., 1950. 'The cycle of phosphorus in the waters of the English Channel.' *J. Mar. biol. Ass. U.K.*, **29**, 145–62.

3. Cooper, L. H. N., 1937. 'Organic phosphorus in sea water from the English Channel.' *J. Mar. biol. Ass. U.K.*, **21**, 673–8.

4. Fiske, C. H., and Subbarow, Y., 1925. 'The colorimetric determination of phosphorus.' *J. biol. Chem.*, **66**, 375–400.

5. Gorgy, S., Rakestraw, N. W., and Fox, D. L., 1948. 'Arsenic in sea water.' *J. Mar. Res.*, **7**, 22–3.

6. Hansen, A. L., and Robinson, R. J., 1953. 'The determination of organic phosphorus in sea water with perchloric acid oxidation.' *J. Mar. Res.*, **12**, 31–42.

7. Harvey, H. W., 1948. 'The estimation of phosphate and of total phosphorus in sea waters.' *J. Mar. biol. Ass. U.K.*, **27**, 337–59.

8. Kalle, K., 1935. 'Meereskundliche chemische Untersuchungen mit Hilfe des Zeisschen Pulfrich-Photometers. Mitteilung V. Die Bestimmung des Gesamt-Phosphorgehaltes, des Plankton Phosphorgehaltes (lebende Substanz) und Trübungsmessungen.' *Ann. Hydrogr., Berl.*, **63**, 195–204.

9. Ketchum, B. H., Corwin, N., and Keen, D. J., 1955. 'The significance of organic phosphorus determinations in ocean waters.' *Deep-sea Res.*, **2**, 172–81.

10. Kreps, E., and Osadich, M., 1933. 'The organic phosphorus in the sea.' *Int. Rev. Hydrobiol.*, **29**, 221–8.

11. Kuney, J. H., 1947. 'Perchloric acid, friend or foe?' *Chem. Engng. News*, **25**, 1658–9.

12. Matida, Y., 1952. 'A critical study of the determination of total phosphorus in natural water.' *Bull. Jap. Soc. Sc. Fish.*, **18**, 175–81.

13. Rakestraw, N. W., and Lutz, F., 1933. 'Arsenic in sea water.' *Biol. Bull.*, *Woods Hole*, **65**, 397–401.

14. Redfield, A. C., Smith, H. P., and Ketchum, B. H., 1937. 'The cycle of organic phosphorus in the Gulf of Maine.' *Biol. Bull.*, *Woods Hole*, **73**, 421–43.

15. Smales, A. A., and Pate, B. D., 1952. 'The determination of sub-microgram quantities of arsenic by radioactivation. Part II. The determination of arsenic in sea water.' *Analyst*, **77**, 188–95.

INORGANIC SILICON: SILICATE

Range, 0–200 μg.-atom Si/l

At. wt. Si$=28\cdot06$.

Factor, g. Si to g.-atom Si$=0\cdot03564$.

Factor, g. Si to g. $SiO_2=2\cdot1404$.

Factor, g. SiO_2 to g. Si$=0\cdot4672$.

Silicon in sea water may be present either in suspension or solution, in the latter case as silicate in which form it is estimated. The soluble yellow silicomolybdic acid formed on the addition of ammonium molybdate in acid solution has been largely used for the estimation (2, 6). The method is simple, but visual matching when the concentrations are low is somewhat difficult, since the colour is faint and not easy to match. For this reason and to obtain greater sensitivity, Armstrong (1) and Mullin and Riley (4) have recently utilized a method analogous to that for phosphate estimations in which silicomolybdic acid is formed and reduced to molybdenum blue.

SILICOMOLYBDIC ACID METHOD (2, 6)

This method is adequate for waters containing large quantities of silica, that is, greater than 50 μg.-atom Si/l.

Reagents

1. *Sulphuric acid.* 6 N. Add 5 ml. of concentrated acid to distilled Si-free water and make up to 30 ml.

2. *Ammonium molybdate.* Dissolve 10 g. of clear crystals in Si-free water and make up to 100 ml. Store in a polythene bottle.

3. *Standard solutions.* To standardize directly against silicate solutions, either pure silica must be prepared and dissolved by fusion with sodium carbonate or a sodium silicate solution must be analysed gravimetrically. This is a tedious process and it is often the practice to use standard solutions of potassium chromate or picric acid whose silica equivalents are known. Swank and Mellon (7) recommend buffered solutions of the former.

(a) *Sodium borate solution.* 10 g. of $Na_2B_4O_7.10H_2O$ are dissolved in distilled water and made up to 1 litre.

(*b*) *Potassium chromate solutions.* 0·945 g. of K_2CrO_4, previously dried at 105°C. is dissolved in distilled water and made up to 1 litre (I). 1 ml. of this solution (I) is 'equivalent' to 2·5 μg.-atom Si; when 0·2–4·0 ml. of this solution are diluted with 25 ml. of the borate solution and made up to 50 ml. or 100 ml. with distilled water, the solutions are equivalent to 10–200 or 5–100 μg.-atom Si/l. respectively.

Procedure

The analyses should be made as soon as possible after collection. Samples should be collected in polythene or heavily waxed bottles and, if delay is unavoidable, stored in the dark to prevent consumption of silica by diatoms or solution of particulate siliceous matter. The acid may be added before storage to assist in preservation (*see* below).

To 100 ml. of the sample add 1·0 ml. of molybdate reagent, followed by 0·5 ml. of the 6 N sulphuric acid; stand for 10–60 minutes. The transmittancy is usually measured at 430 mμ or with a violet filter (Ilford 601, Zeiss S-43). Dr J. P. Riley has pointed out that when a spectrophotometer is available, measurement of the transmittancy at 404 mμ increases the sensitivity almost fourfold with comparatively little increase in the reagent blank. It is then important to maintain the same slit width since the absorption changes rather rapidly with wave-length.

Remarks

1. Phosphate and ferric ions do not interfere at the concentrations in which they are present in sea water.

2. The reagents should be made up in silica-free distilled water and kept in polythene or waxed bottles.

3. It is generally agreed that there is a salt effect, but there is no agreement regarding its magnitude and its variation with chlorinity; no corrections have therefore been applied to the chromate standards.

4. The reagent blank should be tested from time to time.

5. Standard chromate solutions are preferable to those prepared from picric acid: pure potassium chromate is more easily obtained and its solutions are more stable.

6. Above 70 μg.-atom Si/l. a greenish tinge may occur which is difficult to deal with by visual comparison but not by photometer; with the former method an aliquot should be taken for analysis.

7. Temperature has little effect upon the final colour, but when low somewhat retards its development. Half an hour is required at

5° C. Prolonged standing should be avoided in order to reduce errors due to the solution of silicates.

8. With some filters the transmittancy-Si content curve may not be linear; this is not so when working at 430 mμ with a spectrophotometer.

9. Mullin and Riley (5) have investigated the silica changes on storage in various types of bottles; with glass bottles there is a gradual solution of silica, the rate of increase depending upon the type of glass and the conditions of its interior surface. Acidification reduces the rate of solution. They recommend filtering (Whatman No. 2 or 41) the raw sample (120 ml.) through a polythene funnel into a polythene bottle containing 2 drops (0·05 ml.) of concentrated hydrochloric acid, after first washing the filter paper with 20 ml. of the water.

THE MOLYBDENUM BLUE METHOD (4)

This method is useful for low concentrations of silica; it will deal with about 50 μg.-atom Si/l. in a 1 cm. cell. For higher concentrations the sample must be diluted or the silico-molybdate method should be used.

The problems to be faced in using a reduction method are similar to those encountered in the estimation of phosphates; a variety of reducing agents may be used. Armstrong (1) has used stannous chloride which gives the greatest sensitivity, but the colour fades rather rapidly. Mullin and Riley (4) after investigating a number of reducing agents, recommend metol (p-methylaminophenol sulphate); it is cheap, readily available, stable, and the resultant colour is also stable It should be noted that the absorption maximum is in the near infra-red and that maximum sensitivity will not be obtained with photo-voltaic cells which have low sensitivity in this region.

Reagents

1. *Acid ammonium molybdate.* Shake 2 g. of ammonium molybdate with about 70 ml. of distilled water and complete the solution with 6 ml. of concentrated HCl. Dilute to 100 ml. and filter if necessary. Store in a polythene bottle.

2. *Oxalic acid.* Dissolve 10 g. of $(COOH)_2.2H_2O$ in water and make up to 100 ml.

3. *Sulphuric acid.* 25 % v/v.

4. *Metol-sulphite solution.* Dissolve by shaking 5 g. of metol in about 240 ml. of water containing 3 g. of anhydrous sodium sulphite: dilute to 250 ml. Filter and store in an amber bottle.

For use, mix 100 ml. of the metol-sulphite solution with 60 ml. of the 10% oxalic acid. Add, whilst cooling, 120 ml. of 25% sulphuric acid; dilute to 300 ml. This reagent should be freshly prepared every fortnight.

5. *Standard sodium silicate solution.* Fuse 0.1201 g. SiO_2 with 0.6 g. anhydrous sodium carbonate in a platinum crucible; dissolve the melt when cold in distilled water and make up to 100 ml. 1 ml. of this solution contains 20 μg.-atom Si. As a source of silica powdered 'Vitreosil' (99.8% SiO_2) may be used; it should be heated and cooled in a desiccator before weighing.

Treatment of Apparatus

All flasks—standard and otherwise—should be allowed to stand overnight in a 1 : 1 mixture of sulphuric and nitric acids to render them insoluble. They should then be well washed with tap and distilled water. They should not be allowed to dry before use.

Procedure

Pipette 20 ml. of the sample (up to 60 μg. Si) (or 15 ml. plus 5 ml. of distilled water, *see* below) into a 50 ml. graduated flask containing 3 ml. of the acid molybdate reagent and mix thoroughly. After 10 minutes add rapidly 15 ml. of the reducing agent mixture and make up to 50 ml. with distilled water. Measure the transmittancy at 812 mμ after 1 hour. Run a blank.

Remarks

1. The maximum colour is developed in sea water after 1 hour and no fading takes place in 24 hours.

2. There is a salt effect resulting in a reduction of colour: the calibration should be made by silica additions to low silica sea water. The variation of salt error is a linear function of chlorinity. Mullin and Riley (4) give

$$D_d = D_o(1 + 0.00578 Cl\%_0)$$

as the relation between the optical density in distilled and sea waters of varying chlorinity, where D_d is the corrected optical density, D_o the observed optical density at 812 mμ and Cl is the chlorinity of the sample. In most cases the factor may be taken as 1.1.

3. To obtain the greatest accuracy in sea water, 15 ml. of the sample should be diluted with 5 ml. of distilled water before carrying out the procedure.

4. With 7.0 μg.-atom Si/l. the coefficient of variation is $\pm 0.48\%$.

REFERENCES

1. Armstrong, F. A. J., 1951. 'The determination of silicate in sea water.' *J. Mar. biol. Ass. U.K.*, **30**, 149–60.
2. Atkins, W. R. G., 1926. 'Seasonal changes in the silica content of natural waters in relation to the phytoplankton.' *J. Mar. biol. Ass. U.K.*, **14**, 89–99.
3. Chow, D. T.-W., and Robinson, R. J., 1953. 'Forms of silicate available for colorimetric estimations.' *Analyt. Chem.*, **25**, 646–8.
4. Mullin, J. B., and Riley, J. P., 1955. 'The colorimetric determination of silicate with special reference to sea and natural waters.' *Analyt. chim. acta*, **12**, 162–76.
5. ——, ——, 1955. 'Storage of sea-water samples for the determination of silicate.' *Analyst*, **80**, 73–4.
6. Robinson, R. J., and Thompson, T. G., 1948. 'The determination of silicate in sea water.' *J. Mar. Res.*, **7**, 49–55.
7. Swank, H. W., and Mellon, M. G., 1934. 'Colorimetric standards for silica.' *Industr. Engng. Chem. (Anal.)*, **6**, 348–50.

note this is not the same Atkins paper referenced by Claves (1938)

13

ORGANIC CARBON OF SEA WATER AND PLANKTON

The problems associated with the estimation of the organic carbon content have recently been discussed by Kay (3). Simple titration of the oxidizable material with, say, potassium permanganate is inadequate. Prior to the work of Kay the only satisfactory method was that of Krogh and Keys (4) which can be carried out on 20–25 ml. (2–3 mg. C/l.) of water. The method requires much skill and practice and is not really suitable for a large number of serial analyses. This method is given below. For a satisfactory routine method Kay considers the following to be the main desiderata:

1. Because of the small quantities of carbon involved, contact with air should be avoided throughout the analysis; all transfers should be made within the apparatus.

2. A concentration of the material (as in Krogh's method) should if possible be avoided in order to reduce possible contamination.

3. Contamination with atmospheric carbon dioxide should be avoided.

4. Precipitation of chloride should not be made prior to analysis; this may lead to contamination.

5. The amount of water should be sufficiently great to give the required accuracy but should not be so large as to give high blanks.

6. The apparatus should be simple and reliable.

THE METHOD OF KROGH AND KEYS (4)

Reagents

1. *Phosphoric acid.* Pure acid dissolved in distilled water and diluted to give about 0.1 N.

2. *Methyl red indicator.* 0.1% solution.

3. *Thallous sulphate.* The purest preparation available is melted in a crucible and well stirred to remove any organic matter by combustion. After cooling the solid is pulverized and stored.

4. *Oxidizing solution.* Mix 10 g. $K_2Cr_2O_7$, 4 g. Ag_2CrO_4 and 1 g. of chromic acid together in a crucible and melt. Pulverize the resultant solid. To 50 ml. of distilled water add 50 ml. of sulphuric

acid, 6 g. of the chromic acid mixture and 3 g. of ceric sulphate, heat the mixture in its storage bottle whilst aerating with CO_2-free air for about 24 hours. The mixture is kept protected against CO_2 (see Fig. 35).

5. *Potassium dichromate*. Pure, as a fine powder.

6. *Hydrochloric acid*. 0·33 N kept in a stoppered bottle.

7. *Baryta solution*. About 0·09–0·06 N with a little cresolphthalein indicator: this reagent should be stored in a CO_2-free atmosphere (see Fig. 35).

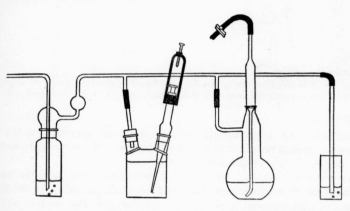

FIG. 35. Arrangements for storing reagents. (Redrawn from Krogh, A. and Keys, A., *Biol. Bull.*, 1934.)

Apparatus

The oxidation is conducted in a combustion flask fitted with a side arm (Fig. 36). The flasks should be cleaned with thiosulphate solution, followed by ordinary bichromate cleaning fluid, and just before use they should be rinsed with a little distilled water which is poured off as completely as possible and the flasks dried by filter pump. Whilst the combustion mixture in the flask is heated on a glycerine bath, air freed from carbon dioxide by soda lime (B) is swept through the entire system. The combustion tube (C) is filled in the following order with asbestos shreds, lead chromate dispersed in asbestos, cupric oxide, asbestos, platinum foil, asbestos impregnated with finely divided silver, and finally asbestos. The air and combustion gases pass through these fillings in the order given to ensure that all traces of halogens and halogen acids are removed and that any carbon monoxide is converted to carbon dioxide. The working part (14 cm.) of this tube (Pyrex or hard glass) is surrounded by a copper tube (D) and heated by the burner (E) to a temperature of 450° C.

registered on a thermometer in this tube. The flow of air is regulated by a clip and may be observed in the absorption tube (G).

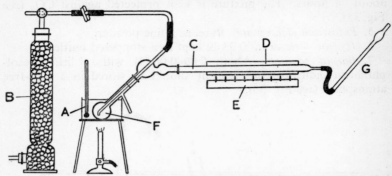

FIG. 36. Combustion apparatus for the determination of dissolved organic carbon in sea water. (Redrawn from Krogh, A. and Keys, A., *Biol. Bull.*, 1934.)

Procedure

Determine the approximate salinity and the amount of 0·1 N phosphoric acid required to give a permanent red colour with methyl red per 20–25 ml. of the water sample.

Transfer a 20–25 ml. sample to a centrifuge tube, add the same amount of phosphoric acid followed by thallous sulphate in 30% excess of that required to precipitate the chloride. For normal waters 2·5 g. thallous sulphate is adequate. Shake the mixture slowly for ten or more hours. Centrifuge, and pipette off 20 ml. of the supernatant liquid and evaporate it to dryness. Transfer the dry solid to the combustion flask and add about 0·2 g. of potassium dichromate. Thoroughly mix the two and place 3 ml. of the oxidizing solution in the side arm. Raise the temperature of the glycerine bath whilst maintaining a fairly rapid current of air and, with a drop of water in the absorption tube, heat the tube (D) by the burner (E). When the temperature of the glycerine bath has reached 80–90° C., reduce the flow of air and transfer a known quantity of barium hydroxide to the absorption tube. Turn the combustion flask and gradually transfer oxidation liquid from the side bulb into the combustion flask. Mix the contents of the latter thoroughly. After reaching a temperature of 120° C. continue the combustion for a further 30 minutes; this is sufficient to drive off all the carbon dioxide.

Place a clip on the rubber tube of the absorption tube, remove from the combustion line, and titrate with 0·33 N hydrochloric acid under a current of carbon dioxide-free air.

Blank estimations should be run on the reagents; the chromic acid will give off the equivalent of 2–10 μg. C., and since this amount is dependent upon the working conditions it is essential to maintain time and temperature conditions the same in all runs.

Remarks

1. The precipitate of thallous chloride is readily converted back to the sulphate. Wash the precipitate several times with minimal amounts of cold distilled water. Transfer the washed precipitate to a casserole, add a 50 % excess concentrated sulphuric acid and heat at 400° C. for 24 hours. Raise the temperature to 450° C. and boil off all the excess sulphuric acid. Cool and pulverize.

2. Krogh and Keys (4) recommend a simple radiation oven for evaporation of the supernatant liquid from the thallous sulphate precipitation.

3. Great care should be taken when the oxidizing mixture is transferred from the side arm to the combustion flask since it lowers the temperature and absorbs any water vapour present; there is a tendency for the baryta to be sucked back from its tube.

4. 1 c.mm. of 0·33 N hydrochloric acid is equivalent to 2 μg. C. The volume of barium hydroxide solution should be equivalent to 90–100 c.mm. of the 0·33 N acid.

5. In collecting the water samples great care must be exercised to prevent contamination by oil or grease.

6. Particulate matter and some colloidal matter is carried down with the precipitate; however, some approach to an estimation of soluble and colloidal organic matter could be made by the use of graded ultra-filters. Care would have to be taken to prevent contamination (2).

7. Planktonic material may be prepared as described for nitrogen estimation; alternatively, since there are virtually no salts present, a dry combustion method may be used (von Brand, 2).

8. The precision is about ± 3 μg. C on 10–100 μg. of C.

9. When large samples of material are available the standard micro-methods for carbon estimations commonly used in organic chemistry may be employed for plankton and tissues.

THE METHOD OF KAY (3)

The water sample is freed from carbon dioxide and the organic matter oxidized with a silver-containing chromic acid mixture in a stream of oxygen, the chloride being simultaneously precipitated. The oxidation products are separated from any chloride by potassium iodide, and fully oxidized to carbon dioxide which is absorbed in barium hydroxide. Up to 20 ml. of sample may be used containing 1–200 μg. C; the accuracy is stated to be 1 μg. C.

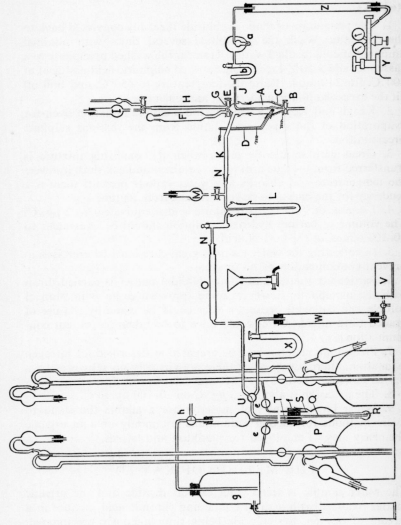

FIG. 37. The Apparatus of Kay for carbon estimation. (Redrawn from Kay, H., *Kiel. Meeresforsch.*, 1954.)

Apparatus and Manipulation (Figs. 37 and 38)

1. *The wet digestion vessel* (A). This is funnel-shaped and has a draining cock (B) at its lower end. The vessel is electrically heated by means of resistance wire (C) and the temperature is controlled by a mercury thermometer (D) inserted through a side arm and connected to a suitable relay. All cocks are sealed with sulphuric acid.

2. *Introduction of oxidation mixture and sample.* The head of the digestion vessel carries a double stopcock (E) which leads to the oxidation mixture reservoir (F) graduated in 0·5 ml. and closed by a ground cap and to a small ground section (G) which takes the sample pipette (H). The latter, made to deliver either 5 or 10 ml., is exactly similar to the Knudsen pipette used for measuring the samples for salinity determinations (*see* p. 86); its side arm is protected by an absorption tube (I) to prevent any contamination by atmospheric carbon dioxide. The pipette is calibrated in the usual way. A gas inlet tube (J) leads into the digestion vessel and from it is a wider condenser tube (K) connecting with the halogen absorption vessel. The oxidation mixture and silver chloride precipitation are in contact throughout the digestion process.

3. *The halogen absorption vessel* (L). This is a 50-ml. wash bottle connected to the tube (K) leading out to the oxidation vessel and having a side arm with a cock leading to the absorption tube. The joints are so constructed that when working with halogen-free material the digestion vessel can be connected directly to the catalyst tube (N to N).

4. *The catalyst tube* (O). This is a heavy combustion tube, connected at one end to the iodine absorption vessel and leading at the other to the carbon dioxide absorption vessel via a rubber connection. The platinum catalyst is in the form of a curled platinum gauze 7 cm. long, with 2 mm. thick asbestos stoppers each with 3 cm. of silver wool. The combustion tube is surrounded on the outside with wire gauze during heating. It should be separated from other parts of the apparatus by heat-insulating material. The platinum is heated to a dull red glow.

5. *The carbon dioxide absorption system.* The narrow absorption vessel is shown at (P), the lower portion containing about 8 ml. for convenience in titration. The thick-walled capillary tube (Q) leading from the combustion section passes to the bottom of the absorption vessel and has fused to its end a small sinter glass filter to give small gas bubbles, and so ensure effective absorption. The vessel is closed by a rubber stopper through which pass the carefully ground tips of the burettes (S). A fourth hole in the stopper (to h) leads to the gas remover. A three-way stopcock in the introduction tube allows the absorption vessel to be put into connection with either the gas stream or the rinsing device.

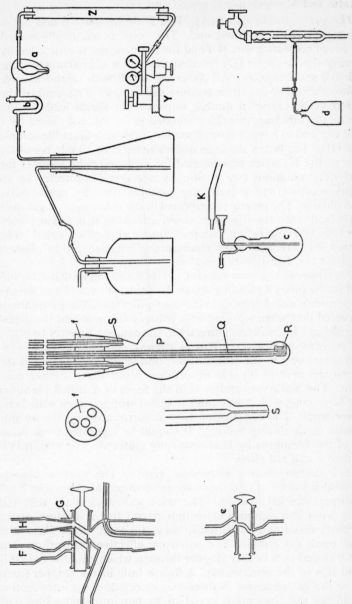

FIG. 38. The Apparatus of Kay for carbon estimation. (Redrawn from Kay, H., *Kiel. Meeresforsch.*, 1954.)

6. *The rinsing device.* An air pump (V) of conventional pattern is connected via a carbon dioxide absorption tube (W), 25 cm. long, and a drying tube (X) to one side of the three-way stopcock (U). Stopcocks on the pump exit allow gas regulation.

7. *The stream of gas.* Oxygen is taken directly from a cylinder (Y) with a pressure regulator, and passes through a tube (Z) containing finely ground calcium chloride and soda asbestos, through the bubble counter (*a*) and then through a calcium chloride absorption tube (*b*) before going into the digestion vessel. The purity of the oxygen should be checked for each cylinder. It must not contain more than 3 μg. C/300 ml. The pressure balance is restored by the suction pump and the flask (g), which is connected to the washing valve (h) and absorption tube.

The Reagents

1. *Silver chromate.* Add a solution containing 48 g. potassium dichromate in 800 ml. of water to a boiling solution of 48 g. silver nitrate in 500 ml. of water (to which a little nitric acid has been added) stirring vigorously. Cool, separate the dark red precipitate on a sinter glass filter and dry at 100° C. (yield about 48 g.).

2. *The digestion mixture.* Mix together in a 500 ml. flask (c) 48 g. of silver dichromate, 16 g. of potassium dichromate and 400 ml. of sulphuric acid (S.G. 1·84). Connect to the apparatus at the condenser (K) and heat to 125° C. whilst passing a stream of purified oxygen. The mixture should be kept in this flask closed with ground-glass caps as shown in Fig. 38. The acid so prepared is almost carbon free.

3. *Potassium iodide solution.* Dissolve 20 g. KI in 50 ml. of 10% sulphuric acid. The antimony cartridge is prepared from pure finely powdered metallic antimony.

4. *Platinum catalyst.* A 7×3 cm. roll of 1024 meshes/cm.^{2}.

5. *Barium hydroxide solution.* 0·05 N. Dissolve 16 g. of barium hydroxide and 20 g. of barium chloride in distilled water and make up to 2 litres. The air-free liquor is kept in a storage vessel.

6. *Hydrochloric acid solution.* 0·025 N. Transfer 250 ml. of 0·1 N HCl to a litre volumetric flask, add 30 g. of barium chloride dissolved in double-distilled water and make up to mark with double-distilled water. A little mercuric chloride may be added as preservative.

7. *Indicator.* Mix one volume of 0·1% thymol blue in 50% alcohol with three volumes of 0·1% phenolphthalein in 50% alcohol. The purest alcohol should be used and its neutrality checked.

8. *Absorption material.* For carbon dioxide, soda asbestos; for water, finely ground calcium chloride dried at 200° C. in a porcelain dish.

9. *Potassium hydroxide for bubble counter.* A solution of 10 g. of potassium hydroxide in 10 ml. of water to which is added a little finely powdered barium hydroxide. The mixture is heated, cooled and centrifuged.

Procedure

1. *Removal of inorganic carbon compounds.* Transfer 50 ml. of sea water to a 100 ml. Jena flask (d), add 1 ml. concentrated sulphuric acid and preserve at $0°C$. until required. When ready, connect to a vacuum pump and heat to boiling to remove the carbon dioxide.

2. *Analysis.* Bring the flask (g) into suction by the tap (h). Place 0·2 ml. of alcohol and 4 drops of indicator in the absorption vessel (P) and connect to its stopper. Pass oxygen at the rate of 15 ml./min. 100 ml. of oxygen are required to sweep out the apparatus. Admit about 8 ml. of barium hydroxide into the absorption vessel then fill and attach the pipette (H) with the sea water. After beginning to heat up the catalyst tube, transfer the sea water to the digestion vessel, opening the taps (E) and of (M) and add 5 or 10 ml. of oxidation mixture. Close the taps and remove the pipette. Heat the digestion flask. Balance the pressure and set the oxygen supply first at 2 ml./min. and after 40 minutes to 2·5 ml./min. so that after 140 minutes 330 ml. oxygen have passed through the apparatus. After 300 ml. of oxygen have passed begin the titration (keep the burettes at $20°C$.). After running out the first burette full, cut off the catalyst and digestion heaters and run off the liquid at (B) with a slightly increased oxygen pressure. Complete the titration with a second burette of hydrochloric acid. After completing the titration, cut off the oxygen. Wash out the titration vessel, adjusting the taps (U) and at (V) with 0·025 N hydrochloric acid, distilled water and alcohol. Set up again ready for analysis.

3. *Standardization.* This should be done in the closed apparatus and a check should be made every few days.

4. *Blanks.* Take the appropriate quantity of the digestion mixture through the whole procedure. A value of 2·5 μg. C/5 ml. acid per 300 ml. oxygen should not be exceeded. With the same mixture carefully stored and the same oxygen supply this blank remains constant.

Remarks

1. The accuracy is said to be 1 μg. of C. It may be noted that the following points all help to increase the sensitivity of the method:

(*a*) The volume of the titration liquid is kept low.

(*b*) The burettes are 1 metre long, 10 ml. capacity graduated in 0·01 ml.; the readings can be estimated to 0·002 ml. (0·3 μg. carbon when using 0·025 N HCl).

(c) The use of the mixed indicator.

(d) The tips of the burettes are drawn and cut off (S) so that drops of 0·008 ml. can be delivered.

2. In preparation, storage, and analysis, great care is taken against contamination by using always a closed apparatus.

3. The indicator changes from red-violet to yellow (acid). The solution should be titrated to a weak yellow. Kay considers that the exact end-point can be estimated to within 0·004 ml. of 0·025 N acid by comparing the colour before and after the addition of the drop.

REFERENCES

1. Belcher, R., and Godbert, A. L., 1945. *Semi-Micro Quantitative Organic Analysis*. Longmans, Green & Co., London, 1947 Impression, 168 pp.
2. von Brand, T., 1935. 'Methods for the determination of nitrogen and carbon in small amounts of plankton.' *Biol. Bull.*, *Woods Hole*, **69**, 221–32.
3. Kay, H., 1954. 'Eine Mikromethode zur chemischen Bestimmung des organisch gebunden Kohlenstoffs im Meerwasser.' *Kiel. Meeresforsch*, **10**, 26–36.
4. Krogh, A., and Keys, A., 1934. 'Methods for the determination of dissolved organic carbon and nitrogen in sea water.' *Biol. Bull.*, *Woods Hole*, **67**, 132–44.

14

OXYGEN

Range, 0–0·90 mg.-atom O_2/l.

At. wt. O$=16·00$.

Factor, g. O_2 to g.-atom $O_2=0·0625$.

Factor, 1 g. O_2 to ml. at S.T.P. (0°C. and 760 mm. Hg)$=700$ ml.

1 ml. 0·01 N-$Na_2S_2O_3=0·08$ mg. O_2.

STANDARD WINKLER METHOD (MACRO-)

The standard method for the estimation of dissolved oxygen in natural waters is that of Winkler, in which manganous hydroxide is allowed to react with the oxygen giving a tetravalent manganese compound; in the presence of acid potassium iodide an equivalent quantity of iodine is liberated which is titrated with standard sodium thiosulphate. The reactions involved are as follows:

$$Mn^{++}+2OH^-\rightarrow Mn(OH)_2,$$
$$2Mn(OH)_2+O_2\rightarrow 2MnO(OH)_2,$$
$$MnO(OH)_2+4H^++3I^-\rightarrow Mn^{++}+I_3^-+3H_2O,$$
$$I_3^-+2S_2O_3^{--}\rightarrow 3I^-+S_4O_6^{--}.$$

A great many modifications of this technique have been introduced; a standard procedure has been recommended for sea-water samples (8, 15).

Volume Estimation

Two methods of measuring the volume of a sample are used (15):

1. Each bottle is calibrated for its volume, the calibration being etched on both bottle and stopper and painted black. After addition of the reagents (see below) the whole contents of the bottle are titrated. Allowance is made for the water displaced by the added reagents. The advantages of this method are:

   (a) that for titration with 0·01 N sodium thiosulphate a 100 ml. sample is adequate;
   (b) no pipetting or measuring from the bottle is required.

In order to attain a volume accuracy comparable with that of the titration the bottle must, however, be calibrated to deliver the stated volume to within 0·5 ml. Furthermore, the calibration constant for each bottle must be included in the calculation and this is a disadvantage when large numbers of samples have to be dealt with.

2. 250 ml. sample bottles are used; after adding the reagents, 100 ml. of solution, which may be taken sufficiently accurately with a measuring cylinder, are used for the titration. Clearly this is wasteful of the water sample. On the other hand it has the following advantages:

(a) the volume of the bottle need not be known with any great accuracy;

(b) no individual bottle calibration need appear in the calculation (see below);

(c) there is no error due to the collection of a gas bubble at the stopper after addition of the acid;

(d) replicate titrations may be made if desired.

This second procedure has been officially recommended (8).

Collection of the Samples

A sample for oxygen estimation should be taken directly from the water bottle before drawing water for any other analyses; this is to avoid:

(a) loss of oxygen through decreased solubility consequent upon increase in temperature or decrease in pressure when the sample is brought to the surface;

(b) change in oxygen content resulting from the presence of organic material and bacterial activity;

(c) errors due to contact of the water with the metallic sampling apparatus.

In order to collect the sample, attach 20–30 cm. of rubber tube to the outlet of the sampling bottle (for moderate depths when using an insulated water bottle this may be left 'permanently' in place). Displace air from the rubber tube by water and introduce the former into the sampling bottle until it touches the bottom. Rinse the bottle with the sea water. Fill the bottle slowly, avoiding air bubbles, gradually withdrawing the tube as the level rises until the water overflows; rapidly withdraw the rubber tube and stopper the bottle quickly. No air bubbles should be left in the bottle, the carefully ground stopper of which should be pushed well home. Amber bottles should preferably be used: if these are not available, the bottles should not be exposed to light during any subsequent storage.

Reagents

 1. *Manganous sulphate solution.* Dissolve 450 g. of $MnSO_4 . 4H_2O$ in distilled water and make up to 1 litre.

 2. *Alkaline iodide solution.* Dissolve 700 g. of KOH (or 500 g. of NaOH) and 150 g. of KI in distilled water, mix and make up to one litre.

 3. *Sulphuric acid.* Concentrated (36 N).

 4. *Starch solution.* Grind 0·5 g. of soluble starch to a paste with small gradual additions of distilled water. When thoroughly fluid, pour the paste into 200 ml. of distilled water which has been brought to the boil. Boil for one minute. Fresh starch gives a bright blue colour with iodide and is best made up daily; it may be preserved by the addition of 1 mg. of mercuric iodide per 100 ml., but even so a stored reagent is less satisfactory.

 Dr Rakestraw prefers a good batch of 'potato' starch rather than the material sold as 'soluble' starch. The solution is prepared as above, using 10 g. per 2 litres and preserved by the addition of 7 ml. of 30% formaldehyde. He considers that once a good batch has been obtained these solutions give a better end-point and have better keeping qualities than soluble starch solutions.

 5. *Sodium thiosulphate solution.* Dissolve 3·5 g. $Na_2S_2O_3 . 5H_2O$ in boiled-out distilled water and make up to 1 litre. Add a drop or two of carbon bisulphide as preservative and store in an amber bottle. This is about 0·015 N and should be accurately standardized as given below. The strength should be checked at frequent intervals particularly in warm weather.

 6. *Potassium bi-iodate solution.* Weigh out accurately about 0·325 g. of pure $KH(IO_3)_2$, dissolve in distilled water and make up to 1 litre (about 0·01 N). The strength of the solution is

$$\frac{w}{32·5}N,$$

where w is the weight in grams of the bi-iodate.

Standardization of the Thiosulphate

Transfer 97 ml. of typical sea water (if this is highly contaminated use distilled water) to a 250 ml. Erlenmeyer flask with stopper and add 1 ml. of concentrated sulphuric acid. Mix well and add 1 ml. of the alkaline iodide reagent and again thoroughly mix. Add 1 ml. of the manganous sulphate solution and again mix. Add 10 ml. of the standard potassium bi-iodate solution, swirl gently, stopper and allow to stand 10 minutes in the dark. Titrate the liberated iodine with the thiosulphate to a pale straw colour using a 50 or 25 ml.

burette; after adding 0·5 ml. of the starch solution as indicator, complete the titration to the disappearance of the blue colour.

A blank should be determined by repeating the process, but omitting the bi-iodate. If more than 0·1 ml. is required ascertain the reagent responsible, and replace.

Suppose x ml. of the sodium thiosulphate (corrected for the blank, if any) are equivalent to 10 ml. of bi-iodate containing w g. per litre. Then the normality of the thiosulphate is

$$\frac{10 \times w}{x \times 32 \cdot 5} N = F.$$

Procedure

The samples should be treated with reagents directly after drawing. Add as rapidly as possible 1 ml. of the manganous sulphate solution by a pipette with its tip well below the surface of the water: the reagent rapidly sinks to the bottom of the bottle. Add 1 ml. of alkaline iodide solution in the same manner. Stopper quickly neglecting any overflow, and taking care not to trap any air bubbles. Shake the bottle vigorously and after the precipitate has partially settled repeat the shaking. Allow the precipitate to settle as completely as possible. Introduce 1 ml. of concentrated sulphuric acid and again shake until the precipitate dissolves and iodine is liberated. The subsequent titration should be made as soon as possible, storing in the dark if there is any delay.

Transfer 100 ml. by cylinder, or the whole contents of the bottle, to an Erlenmeyer flask and titrate the free iodine with the standard thiosulphate using the starch indicator. If the whole contents of the bottle are used then either rinse out with a little distilled water, or after the first end-point return some of the solution to the bottle, rinse and after transferring back to the Erlenmeyer flask complete the titration. This rinsing is avoided if the bottles are calibrated to *deliver* the stated volume. A 25 or 50 ml. burette should be used and read to 0·02 ml. Titrate a sea-water blank reversing order of reagent addition. Under normal conditions a single blank will suffice for a whole series of estimations.

Calculation

1. When the whole contents of the bottle are used: let V be the volume of the bottle, and n the ml. of thiosulphate of normality F required to titrate the liberated iodine corrected for the blank. The volume of the sample whose oxygen content is being measured is

$$(V-2) \text{ ml.}$$

(The added acid only displaces oxygen-free water.)

Then the oxygen content is

$$C=\frac{n.F.1000}{2(V-2)} \text{ mg.-atom } O_2/l.$$

or

$$C=\frac{n.F.1000\times22,400}{(V-2)4.1000}$$

$$=\frac{n.F.5600}{(V-2)} \text{ ml. } O_2 \text{ at S.T.P./l.}$$

2. When the reagents are added to a 250 ml. sample and 100 ml. are taken for titration, then, if the bottles are chosen as described below, the volume of the sample is

$$100\times\frac{(250-2)}{250}=f=99\cdot2,$$

and this factor is used for all the bottles. The oxygen content is given by

$$C=\frac{n.F.1000}{2.f}$$

$$=n.5\cdot04.F \text{ mg.-atom } O_2/l.$$

or

$$C=\frac{n.F.1000.22,400}{f.4.1000}$$

$$=n\times56\cdot45.F \text{ ml. } O_2 \text{ at S.T.P./l.}$$

Remarks

1. The method is suitable for estimating oxygen in the absence of oxidizing or reducing substances: the former liberate iodine from iodide and the latter reduce iodine to iodide. In normal sea water little trouble is experienced although in highly polluted waters one of the modifications given below should be used.

2. Sulphuric acid may be conveniently replaced by concentrated hydrochloric acid. If this is done it should be ascertained that the latter is free from ferric iron (a common impurity) since this readily oxidizes iodide to iodine.

3. Nitrogen oxides may be present in the sulphuric acid, in which case the latter should be either fumed alone or with a crystal of ammonium sulphate.

Manganous sulphate may occasionally contain ferric iron (it is preferable to the chloride in this respect); if so, it should be re-crystallized.

4. If 100 ml. bottles are used they may be calibrated by filling with distilled water, carefully inserting the stopper, drying the outside and weighing. Alternately they may be calibrated to deliver a stated volume by weighing full and after a standard delivery procedure (*see* p. 68). The density of water at 20°C. ±5°C. may be taken as 0·9972; the calibration should not be in error by more than 1·0%. The etched volume figure should be blackened since etching does not easily show when the bottle is wet, and the volume of the individual bottle has to be entered at the time of the titration.

If 250 ml. ±25 ml. bottles are chosen and 100 ml. samples taken for the titration, the constant factor for the water volume may be used without significant error.

5. Iodine is volatile and any titration, either of sample or standards, should be performed as quickly as possible, preferably using stoppered Erlenmeyer flasks.

6. Potassium bi-iodate (or iodate) is by far the most convenient and reliable substance with which to standardize thiosulphate. If it is not available, either potassium dichromate (with iodine as an intermediate) or arsenious oxide may be used. Iodine is not recommended as a primary standard because of its volatility. Arsenious oxide is reliable and easily purified by resublimation but requires an intermediate iodine standard. Potassium dichromate is readily available; however, its reaction with iodides is not instantaneous and it is sometimes stated that there is a danger of air-oxidation of hydriodic acid particularly in the presence of chromic salts.

Standardization with potassium dichromate. Dissolve about 0·5 g., accurately known, of pure potassium dichromate (dried at 130°C. for 30 minutes) in distilled water and make up to 1 litre. A 0·01 N solution contains 0·4903 g./l. Place 100 ml. of cold, boiled-out distilled water (or sea water) in a stoppered flask and add 1 g. of iodate-free potassium iodide and 0·3 g. pure sodium bicarbonate: shake until dissolved. Add 1 ml. concentrated sulphuric acid slowly. Run in 10 ml. of standard dichromate, mix well, wash down, and after stoppering allow to stand in the dark for 5 minutes. Titrate the liberated iodine with the thiosulphate solution. Starch should be added as usual towards the end-point, at which the colour change is from a greenish-blue to a light green. The end-point is quite satisfactory when observed against a white background.

Standardization with arsenious oxide. Dissolve about 0·5 g., accurately weighed out, of pure resublimed arsenious oxide in approximately 10 ml. of N sodium hydroxide, dilute to about 100 ml. and make just acid to litmus paper with N hydrochloric acid. Wash off the paper, add 2 g. of sodium carbonate, transfer to a volumetric flask and make up to 1 litre. A 0·01 N solution contains 0·4945 g.

As_2O_3/l. Weigh out about 1·27 g. iodine into a weighing bottle containing 4 g. of iodate-free potassium iodide dissolved in 5 ml. of water. Dissolve and make up to 1 litre. Transfer 10 ml. of the sodium arsenite (alkali+arsenious oxide) to an Erlenmeyer flask, add 50 ml. of distilled water, 5 g. sodium bicarbonate, and 1 ml. of the starch solution; titrate with the iodine to a pale blue colour. Calculate the normality of the iodine solution. Transfer 10 ml. of the standardized iodine solution to an Erlenmeyer flask and titrate in the usual way with the thiosulphate. Calculate the strength of the thiosulphate solution.

7. Sodium starch glycollate may be used to replace starch as the indicator (11). It has the advantage that it may be added at the beginning of the titration (*see*, however, below).

8. Knowles and Lowden (9) have recently made a study of the detection of the end-point in iodine-thiosulphate titrations. They find that a simple amperometric circuit is the best indicator; starch can lead to results on the low side (-20 to -40 μg. I_2 in volumes between 50 and 200 ml.) and sodium starch glycollate is worse. The amperometric titration, capable of detecting 1 μg. of iodine in 40 ml.

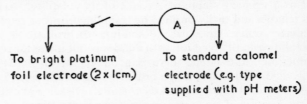

To bright platinum foil electrode (2 x 1cm.)

To standard calomel electrode (e.g. type supplied with pH meters)

Fig. 39. Circuit for amperometric titration. A, micro-ammeter, F.S.D. 5 μA. (that used had a resistance of 3000Ω). (Redrawn from Knowles, G., and Lowden, G. F., *Analyst*, 1953.)

of solution is simple. The circuit is shown above (Fig. 39). For use, place both electrodes in the solution, which should be at least 0·4% by weight with respect to iodide and about 0·15 N with respect to acid at the end of the titration. Add an excess of standard sodium thiosulphate solution, close the amperometric circuit and titrate with standard potassium iodate solution until a permanent increase in current is obtained (Fig. 40).

9. *The Degree of Saturation.* This is the ratio of the concentration of the oxygen present in a water sample to the saturation value at the temperature *in situ* and when in equilibrium with atmospheric oxygen at pressure of 760 Torr. The saturation value at a given temperature depends upon the chlorinity and may be obtained from tables (*see* Tables 18 and 19, pp. 300–1), originally published by Fox (5, 6). The degree of saturation is usually expressed as a percentage.

The oxygen content, the temperature *in situ*, and the chlorinity being known, the tables may then be used to find the saturation value when the degree of saturation is readily calculated.

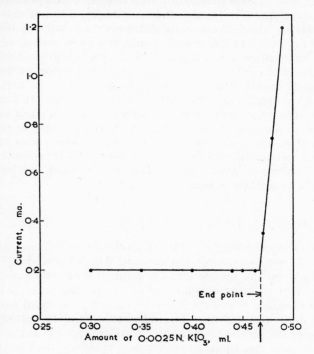

FIG. 40. Results of amperometric titration.

10. It has recently been pointed out (17, 18) that the values given by Fox may be slightly in error and re-calculated values are given. (*See* Tables 20 and 21, pp. 302–3.)

OXYGEN (POLLUTED WATERS)

The foregoing method may be used for ocean and most inshore waters. In the presence of unusual phytoplankton blooms or abnormal concentrations of other organic matter errors may result. Furthermore, the hydrographer is being increasingly consulted—and quite rightly so—on problems of inshore and estuarine hydrography with particular reference to the disposal of industrial wastes, and a knowledge of the oxygen content of the water in such situations is of great importance. The presence of many industrial wastes, containing oxidizing or reducing substances, completely invalidates the standard Winkler procedure: the analytical problems become relatively difficult especially in polluted inshore waters when there has been little time for natural processes to effect decomposition or to allow any settling (2). Three methods for dealing with polluted water will be given. The first, the iodine difference method (Ohle, 10), may be used for a moderate degree of natural or artificial pollution; there is little information on its efficacy with waters heavily polluted with industrial waste. The second—the Alsterberg azide method—is particularly suitable when water is contaminated with nitrites; other reducing or oxidizing substances should be absent. If 1 ml. of fluoride solution is added before acidifying the sample and there is no delay in titration up to 200 mg./l. of ferric iron may be present. Industrial wastes from paper mills and chlorination plants contain sulphur compounds, such as sulphites, thiosulphates, polythionates or free chlorine or hypochlorite. The third method, the alkaline-hypochlorite method, is used in such cases.

THE IODINE DIFFERENCE METHOD (OHLE, 10)

In this method a small addition of a solution of iodine is made to the sample and to a control; the standard Winkler procedure is then carried out on the sample and the residual iodine titrated in the control. Any reducing substance which would react with the iodine in the unmodified Winkler method does so with the added iodine in both sample and control. The difference therefore between the titration of the sample (after adding Winkler reagents) and the control gives the iodine equivalent of the sample automatically corrected for the effect of any interfering substances. It is essential for the success of the method that the interfering substances react with the preliminary iodine addition to the same extent in both sample and control and it is necessary, therefore, to maintain the conditions and timing the same in both.

Reagents

In addition to the standard Winkler reagents already given an approximately 0·01 N solution of iodine in KI prepared as previously described (*see* p. 184) is required. The solution should be kept well stoppered.

Procedure

Fill two sample bottles of about the same volume in the usual way. To each add exactly 1·0 ml. of the 0·01 N iodine solution; if the iodine all disappears add a further 1·0 ml. to each. It is essential for the two bottles to be dealt with at the same time since the reactions should go on for the same period in each bottle. One bottle (the main bottle) is treated exactly as for the Winkler method. The second bottle (control) is treated similarly except that no manganous sulphate reagent is added, but instead 1·0 ml. distilled water. (An alternative is to add the equivalent volume of diluted acid so that the added volumes are the same in both bottles.) The iodine in each is titrated with thiosulphate as in the standard Winkler procedure.

It should be noted that in contradistinction to the Winkler method the acid is added *before* the precipitate in the main bottle is allowed to settle completely. Ohle found that if this is not done much of the organic matter in polluted waters is carried down with the precipitate and, as a result, its effect on the iodine is not identical with that in the parallel bottle in the absence of a precipitate. The longer the interval between the formation and settlement of the precipitate, and the addition of the acid, the greater will be the error from this source.

Calculation

Any substances which would have reacted with the iodine in the unmodified Winkler method will do so with the additional iodine added initially. The iodine equivalent of the oxygen is only liberated in the main bottle and, if the reaction times are the same, then the difference in titre between the two bottles gives the iodine equivalent of the oxygen in the water plus that present in the reagents. Suppose x ml. of the thiosulphate whose strength is F normal, are used for the main bottle and y ml. for the parallel bottle. It is sufficiently accurate to take the difference without considering the volume of the parallel bottle. Then, since $(x-y)$ ml. are used for the oxygen titration, the oxygen content is

$$C = \frac{(x-y)F.1000}{2V} \text{ mg.-atom } O_2/l.$$

or

$$= \frac{(x-y)F.5600}{V} \text{ ml. at S.T.P./l.,}$$

where V is the volume of the sample bottle corrected for reagent additions.

If extreme accuracy is required allowance should be made for the oxygen content of the reagents which is given by Ohle as about 0·1 mg. O_2/l.

THE ALSTERBERG AZIDE METHOD (1, 3, 12)

Reagents

As for the Winkler method and in addition:

1. *Alkaline iodide-sodium azide reagent.* Dissolve 10 g. of sodium azide in 40 ml. of distilled water and add this solution to 950 ml. of the alkaline iodide solution prepared as for the Winkler estimation (Reagent 2, p. 180).

2. *Potassium fluoride solution.* Dissolve 40 g. of $KF.2H_2O$ in distilled water and make up to 100 ml.

Procedure

If ferric iron is present add 1 ml. of the fluoride solution.

Proceed as in the direct Winkler method (p. 181) using the alkaline iodide-sodium azide reagent to replace the normal Winkler iodide reagent. Use the same quantities of manganous salt and acid. If necessary allow for the water displaced by the fluoride solution.

THE ALKALI-HYPOCHLORITE METHOD (14)

In this method the polluting substances are oxidized with a hypochlorite solution. Excess of the latter is destroyed with iodine, excess of which is in turn removed with sodium sulphite. The method may be used to replace the Alsterberg azide technique given above, but the latter is simpler when it is only necessary to deal with nitrites and iron salts. The method tends to give low results. Delay at any point in the procedure should be avoided. With waste containing chlorine and hypochlorite the preliminary treatment with hypochlorite is omitted, so that the procedure may be begun at the iodine addition stage. (Thiosulphate should never be used for the removal of iodine liberated by chlorine or its derivatives in alkaline solutions. Sulphite should always be used.)

Reagents

The following additional reagents are required:

1. *Alkaline hypochlorite solution.* 1 N-NaOCl and 0·1 N-NaOH. Pass chlorine through a 0·1 N caustic soda solution until a 1 ml. test portion requires about 20 ml. 0·1 N thiosulphate to remove the iodine released upon acidification in the presence of an iodide. Satisfactory proprietary preparations of hypochlorite are sold. The strength of this reagent should be checked regularly.

2. *Iodide solution.* Dissolve 17 g. of KI in distilled water and make up to 100 ml. Add 1 ml. 1 N-NaOH to each 100 ml. of solution to preserve.

3. *Sodium sulphite solution.* Dissolve 6·3 g. Na_2SO_3 in distilled water and make up to 1 litre.

4. *Sulphuric acid.* 3·6 N solution. Dilute 100 ml. concentrated acid to 1 litre with distilled water.

Procedure

The sample is collected as for Winkler procedure. Add enough of the alkaline hypochlorite to oxidize the sample, avoiding excess. Water polluted with sulphite waste usually requires about 0·2 ml. Mix well; the duration of this treatment should not exceed 20 seconds, otherwise the results will be low as a result of the absorption of oxygen by the decomposition products of the organic matter. Acidify the sample with 1 ml. of 3·6 N-H_2SO_4 and follow by 1 ml. of the potassium iodide solution. Shake. Remove the liberated iodine with the sodium sulphite solution using starch indicator. The reaction between sulphite and iodine in dilute solution is a comparatively slow reaction. Proceed as for Winkler adding one and a half times the alkaline iodide reagent in order to neutralize the acid used in the preliminary treatment. Allow for reagent additions in calculating the volume of the sample.

WINKLER METHOD (MICRO-)

The macro-method given above is the standard method in hydrographic work and is that recommended when the required volume of water sample can be collected. In some inshore studies and in experimental work, however, only small volumes of water may be available and the following micro-method of Fox and Wingfield (7, *see also* 19) may then be recommended. An accuracy of 1–2 % using 1–2 ml. of water may be attained.

Reagents

1. *Sodium thiosulphate solution.* Dissolve about 6·5 g. of sodium thiosulphate in distilled, boiled-out water and make up to one litre. The solution is about 0·025 N.

2. *Potassium bi-iodate solution.* Dissolve about 0·8 g. of potassium bi-iodate (accurately known) in distilled water and make up to one litre. A normal solution of bi-iodate contains 32·5 g./l.

3. *Manganous chloride.* A solution containing 200 g./l. in distilled water.

4. *Alkaline iodide solution.* 8 g. of sodium hydroxide and 2·5 g. potassium iodide are dissolved in distilled water, mixed and made up to 100 ml.

5. *Phosphoric acid.* 85 % w/w solution of H_3PO_4.

Apparatus

1. *The syringe pipette.* Both the water sample and the reagents are taken into the pipette where the reactions leading to the liberation of iodine take place: the solution is only expelled for titration.

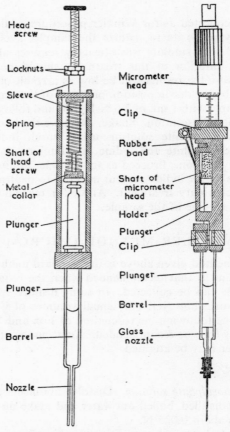

Fig. 41. Syringe pipette (*left*) and burette (*right*). (Redrawn from Fox, H. M., and Wingfield, C. A., *J. exp. Biol.*, 1938.)

The pipette (Fig. 41), fitted with a thick-walled capillary nozzle, is mounted in a metal and ebonite frame. Control of volume is obtained by a head screw and lock-nuts which fix the travel of the plunger so that the same volumes are taken in with successive samples. The actual volumes are determined by taking in a standard solution of potassium bi-iodate and titrating. The head screw, which can be rotated, moves in a sleeve rigidly attached to the frame. The end of the glass plunger of the syringe is kept in contact with the end of the head screw shaft by a spring attached at one end to the plunger and at the other end to the frame. The required volume is selected by adjusting the lock-nuts which are secured in position on the head screw. 1·5 ml. is a convenient volume for a water sample.

Calibration of the syringe pipette. The total volume, i.e. barrel plus dead space in the nozzle, of the adjusted syringe is first determined.

Turn the head-screw down until the lock-nuts are in contact with the sleeve and fill with standard potassium bi-iodate. Wipe off the syringe and deliver the solution plus rinsings into a titration vessel which may be a small beaker or a short specimen tube. Add 1 ml. of 1 % potassium iodide solution followed by three drops of phosphoric acid and titrate from a 5 ml. burette with the standardized sodium thiosulphate using starch indicator. Calculate the volume of the pipette. After washing out the syringe fill the dead space only with the same iodate solution, eject, wash out, and titrate with the micrometer syringe burette (*see* below). Calculate the volume of the dead space: the volume of the barrel is found by subtraction (*see* below).

2. *The Agla syringe burette* (Fig. 41). This consists of a small-bore glass injection syringe whose plunger is actuated by a micrometer head. The glass syringe is mounted in a metal holder which is attached to the micrometer head by a metal clamp. The syringe is filled by screwing the shaft of the micrometer head downwards until the plunger of the syringe reaches nearly to the end of the syringe barrel. Standard solution is then drawn into the syringe by screwing the micrometer head upwards. The head of the glass plunger is held in contact with the shaft of the micrometer head by means of a rubber band. Any air bubbles are expelled by inverting the syringe and turning the screw. The bore of the syringe should be checked for uniformity by weighing the water ejected over various parts of the travel of the piston. Only glass (not steel) tips should be used.

Procedure

Turn down the head screw of the syringe pipette until the lock-nuts touch the sleeve. Fill the dead space with the manganous chloride solution by drawing a small quantity of it into the barrel, inverting the syringe and expelling any air bubbles and solution so that only the dead space remains filled. Wash the outside of the nozzle with water and take the water sample into the syringe by withdrawing the plunger until its head comes in contact with the shaft of the head screw. During this procedure the sample is of course mixed with the manganous chloride previously contained in the dead space. Alkaline iodide solution is then drawn into the syringe by unscrewing the head screw, the volume introduced being about twice that of the manganous chloride; about one turn of the head screw is required. Shake the pipette until the precipitate is evenly distributed and then lay it on its side for three minutes in the dark to allow complete absorption of the oxygen. After further shaking, take in phosphoric acid by three turns of the head screw and shake by inversion until all the precipitate has disappeared. Eject the solution and washings into the titration vessel.

For the titration any micro-burette such as the Rehberg may be used but the Agla described above is very convenient. The burette is best held in a stand with the top of the needle just dipping below the surface of the solution to be titrated. Add 1 drop of the starch solution and titrate, stirring throughout, whilst comparing the colour with distilled water to which one drop of starch has also been added. Repeat with distilled water adding the acid first to determine the blank. Correct the titration for the oxygen content of the reagents which is 5·4 ml./l.

Standardization of the Thiosulphate

This may be done with a 5 ml. ordinary micro-burette. Transfer 2 ml. of the standard potassium bi-iodate to the titration vessel and add 1 ml. of 1% potassium iodide solution and 2–3 ml. of distilled water. Add 5 drops of phosphoric acid and titrate with the thiosulphate solution, adding starch towards the end of the titration. Repeat for blank omitting the bi-iodate.

Calculation

Let the strength of the standard bi-iodate be F Normal.

All the figures are assumed to be corrected for the appropriate blanks. Then if y ml. of thiosulphate are required for the titration of the iodine liberated from 2 ml. of this bi-iodate the thiosulphate is,

$$(2 \cdot 00/y) \ F \ \text{Normal} = A.$$

Let p ml. be the volume of thiosulphate required to titrate the bi-iodate of the dead space in the nozzle.

Then the volume of the dead space is

$$p \times \frac{2 \cdot 00}{y} \ \text{ml.}$$

Let q ml. be the volume of the thiosulphate required to titrate the bi-iodate in the adjusted barrel together with the nozzle dead space.

Then the volume of adjusted barrel plus dead space is

$$q \times \frac{2 \cdot 00}{y} \text{ ml.}$$

Hence the volume of the barrel, i.e. water sample, is

$$\left(q \times \frac{2 \cdot 00}{y}\right) - \left(p \times \frac{2 \cdot 00}{y}\right) = \frac{2 \cdot 00}{y}(q - p) = V \text{ ml.}$$

If n is the number of ml. of thiosulphate required for the water sample, the oxygen can be calculated exactly as before and is

$$C = \frac{n \cdot A \cdot 1000}{2 \cdot V} \text{ mg.-atom } O_2/l.$$

$$C' = \frac{n \cdot A \cdot 5600}{V} \text{ ml. } O_2 \text{ at S.T.P./l.}$$

Remarks

1. Potassium iodate was originally suggested for standardization purposes: potassium bi-iodate may be used.

2. Sodium starch glycollate may be used and added before approaching the end-point (see, however, p. 184).

3. Thorpe and Crisp (16) point out that for accurate work when using very dilute solutions of sodium thiosulphate (0·005 N) it is essential to compare the end-point with that obtained in known solutions of iodine and thiosulphate.

4. Van Dam (4, see also 7) states that if alkaline iodide solution comes into contact with sulphuric acid in the nozzle of the syringe pipette, free iodine may be liberated, and he recommends that the nozzle of the syringe pipette be first filled with the alkaline iodide solution instead of the manganous chloride solution, and that the latter reagent be taken in as the second reagent; in this way direct contact of the alkaline iodide with the acid is avoided. This has been confirmed by Fox and Wingfield who state, however, that the error is completely eliminated by the substitution of phosphoric acid as recommended in their procedure.

5. Stirring of the small volume of titration liquid may be effected by means of a magnetic stirrer, or more simply a neat-fitting glass rod may be used.

THE MICRO-GASOMETRIC ESTIMATION OF DISSOLVED OXYGEN (AND NITROGEN)

A reliable micro-gasometric method (13) has recently been described which may be used in the field or the laboratory. It can be used for polluted waters. The water sample, followed by acid, is drawn anaerobically into an extraction syringe pipette, containing bicarbonate in the dead space; the dissolved gases escape into the large carbon dioxide phase generated by the reagents. After ejecting the liquids, the carbon dioxide is absorbed by strong potassium hydroxide leaving the oxygen and nitrogen as a bubble. This is moved into the capillary of the extractor. The gas bubble is transferred to a syringe analyser, where the oxygen is absorbed.

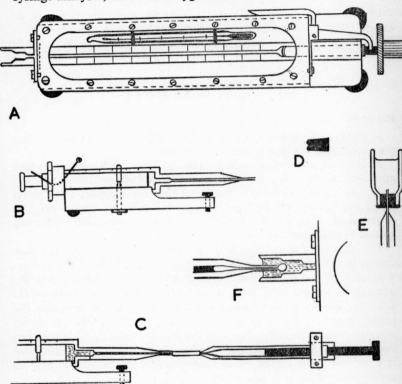

Fig. 42. The micro-gasometric oxygen apparatus. (Redrawn from Scholander, D. L. *et al.*, *Biol. Bull.*, 1955.)

Apparatus

This consists of two parts, namely a combined water sampler and gas extractor, and a gas analyser. The extractor (Fig. 42) has a 5 ml. syringe, with a fused capillary tip 5 cm. long, and of 0·7 mm. bore. It is provided with a releasable spring drag, made by passing a wire through a rubber cuff. The syringe is mounted on a wood or plastic base provided with a levelling screw, so that the tip of the capillary can be set to match the cup on the gas analyser. The capillary tip can be closed with a rubber stopper which has a small hole slit at one end, and can also be provided with a glass cup for potassium hydroxide (Fig. 42, D and E).

The gas analyser (Fig. 42, A) consists of a millimetre-graduated 0·6 mm. precision bore capillary, fused to a 3/16-inch precision bore glass tubing, which acts as a barrel for a stainless steel plunger, terminating in an 8/40 screw; the screw is engaged by a spring-loaded lever arm. The analyser is temperature-stabilized by a plastic water jacket, fluted along the edges and rests on legs to insulate it from direct contact with hands and table.

Reagents

Reagents 1–3 are required for extracting the gases from the sample and reagents 4–7 for the gas analysis.

1. *Carbonate solution.* Dissolve 8 g. sodium citrate $Na_3C_6H_5O_7$. $2H_2O$ and 5 g. anhydrous potassium carbonate in 20 ml. of water.

2. *Acid solution.* Dissolve 10 g. citric acid and 3 g. sodium citrate in 20 ml. water.

3. *Strong potassium hydroxide solution.* Dissolve 100 g. of potassium hydroxide in 60 ml. water.

4. *Acid citrate.* Dissolve 170 g. of sodium citrate and 6 g. of citric acid in 200 ml. water.

5. *Alkaline citrate.* Dissolve 70 g. of sodium citrate and 5 g. potassium hydroxide in 120 ml. water.

6. *Oxygen absorptent.* Add 15 g. pyrogallol to 100 ml. of 20% sodium hydroxide in a rubber-stoppered bottle and cover with a layer of paraffin oil 2 cm. thick. Dissolve the pyrogallol under the oil by stirring with a glass rod.

7. *Acid rinsing solution.* Add 1 ml. concentrated sulphuric acid to 500 c.c. water followed by 10 mg. potassium permanganate.

Solutions 1 and 2 are highly concentrated in order to keep the gas solubility low; the salts may crystallize out when cold, so it is often necessary to redissolve them by heating. The solutions are boiled when made up, to overcome the gas supersaturation that results from dissolving the salts.

Calibration

The capillary of the gas analyser is most easily calibrated by means of a micrometer burette. With the analyser mounted horizontally on a stand, and the screw plunger removed, a stiff rubber connection is made between the water-filled cup of the capillary and the tip of the burette, taking care not to trap any air bubbles in the connection. The water is *slowly* and *evenly* moved back in the capillary by means of the micrometer, reading off partial as well as total calibration.

For accurate work it is best to draw the sample into an accurately calibrated syringe burette, with or without automatic stops, as in Fig. 42, C, and from there deliver it into the extractor syringe. In many cases it will, however, suffice to measure the water sample directly into the extractor, which has been calibrated by delivering water from the 1 ml. mark until the plunger touches bottom. During this operation the number on the plunger is kept facing up. The water is delivered into a cylindrical shell vial, about 1×3 cm., silicone-coated on the inside. The vial is handled only by forceps. The tall sides and absence of thermal convection effectively prevent evaporation loss during weighing. For repeated deliveries remove the water by means of suction.

Procedure

Collection of sample and extraction of gas. Pour the boiled acid and alkaline reagents (1 and 2) into two 10 ml. beakers, which are kept covered. Rinse the extractor with water. Draw in 0·5 ml. of carbonate solution and discard; fill the dead space with carbonate solution, orienting the plunger with the number up. Either draw in the 1 ml. water sample directly or push it in from the burette (Fig. 42, C) through a short piece of rubber or plastic tubing. (Note: do not use a long piece of thin-walled polyethylene tube, which is seriously pervious to gases.) Avoid trapping air bubbles. Hold the extractor vertically with the tip in the acid, and carefully draw in 0·2 ml. This forms a layer under the carbonate solution, and there is time to close the capillary tip with the rubber stopper before the evolution of carbon dioxide begins. The loss of a few cubic millimetres of gas or liquid at this point is immaterial. With the plunger clip released, the extractor is shaken until no more carbon dioxide is evolved, which with the proper strength of carbonate solution should be at a gas phase of about 4 ml. Shake for two minutes. Hold the extractor tip down, and force the plunger in to give a slight excess pressure. Remove the stopper and allow the extracted water to run down into a finger bowl of water, whilst keeping the tip under water; leave only a seal in the capillary. Turn the extractor tip up, readjusting the plunger so as to maintain the liquid seal in the capillary, and attach the potassium hydroxide cup (Fig. 42, E). Fill this half-way up with strong potassium hydroxide reagent. Expel any air trapped in the capillary into the potassium hydroxide solution. Draw down the potassium hydroxide over the carbon dioxide in the barrel, letting in the plunger as the gas is absorbed. At the very last stage of the absorption, run the remaining bubble of oxygen and nitrogen up into the capillary, where it is safely protected from diffusion exchange until transferred to the analyser.

Transfer and analysis of gas bubble. Rinse the analyser and fill the dead space plus the cup with the alkaline citrate reagent. With the extractor and analyser placed on a table, introduce the extractor tip into the citrate, which fills the cup of the analyser, and carefully transfer the gas bubble into the cup by gently twisting in the extractor plunger (Fig. 42, H). The analyser is held cup down, and the gas bubble is drawn into the capillary. With the cup up, draw the bubble down into the barrel, and then bring it back very *slowly and evenly* into the capillary for a reading. Any abrupt movement of the meniscus leaves excess liquid on the sides of the capillary, and the volume of the bubble will be over-estimated. Enough of the citrate above the gas bubble is drawn off so that both menisci of the seal remain within the capillary during the reading. If the upper meniscus is in the cup, the gas volume will read significantly too large. The readings are made with a hand lens and with the analyser resting on the table. The length of the bubble is checked by repeating the procedure, and the smallest reading (V_1) is used. Absorb the oxygen by slowly and steadily drawing one cupful of pyrogallol down over the bubble, with the instrument held cup up. The pyrogallol forms a layer around the bubble in the barrel on top of the citrate. By this procedure fresh pyrogallol, in excess, runs over the bubble, so effectively preventing the formation of monoxide. The remaining nitrogen (and inert gas) bubble is slowly moved up into the capillary, and the volume (V_2) read with all three menisci in the capillary. Read the temperature of the analyser.

After analysis, rinse the analyser several times in water, disconnecting the screw-feed and removing the plunger. If the water supply is limited, rinsing with permanganate solution until this retains its colour may be necessary.

Calculations

The oxygen contained in the sample equals

$$(V_1 - V_2 - C) \times (F_s \times i) \times F_a,$$

where $C =$ the blank correction for oxygen in the reagents, $F_s =$ the factor reducing measured gas volumes to standard conditions, $i =$ the factor for gas remaining in the liquid phase (near to $1 \cdot 0075$ when liquid volume/gas volume is $0 \cdot 25$), $F_a =$ the calibration of the analyser capillary. F_s is based on (1) a temperature-corrected barometer reading, from which is subtracted the water vapour tension at the analyser temperature, and (2) the temperature of the analyser.

The nitrogen contained in the sample equals

$$(V_2 - C) \times (F_s \times i) \times F_a,$$

where C is the blank correction for nitrogen in the reagents, F_s as above, i near to $1 \cdot 004$, and F_a is as above.

When the analysis is performed at a temperature between 15° and 30°C. the following empirical terms may be used, with less than $0 \cdot 2 \%$ error, as substitutes for $(F_s \times i)$; for oxygen $F_s \times i = 0 \cdot 215 B/t + 160$, and for nitrogen $F_s \times i = 0 \cdot 214 B/t + 160$, where B is the uncorrected barometric pressure in mm.Hg, and t is the temperature of the analyser in degrees centigrade.

Determination of Reagent Blank (C)

Boil half a litre of water in an Erlenmeyer flask, provided with a cork through which a capillary glass siphon fits loosely. The free end of the siphon has a short piece of rubber tubing with a pinchcock. After half an hour of steady boiling, transfer anaerobically 10 ml. of the still boiling water through the siphon to a 10-ml. syringe, which has been closed with a fine bore rubber tube and glass plug and is cooled under the tap. Quickly transfer the gas-free water from this into the extractor by means of a short piece of heavy-walled tubing. Air bubbles must be scrupulously avoided. Proceed with the extraction and analysis as described above. The authors report blanks of $0 \cdot 8$ c.mm. for oxygen and $2 \cdot 4$ c.mm. for nitrogen. A check may be made by analysing water equilibrated with air by shaking at a known temperature. Do not use bubbled air, because this may be supersaturated to an unknown extent.

Precision

The authors tested the method on air-equilibrated water and report that out of 21 consecutive oxygen analyses 16 were within $\pm 1 \%$ of the theoretical value, 4 were within $\pm 2 \%$. The average for 20 determinations was $100 \cdot 1 \%$.

In the same series 17 nitrogen determinations were within $\pm 1 \%$ of the expected value and 3 were within $+2 \%$. The average of 20 determinations was $100 \cdot 6 \%$.

REFERENCES

1. Alsterberg, G., 1925. 'Methoden zur Bestimmung von in Wasser gelösten elementaren Sauerstoff bei gegenwart von salpetriger Säure.' *Biochem. Z.*, **159**, 36–47.
2. American Public Health Association and others, 1955. *Standard Methods for the Examination of Water, Sewage and Industrial Wastes.* Amer. Publ. Health Ass., Inc., New York, 10th ed., 1955, 522 pp.

3. Barnett, G. R., and Hurwitz, E., 1939. 'The use of sodium azide in the Winkler method for the determination of dissolved oxygen.' *Sewage Wks. J.*, **11**, 781–7.

4. van Dam, L., 1933. *Hand. 24ᵉ ned. nat.-en geneesk. Congr.* p. 150.

5. Fox, C. J. J., 1907. 'On the coefficients of absorption of the atmosphere gases in distilled water and sea water.' *Publ. Circ. Cons. Explor. Mer*, No. 41, 1–27.

6. ——, 1909. 'On the coefficients of absorption of nitrogen and oxygen in distilled water and sea water and atmospheric carbonic acid in sea water.' *Trans. Faraday Soc.*, **5**, 68–87.

7. Fox, H. M., and Wingfield, C. A., 1938. 'A portable apparatus for the determination of oxygen dissolved in a small volume of water.' *J. exp. Biol.*, **15**, 437–45.

8. Jacobsen, J. P., Robinson, R. J., and Thompson, T. G., 1950. 'A review of the determination of dissolved oxygen in sea water by the Winkler method.' *Publ. sci. Ass. Océanogr. phys.* No. 11, 22 pp.

9. Knowles, G., and Lowden, G. F., 1953. 'Methods for detecting the end-point in the titration of iodine with thiosulphate.' *Analyst*, **78**, 159–64.

10. Ohle, W., 1953. 'Die chemische und die elektrochemische Bestimmung des molekular gelösten Sauerstoffs der Binnengewässer.' *Int. Ver. f. Theor. u. Angew. Limnologie.* Mitteilungen No. 3, 44 pp.

11. Peat, S., Bourne, E. J., and Thrower, R. D., 1947. 'A new indicator for iodometric analysis.' *Nature, Lond.*, **159**, 810–11.

12. Placak, O. R., and Ruchhoft, C. C., 1941. 'Determination of biochemical oxygen demand. Comparative study of azide and Rideal-Stewart modifications of the Winkler method.' *Industr. Engng. Chem. (Anal.)*, **13**, 12–15.

13. Scholander, D. L., van Dam, L., Claff, C. L., and Kanwisher, J. W., 1955. 'Micro-gasometric determination of dissolved oxygen and nitrogen.' *Biol. Bull., Woods Hole*, **109**, 328–34.

14. Theriault, E. J., and McNamee, P. D., 1932. 'Dissolved oxygen in the presence of organic matter, hypochlorites and sulphite wastes.' *Industr. Engng. Chem. (Anal.)*, **4**, 59–64.

15. Thompson, T. G., and Robinson, R. J., 1939. 'Notes on the determination of dissolved oxygen in sea water.' *J. Mar. Res.*, **2**, 1–8.

16. Thorpe, W. H., and Crisp, D. J., 1947. 'Studies on plastron respiration. II. The respiratory efficiency of the plastron in Aphelocheirus.' *J. exp. Biol.*, **24**, 270–303.

17. Truesdale, G. A., and Downing, A. L., 1954. 'Solubility of oxygen in water.' *Nature, Lond.*, **173**, 1236.

18. ——, and Lowden, G. F., 1955. 'The solubility of oxygen in pure water and sea water.' *J. Appl. Chem.*, **5**, 53–62.

19. Whitney, R. J., 1938. 'A syringe pipette method for the determination of oxygen in the field.' *J. exp. Biol.*, **15**, 564–70.

15

ALKALINITY

Sea water is alkaline and the quantity of acid required to bring a given volume to some specified end-point may readily be determined. The alkalinity should be reported in mg.-atom/l. or milli-equiv./l. of acid. The terms buffer capacity, titratable base, and titration alkalinity, have been used in the past but should be discontinued.

There is general agreement on the above statement with regard to alkalinity—it is merely a statement of fact; however, as Rakestraw (7) has so cogently pointed out, the interpretation and terminology have given rise to a good deal of confusion, much of which has arisen through a lack of appreciation of some of the modern concepts of acids and bases. It may not be out of place to indicate briefly the modern viewpoint.

An acid is a substance with a tendency to lose a proton, and a base a substance with a tendency to gain a proton (H^+). Thus

$$A \rightleftharpoons H^+ + B$$
$$\text{acid} \quad \text{proton} \quad \text{base}$$

The acid and base differing by a proton are said to be conjugate. It is unlikely that free protons can exist in solution so that acidic or basic properties are not manifest unless the solvent molecules can accept or donate protons. Water, which can act as either a donator or acceptor is said to be an amphiprotic solvent. When HCl is dissolved in water, we have

$$HCl + H_2O \rightleftharpoons H_3O^+ + Cl^-,$$

where H_3O^+ is the hydrated proton. Clearly the chloride ion, Cl^-, is the conjugate base of HCl; since the equilibrium lies very much to the right in the above equation, a large number of H_3O^+ ions are present, hydrochloric acid is said to be a strong acid and Cl^- a very weak base. With a weak acid such as phenol

$$C_6H_5OH + H_2O \rightleftharpoons H_3O^+ + C_6H_5O^-,$$

the equilibrium lies more to the left; phenol is a weak acid and its conjugate base the phenate ion $C_6H_5O^-$ has appreciable strength. When ammonia dissolves in water the latter donates protons, thus

$$NH_3 + H_2O \rightleftharpoons NH_4^+ + OH^-$$

so that the ammonium ion is the conjugate acid of the base ammonia.

In the case of a salt such as sodium bicarbonate we have

$$NaHCO_3 + H_2O \rightleftharpoons Na(H_2O)^+ + HCO_3^-$$

or more strictly, since the substance is ionized in the solid state,

$$Na^+HCO_3^- + H_2O \rightleftharpoons Na(H_2O)^+ + HCO_3^-.$$

The hydrated sodium ion is a weak acid of no appreciable strength however, the bicarbonate ion is a stronger base. Hence

$$HCO_3^- + H_2O \rightleftharpoons H_2CO_3 + OH^-$$

and the solution reacts alkaline. The addition of a strong acid displaces the equilibrium until all the HCO_3^- has been converted into undissociated carbonate.

It may be noted that for an acid

$$HA + H_2O \rightleftharpoons H_3O^- + A^-$$

we have

$$K = \frac{a_{H_3O^+} \cdot a_{A^-}}{a_{HA} \cdot a_{H_2O}},$$

where a_x denotes the activity of the species. The activity of water in dilute solution may be taken as unity, so that

$$K_a = \frac{a_{H_3O^+} \cdot a_{A^-}}{a_{HA}},$$

where K_a is the dissociation constant of the acid. Now $a_{H_3O^-}$ is the effective hydrogen-ion concentration in the solvent H_2O, so that $a_{H_3O^-}$ is the quantity equivalent to that written conventionally as a_{H^+}. Hence

$$K_a = \frac{a_{H^+} \cdot a_{A^-}}{a_{HA}},$$

which is the conventional form of the dissociation constant.

In sea water all the hydrated cations present in any appreciable quantity, Na^+, Mg^{++}, Ca^{++}, K^+, and Sr^{++}, are very weak acids (of these the hydrated Mg ions have the strongest acidic properties but are present in too small a quantity to make any significant contribution). The major anions are Cl^-, SO_4^{--}, Br^-, HCO_3^-, CO_3^{--}, and $H_2BO_3^-$; of these only the bicarbonate, carbonate and borate ions are sufficiently strong bases to make any significant contribution to the basic character. In titration the end-point is chosen so that these ions are combined with protons to give H_2CO_3 and H_3BO_3. The excess base in terms of the equivalents of acid added is, therefore,

$$A = [HCO_3^-] + 2[CO_3^{--}] + [H_2BO_3^-] \qquad \ldots(1)$$

per given volume of sample.

The techniques used in the titration of sea water have varied. In the older work the titration was either carried out without removing the carbon dioxide, taking it to an end-point of pH 4·5, or after adding an excess of acid, the carbon dioxide was removed by boiling and the acid back-titrated to pH 7·0 (a variant of this was to titrate directly into a boiling sample to pH 7·0). More recently a known quantity of acid is added and the alkalinity calculated after measuring the resultant pH.

ADDITION OF ACID AND pH ESTIMATION (1, 2)

It is evident from equation (1) that if the excess acid over that required to neutralize the bases in a sample of sea water can be determined, it is possible to calculate the alkalinity. If a known amount of acid is added and the pH then determined this can be done; by subtraction, the acid required to neutralize the sample is then calculated so giving the alkalinity. The total amount of acid added per litre of sample in milli-equivalents is

$$\frac{1000}{\text{vol. of sample (ml.)}} \times (\text{total ml. of HCl added}) \times \text{normality of HCl.}$$
$$...(2)$$

In calculating the excess acid, the ionic strength of the solution must be taken into account. Anderson and Robinson (1) have determined empirically the 'glass electrode hydrogen-ion activity coefficients' (f_{H^+} values) for varying chlorinities, and these are given in Table I. Once f_{H^+} is known the excess acid concentration C_{H^+} can be calculated from the pH, since,

$$pH = -\log C_{H^+} . f_{H^+}. \qquad ...(3)$$

Now the excess acid per litre of sample is

$$\left(\frac{1000}{\text{vol. of sample}}\right) \times (\text{Vol. of sample} + \text{ml. of HCl added}) \times (C_{H^+}),$$
$$...(4)$$

so that, the alkalinity is given by 2 minus 4.

TABLE I

Interpolated f_{H^+} values (2).

$Cl\%_0$	2	4	6	8	10	12	14	16	18	20
f_{H^+}	0·845	0·782	0·770	0·760	0·755	0·752	0·752	0·754	0·754	0·758

Procedure

Transfer exactly 25 ml. of 0·01 N hydrochloric acid to a clean aged 135 ml. glass-stoppered bottle and pipette into it exactly 100 ml. of the water sample. Thoroughly mix by shaking. Measure the pH by glass electrode. The pH should lie between 3·3 and 3·9. Calculate the alkalinity from the equations 2 and 4 so that

$$\text{Alkalinity} = \left[\left(\frac{1000}{\text{ml. of sample}} \right) (\text{ml. of HCl})(\text{Normality HCl}) \right]$$

$$- \left[\left(\frac{1000}{\text{ml. of sample}} \right) (\text{ml. of sample} + \text{ml. of HCl})(C_{H^+}) \right],$$

where C_{H^+} is given by

$$-\log C_{H^+} . f_{H^+} = pH,$$

using the appropriate value of f_{H^+} for the chlorinity of the sample.

Remarks

1. The bottles should be aged for several months by soaking with hydrochloric acid at about pH 3·5.

2. The sample should be brought to laboratory temperature.

3. The glass electrode should be rinsed with the solution before the pH determination is made.

4. Any standard pH meter with glass electrodes may be used. 0·05 M potassium hydrogen phthalate (pH 4·0) may be used for standardization: the buffer should be kept as stock 0·2 molar.

5. The 0·01 N-HCl should be prepared from 0·1 N-HCl which has been standardized, preferably by potentiometric titration.

6. The probable error is stated to be $\pm 1\%$. A variation of $\pm 0·01$ pH unit at pH 3·60 will affect the alkalinity by $\pm 0·5\%$. The same percentage variation will result from $\pm 3°$C. change in temperature or a change of $\pm 2·5\%$ in the f_{H^+} value. The volumes should be measured accurately (automatic pipettes may be used: Ref 10) since an error in measuring the volume of standard acid of $\pm 0·05$ ml. gives an error of $\pm 0·25\%$ while an error of $\pm 0·1$ ml. in the sample volume gives an error of $\pm 0·15\%$ in the alkalinity value.

7. If the stated volumes are adhered to it is possible to construct graphs or draw up tables relating pH to alkalinities for a given f_{H^+} value.

8. The formula given by Anderson and Robinson (1) neglects the effect of bicarbonate ion on the pH; this is legitimate if the final pH is within 3·3 to 3·9. Bruneau, Jerlov and Koczy (2) recommend rather more acid, i.e. 25 ml. of 0·0169 N. If the samples are then above pH 3·9 either more acid must be added or allowance must be made for the contribution of the bicarbonate ion. When this is allowed for only very small changes of f_{H^+} are found with pH, and for ocean waters it may be taken as equal to 0·81 between pH 3·3 and 4·0.

9. The method can be used with indicators but is rather troublesome since comparison of the solution must be made with base-free sea water of the same chlorinity to which known amounts of acid and indicator have been added.

10. Matida (5) has pointed out that organic acids such as humic acid have a considerable effect on the alkalinity.

TITRATION METHODS

It would seem best to avoid some of the factors giving rise to discrepancies by adding excess acid, boiling off the carbon dioxide and back-titrating.

Procedure

Add 5 ml. of 0·07 N-HCl to 100 ml. of sea water in a flask: reflux for 5 minutes to expel carbon dioxide. Cool and titrate the excess HCl with 0·025 N carbonate-free NaOH using either methyl red or methyl orange as end-point indicators.

$$1 \text{ ml. } 0·01 \text{ N-HCl} = 0·01 \text{ milli-equivalents of HCl.}$$

Remarks

1. Addition of excess acid converts the borate to undissociated boric acid, and carbonate and bicarbonate to carbonic acid. By titration to the end-point of methyl red (or orange) the titration is stopped after the hydrochloric acid has been neutralized but before the boric acid is titrated (4).

2. The hydrochloric acid should preferably be standardized in a synthetic sea water to simulate the actual estimation and compensate for errors.

3. The end-point is not easy to determine: West and Robinson (12) therefore used an electrometric titration.

4. Matida (5) has used a mixed indicator of methyl orange and aniline blue for direct titration whilst Saruhashi (8, 9) recommends the Conway diffusion technique.

REFERENCES

1. Anderson, D. H., and Robinson, R. J., 1946. 'Rapid electrometric determination of the alkalinity of sea water using a glass electrode.' *Industr. Engng. Chem. (Anal.)*, **18**, 767–73.
2. Bruneau, L., Jerlov, N. G., and Koczy, F. F., 1953. 'Physical and chemical methods.' *Rept. Swed. Deep Sea Exped.*, **3**, *Physics and Chemistry*, No. 4, 99–112.

3. Buch, K., 1951. 'Das Kohlensäure Gleichgewichtssystem in Meerwasser.' *Merentutkimuslait. Julk.*, N:o. 151, 18 pp.
4. Greenberg, D. M., Moberg, E. G., and Allen, E. C., 1932. 'Determination of carbon dioxide and titratable base in sea water.' *Industr. Engng. Chem. (Anal.)*, **4**, 309–22.
5. Matida, Y., 1953. 'Some notes on the method of alkalinity determination.' *Bull. Jap. Soc. sci. Fish.*, **19**, 703–9.
6. Mitchell, P. H., and Rakestraw, N. W., 1933. 'The buffer capacity of sea water.' *Biol. Bull.*, *Woods Hole*, **33**, 437–51.
7. Rakestraw, N. W., 1949. 'The conception of alkalinity or excess base of sea water.' *J. Mar. Res.*, **8**, 14–20.
8. Saruhashi, K., 1953. 'On the total carbonaceous matter and hydrogen ion concentration.' *Papers in Met. and Geophys. Japan*, **3**, 202–6.
9. ——, 1955. 'On the equilibrium concentration ratio of carbonic acid substances dissolved in natural waters.' *Papers in Met. and Geophys. Japan*, **6**, 38–55.
10. Thompson, T. G., and Anderson, D. H., 1940. 'The determination of the alkalinity of sea water.' *J. Mar. Res.*, **3**, 224–9.
11. Thompson, T. G., and Bonnar, R. U., 1931. 'The buffer capacity of sea water.' *Industr. Engng. Chem. (Anal.)*, **3**, 393–400.
12. West, L. E., and Robinson, R. J., 1941. 'Potentiometric analysis of sea water. II. Determination of titration alkalinity.' *J. Mar. Res.*, **4**, 38–41.

16

THE CARBON DIOXIDE SYSTEM
IN SEA WATER

The carbon dioxide-carbonate-bicarbonate equilibria may be calculated from a knowledge of the excess base, pH, temperature, and chlorinity. The theoretical derivation of the equations will not be considered but it appears useful to state them and to provide the necessary tables. The subject has recently been examined critically by Buch (1).

Symbols

A	alkalinity, excess base (*see* Section 15)	(equivalents/l.).
A'	carbonate alkalinity	

c_{CO_2}	concentration of carbon dioxide	
$c_{HCO_3^-}$	concentration of bicarbonate ion	
$c_{CO_3^{--}}$	concentration of carbonate ion	(g.mols/l.).
ΣCO_2	concentration of total carbon dioxide	

P_{CO_2} partial pressure of carbon dioxide (atmospheres).

c_o	solubility of carbon dioxide at 1 atmosphere pressure in pure water at a given temperature	
c_s	solubility of carbon dioxide at 1 atmosphere pressure in sea water of a given chlorinity and temperature	(g.mols/l.).

K_1' first apparent dissociation constant of carbonic acid.
K_2' second apparent dissociation constant of carbonic acid.
γ correction factor for determining A'.
a_{H^+} activity of the hydrogen ions.
a_{H_2O} activity of the water.

K_1' and K_2'

The most recent values for the first and second apparent dissociation constants of carbonic acid are given in Tables 25 and 26 (p. 306).

The Carbonate Alkalinity (A')

This is the alkalinity due to carbonate and bicarbonate ions. It may be calculated for open waters, assuming:

1. that boric acid makes the only other significant contribution to the alkalinity;

2. that the total boric acid is given by:

$$c_{\Sigma B} = c_{H_2BO_3^-} + c_{H_3BO_3} = 2 \cdot 2 \times 10^{-5} \; Cl\%_0 \; \text{g.mol/l}.$$

Then

$$A' = A - \frac{K_B' \cdot c_{\Sigma B}}{c_{H^+} + K_B'}$$
$$= A - \gamma.$$

Table 27 gives values of γ from which A' may be calculated.

The Partial Pressure of Carbon Dioxide (P_{CO_2})

We have

$$P_{CO_2} = A' \left[\frac{a_{H^+}}{K_1' \cdot c_o \cdot a_{H_2O} \left(1 + \dfrac{2K_2'}{a_{H^+}} \right)} \right].$$

Values of the factor within the brackets, i.e. P_{CO_2}/A' are given in Table 28 (p. 308) from which knowing A', P_{CO_2} may be calculated.

The Total Carbon Dioxide (ΣCO_2)

We have

$$\Sigma CO_2 = A' \cdot \left[\frac{1 + \dfrac{K_2'}{a_{H^+}} + \dfrac{c_s \cdot a_{H^+}}{K_1' \cdot c_o \cdot a_{H_2O}}}{1 + \dfrac{2K_2'}{a_{H^+}}} \right].$$

Values of the factor within the brackets, $\Sigma CO_2/A'$, are given in Table 29 (p. 309) from which the total carbon dioxide may then be calculated.

The Bicarbonate Ion ($c_{HCO_3^-}$)

We have

$$c_{HCO_3^-} = A' \cdot \frac{1}{1 + \dfrac{2K_2'}{a_{H^+}}}.$$

The Carbonate Ion ($c_{CO_3^{--}}$)

We have

$$c_{CO_3^{--}} = A' \cdot \frac{K_2'}{2K_2' + a_{H^+}} = c_{HCO_3^-} \cdot \frac{K_2'}{a_{H^+}}.$$

Dissolved Carbon Dioxide (c_{CO_2})

We have

$$c_{CO_2} = P_{CO_2} \cdot c_s.$$

The last three may be calculated from the foregoing and Tables 25, 26 and 30 (pp. 306, 310) giving values of K_1', K_2' and c_s; a_{H^+} may be obtained from the pH, assuming $c_{H^+}=a_{H^+}$, noting pH $= -1/\log c_{H^+}$. Thus pH $8\cdot6=0\cdot3981$ ($=\log 6)\times10$ g.-ions/l.

REFERENCES

1. Buch, K., 1951. 'Das Kohlensäure Gleichgewichtssystem im Meerwasser.' *Merentutkimuslait. Julk.*, N:o. 151, 18 pp.
2. Harvey, H. W., 1955. *The Chemistry and Fertility of Sea Waters*. The University Press, Cambridge. 224 pp.

17

THE CONSERVATIVE ELEMENTS:
MICRO-METHODS

Estimations of the conservative elements are made by standard analytical methods, taking the precautions appropriate to such a complex mixture as sea water. A list of references to the major contributions is given later (pp. 221–3); for further details standard texts of inorganic analysis should be consulted. In oceanography, analyses for the conservative elements are rarely made, but in physiological work a knowledge of the concentrations of the major cations and anions is frequently required.

For some of these cations flame photometry (18, 21) should be considered by anyone intending to make many analyses; ultra-micro flame photometry has been developed by Ramsay and co-workers (8, 9, 10). A flame photometer is, however, not always available and in the present state of development must still be used with caution in some biological work (12). Only semi-micro chemical methods will be considered here.

The amounts of fluid available for such analyses usually necessitate the employment of micro- or semi-micro-methods; a variety of techniques are available. On the semi-micro scale standard chemical methods are not always satisfactory when applied directly to sea water, and it is felt that the very reliable methods of Robertson and Webb (11) specially designed for work on about 1 ml. of typical sea water or fluids from marine animals without the use of a microbalance or complicated apparatus, may be usefully outlined. The amounts (mg.) of the ions available in 1 ml. of sea water are:

$$Na\ 10.5 \qquad K\ 0.4 \qquad Ca\ 0.4 \qquad Mg\ 1.3$$
$$Cl\ 19.0 \qquad SO_4\ 2.7$$

For the estimation of the cations in biological fluids, the sample is first treated with sulphuric acid to convert all the bases to sulphate so that losses by volatilization during the subsequent dry ashing are avoided. In sea water itself only the sample for potassium need be in the form of sulphate; the other ions may be determined without further treatment of the water sample.

ASHING

For the estimation of sodium, potassium, calcium, magnesium and also of copper (*see* section on magnesium), measure 1 ml. of the sample into a small silica crucible, and add about 0·2 ml. (three to four drops) of 25% sulphuric acid; evaporate down on a steam bath. Drive off the excess acid by very cautious heating over a flame until fumes are no longer given off. Complete the ignition in a muffle furnace at dull red heat. If any specks of carbon remain, cool and add a drop of dilute sulphuric acid; re-evaporate and ash. The acid assists in the oxidation of the carbon, and prevents the formation of carbonates and oxides. If more than one element is to be determined a larger quantity may be ashed in this way, made up to volume and aliquots taken for the separate analyses.

SODIUM

The standard zinc uranyl acetate method is used; even with 0·1 ml. sea water (1 mg. sodium) the precipitate is sufficient to be weighed on an ordinary analytical balance. Potassium does not interfere unless it exceeds 25 g./l. Phosphate, if present, should be removed by shaking with a little powdered calcium hydroxide before adding the precipitating reagent.

Reagent

Zinc uranyl acetate. A prepared reagent may be purchased; otherwise it is made up as follows. Dissolve 80 g. uranyl acetate with heating in 425 ml. of distilled water, to which has been added 14 ml. glacial acetic acid. Dissolve separately 220 g. zinc acetate in 275 ml. distilled water with the addition of 7 ml. glacial acetic acid. Mix the two solutions while hot. A trace of sodium acetate may be added to ensure that the solution is saturated with respect to the triple salt (sodium zinc uranyl acetate), although unless the salts used are of analytical grade, sufficient sodium for this purpose will already be present as impurity. The temperature coefficient of solubility for the triple salt is relatively high and the solution should therefore be stored (preferably at a fairly constant temperature) in contact with excess of the salt; shake well and filter just before use. Prepare a washing fluid by saturating 95% ethanol with the triple salt.

Procedure

Wash a 30 ml. sinter glass filter crucible of medium porosity with ether, suck dry with the filter pump, and weigh after standing for an hour or more in a desiccator. Fit the lower opening with a rubber bung to prevent the passage of fluid through the filter. Transfer 20 ml. of the freshly filtered zinc uranyl acetate reagent to the crucible and add the sample directly to it. Sea-water samples may be delivered directly into the reagent from a pipette; with ashed samples of blood, etc., the ash should be extracted with 1 ml. of water and the resultant solution poured into the reagent, the ashing crucible being then washed out, first with two 0·5 ml. portions of water and then with three 1 ml. portions of the reagent. It is important to ensure that the volume of reagent is at least ten times that of the water added in sample and washings. (If several cations are to be determined a larger sample may be ashed, taken up in dilute acid and, after making up to a known volume in a volumetric flask, aliquots used for the individual cations.)

If considerable quantities of phosphate are present add a small quantity of pure powdered calcium hydroxide to the solution before the latter is added to the precipitant. Shake vigorously several times over a period of half an hour, centrifuge and take an aliquot of the supernatant for sodium precipitation. If necessary evaporate to a small bulk.

Stir the contents of the crucible for 2 minutes with a glass rod, washing off any adherent precipitate with 1·0 ml. of reagent; cover the crucible and allow to stand for 1 hour at a temperature within a few degrees of that at which the reagent was filtered. Remove the bung and draw off the liquid at the pump. When dry, wash the precipitate with five 2 ml. portions of the freshly filtered alcoholic washing fluid, and then with two 5 ml. portions of pure ether. Suck dry, transfer to a desiccator, and after standing for 4 hours, re-weigh.

Wt. of precipitate (mg.) × 0·01495 = Wt. of sodium (mg.) in sample.

POTASSIUM

The precipitation is made with silver cobaltinitrite. The precipitate may be weighed or estimated by titration or colorimetrically. In the present method the nitrite radical is estimated by titration; ceric sulphate is added and the excess back-titrated with ferrous ammonium sulphate.

If the ferrous ammonium sulphate is made up in decinormal acid as directed below it keeps almost indefinitely without change of titre. It should, however, for safety, be titrated against the ceric sulphate solution once a fortnight. Lissamine green or ferrous phenanthroline is used as indicator.

When the silver salt is used it is difficult to obtain a constant factor, either theoretical or empirical, to express the relation between the titre of the precipitate and its potassium content. (Temperature and duration of precipitation time are both of importance in determining the composition of the precipitate.) This difficulty is avoided by running standards containing a known amount of potassium simultaneously with the unknowns, so that fluctuations in the composition of the precipitate arising from chance variations in technique are compensated. With each batch of analyses two standards of known potassium content should be analysed. It is then unnecessary to know the strength in absolute units of either ceric sulphate or ferrous ammonium sulphate solutions.

The presence of silver ions in the precipitant makes it necessary to eliminate chlorides before precipitation. Ashed samples are chloride-free; sea-water samples must be similarly evaporated down with sulphuric acid and the excess acid cautiously driven off.

Reagents

1. *Bromo-cresol green.* A 0·04% aqueous solution.
2. *Sodium hydroxide.* A 1% aqueous solution, potassium free.
3. *Acetone.* Analytical grade.
4. *Silver cobaltinitrite.* Mix, just before use, a 25% w/v aqueous solution of sodium cobaltinitrite with an equal volume of 1% w/v silver nitrate solution; filter if necessary.
5. *Ceric sulphate.* About 0·02 N solution. This is standardized against the ferrous ammonium sulphate and contains about 7 g. (depending on the purity) of commercial ceric sulphate dissolved in a litre of water containing 25–30 ml. of concentrated sulphuric acid.
6. *Ferrous ammonium sulphate.* 8 g. $FeSO_4(NH_4)_2SO_4.6H_2O$ dissolved in 1 litre of distilled water containing 3 ml. of concentrated sulphuric acid.
7. *Lissamine green indicator* (*or ferrous phenanthroline*). 0·1% aqueous solution.
8. *Standard potassium sulphate.* A solution containing 0·8914 g. K_2SO_4/l. (0·4 g. potassium/l.).

Procedure

Take up the ash, which is in the form of solid mixed sulphates, with 2 ml. of water (or take an aliquot of a larger sample) and add one drop of bromo-cresol green indicator. If the indicator shows that any free acid is present in the extract, either evaporate down again and heat more strongly, or neutralize by the cautious addition of 1% potassium-free sodium hydroxide. Transfer the solution to a centrifuge tube, adding the 1 ml. washings from the crucible. Add 1 ml. of pure acetone and stir well. Immerse in a water bath at 65°C. for 2 minutes *during which time* the cobaltinitrite reagent should be made up. Add 2 ml. of this reagent whilst stirring to the contents of the centrifuge tube, rinsing off the rod with the last few drops. Repeat the precipitation with the standard potassium sulphate solution. Remove the tubes from the water bath and allow to stand 18–24 hours at room temperature. Centrifuge and siphon off the supernatant, using an upturned capillary and filter pump; wash the precipitate three times with 3 ml. portions of the washing fluid, which consists of its saturated aqueous solution. (An equally satisfactory, and often more convenient procedure, is to stand the tubes in the refrigerator for 4 hours and wash the precipitate with ice-cold water.) During the last wash, the precipitate should be well agitated and suspended in the liquid by tapping the end of the tube. After completion of the washing, add 5 ml. of 0·02 N ceric sulphate solution to the precipitate; immerse the tube in a water bath at 70°C., and stir until all the precipitate has dissolved. Pour the contents of the tube and washings into a 100 ml. beaker, and back-titrate the excess ceric sulphate with 0·02 N ferrous ammonium sulphate, using a 5 ml. pinchcock burette, graduated in 0·02 ml. divisions, and delivering about 50 drops per ml. It is best to defer addition of the indicator (one drop) until the yellow colour of the ceric ions has almost disappeared.

If x represents the titration figure given by the sample, y that given by 1 ml. of the standard potassium sulphate solution, and z the volume of ferrous ammonium sulphate solution that is equivalent to 5 ml. of the ceric sulphate solution, then the potassium content of the sample is

$$\frac{0\cdot4(z-x)}{z-y} \text{ mg.}$$

CALCIUM

The chief obstacle to the accurate estimation of calcium by precipitation as oxalate is the ease with which magnesium is co-precipitated. Robertson and Webb investigated the precipitation and found that all claims to effect a separation in a single precipitation were the result of a compensation of errors. When a double precipitation method is employed it is essential not only to prevent co-precipitation of magnesium but also occlusion of sodium oxalate in the precipitate. Furthermore, complete precipitation of the calcium must be ensured; incomplete precipitation is most likely to occur under just those conditions which minimize co-precipitation and occlusion errors, namely low pH and considerable dilution. On theoretical grounds, increase in the total salt content might be expected to have the same effect and no buffers other than the ammonium oxalate used as the precipitating agent are employed. Webb (23) has discussed the interference due to strontium; unless the calcium figures are to be interpreted as a calcum after the strontium and barium have been replaced by calcium, the results must be decreased by 1·5% for solutions with an atomic ratio Ca/Sr approximating to 65.

It is not claimed that the method described below eliminates all these errors completely. Spectrographic examination of precipitates and filtrates showed that, even after two precipitations, some magnesium may be detected in the precipitate (although sodium is virtually absent) and that, even with an enormous excess of oxalate ions present, some calcium remains behind in solution after the first, and to a less extent after the second, precipitation. These errors are opposite in sign and more or less equal in magnitude, but it must be emphasized that each is only of the order of 0·5 % so that even if they failed to compensate one another exactly, the accuracy of the method within the limits assigned (1–2 %) would be unimpaired.

As an oxidizing agent for the volumetric estimation of the precipitated calcium oxalate, potassium permanganate is frequently used; it may with advantage be replaced by ceric sulphate. The latter is more stable, gives a sharper end-point with dilute solutions, and does not require careful control of the temperature during titration. These advantages are more than enough to compensate for the necessity of preparing an extra standard solution of ferrous ammonium sulphate.

Reagents

1. *Bromo-cresol green.* A 0·04% aqueous solution.
2. *Hydrochloric acid.* About 2 N.
3. *Ammonium oxalate.* A filtered saturated aqueous solution.
4. *Ammonium hydroxide.* About 2% aqueous solution; 2 ml. of 0·880 S.G. ammonia made up to 100 ml. with distilled water.
5. *Ceric sulphate.* About 0·006 N. Dissolve about 2·0 g. (*see* p. 212) of purified ceric sulphate in one litre of distilled water containing 25–30 ml. of concentrated sulphuric acid.
6. *Ferrous ammonium sulphate.* About 0·006 N. Dissolve 2·5 g. of $FeSO_4(NH_4)_2SO_4.6H_2O$ in a litre of distilled water containing 3 ml. of concentrated sulphuric acid.
7. *Standard sodium oxalate.* 0·1 N. Dissolve 6·6995 g. $Na_2C_2O_4$ (dried at 110°C.) in distilled water and make up to 1 litre.
8. *Lissamine green (or ferrous phenanthroline) indicator.* A 0·1% aqueous solution.

Procedure

Transfer the sample to a centrifuge tube and make up to 4 ml. with water: add two drops of bromo-cresol green indicator, two drops of the 2 N hydrochloric acid, and 1 ml. of the saturated ammonium oxalate solution. Heat in a water bath to about 90°C. and add 2% ammonia drop by drop till the colour has just passed from green to blue. After 10 minutes in the water bath allow to stand at least 4 hours at room temperature. Then centrifuge and siphon off the supernatant: wash the precipitate once with 2% ammonia and then redissolve by adding three drops of twice normal hydrochloric acid, 4 ml. of water and heating in a water bath. As soon as the precipitate has dissolved reprecipitate by the addition as before of indicator, ammonium oxalate and ammonia. After 10 minutes in the water bath again stand for 4 hours at room temperature. Centrifuge and wash the precipitate three times with 2% ammonia. After the final washing add 5 ml. of the ceric sulphate solution, stir and warm on a water bath until the precipitate has dissolved. Titrate the excess ceric sulphate with 0·006 N ferrous ammonium sulphate using 1 drop of lissamine green indicator. The relative strengths of the ceric sulphate and ferrous ammonium sulphate solutions are found by titrating 5 ml. of the former against the latter, and their strengths in absolute units by adding to 1 ml. of standard decinormal sodium oxalate 20 ml. of the ceric sulphate solution, warming for a few minutes until the reaction is complete, and titrating the excess ceric sulphate with ferrous ammonium sulphate.

If the volumes of ferrous ammonium sulphate solution required for the three titrations, in the order in which they are described above, are x, y and z ml. respectively, then the quantity of calcium in the sample is

$$\frac{2 \cdot 004(z-x)}{4(y-z)} \text{ mg.}$$

MAGNESIUM

The accurate estimation by precipitation as magnesium ammonium phosphate is tedious; a preliminary separation of calcium followed by three precipitations is essential. Furthermore, the precipitate is difficult to estimate volumetrically. Precipitation with 8-hydroxyquinoline is employed, purifying the precipitate from calcium by a second precipitation followed by bromination and iodimetric titration. Attention is particularly directed to the following:

1. Only a small amount of acid is used to dissolve the first precipitate: this is in order to reduce the quantity of ammonium salts present (formed when the acid is neutralized) and so avoid their inhibitory action on the precipitation of the magnesium hydroxy-quinolate.

2. The solutions are considerably diluted; precipitation of magnesium hydroxide before the hydroxy-quinolate is thereby prevented without the addition of ammonium salts.
3. Only a small excess of the reagent is used in the second precipitation; co-precipitation of calcium a second time is thereby prevented.

Copper which is present in the blood of some marine invertebrates is precipitated with the magnesium; since the copper is present in relatively small quantities a rough estimation is adequate to apply the appropriate correction.

It is convenient to use the following modification of the original technique, adapted for 0·2–0·3 mg. of magnesium, the whole procedure being carried through in a centrifuge tube.

Reagents

1. *8-hydroxy-quinoline reagent.* A 1·0% solution in 70% ethanol.
2. *Ammonia.* A 50% v/v aqueous solution.
3. *Ammonia.* A 2% v/v aqueous solution.
4. *Hydrochloric acid.* 2·0 N.
5. *Standard potassium bromate-bromide solution.* 2·7836 g. KBrO$_3$ dissolved in 1 litre of distilled water containing about 11 g. KBr per litre.
6. *Potassium iodide solution.* 20% w/v aqueous solution.
7. *Sodium thiosulphate solution.* About 0·1 N.
8. *Starch indicator.* See p. 180.

Procedure

Transfer the sample in aqueous solution, to a centrifuge tube and make the volume up to 7–8 ml. Add 1 ml. of the 8-hydroxy-quinoline reagent followed by 1 drop of 50% ammonia. Hold at a temperature of 70–80° C., stirring vigorously for a few minutes, and then for 10 minutes at 90° C. Allow to cool, centrifuge and wash the precipitate with 2 ml. of 2% ammonia. Dissolve the precipitate in three drops of 2 N hydrochloric acid. Make up to 7–8 ml. and reprecipitate by adding two drops of 50% ammonia followed by 0·3 ml. of 8-hydroxy-quinoline reagent. Stir and heat exactly as before. After cooling, centrifuge, and wash the precipitate three times with 1 ml. portions of 2% ammonia. Dissolve the precipitate in 1 ml. of 2 N hydrochloric acid. Transfer to a stoppered flask and add a further 2 ml. of 2 N hydrochloric acid followed by 2 ml. of the standard bromate-bromide solution. Add 1 ml. of the potassium iodide solution and titrate the liberated iodine with thiosulphate, using the starch indicator.

Standardize the thiosulphate by titrating 2 ml. of the bromate-bromide solution after the addition of 5 ml. 2 N hydrochloric acid followed after 2 minutes by excess potassium iodide.

If x is the titration figure for the sample and y the titration for 2 ml. of bromate-bromide then the apparent magnesium content is

$$\frac{0 \cdot 608(y-x)}{y}.$$

If a copper correction is required the sodium diethyldithiocarbamate method should be used. Only a rough estimate with Hehner tubes is necessary. To 20 ml. of the solution of the sample add successively 5 ml. of a 1 % solution of gum arabic, 7 ml. of 50 % ammonia and 5 ml. of a 0·2 % solution of sodium diethyl dithiocarbamate and adjust the volume to 100 ml. Compare with a standard containing 100 mg. Cu/l., i.e. 0·3928 g. $CuSO_4 . 5H_2O$ per litre. To correct the magnesium value subtract 0·38z mg. from the amount found, where z is the copper content in mg.

CHLORIDE

For the estimation of chloride in sea water a Mohr or Volhard titration may be used with appropriate strengths of reagents for 1–10 mg. quantities. It is of course impossible to determine chloride on ashed material. These methods cannot be used for solutions containing even small amounts of protein. Various methods have been used for the destruction or removal of proteins. In their original paper Robertson and Webb adopted Sendroy's method in which silver iodate is added; silver is never present in quantity in solution and deproteinization is not necessary. This method will be given and also a method based on deproteinization, followed by a Volhard titration.

METHOD USING SILVER IODATE:
DEPROTEINIZATION UNNECESSARY

Silver iodate, although almost insoluble, is less so than silver chloride; on the addition of silver iodate to a soluble chloride, silver chloride is precipitated and iodate ions pass into solution.

$$AgIO_3 + NaCl = AgCl + NaIO_3.$$

When the reaction is complete the solution is filtered and the iodate estimated iodimetrically in an aliquot of the filtrate; however, because of the slight solubility of both silver iodate and silver chloride, it is necessary to correct for the incomplete precipitation of silver chloride. These corrections vary with the initial chloride concentration and differ in sign; in samples containing over 7·5 mg. chloride the correction is always less than 0·5%.

Reagents

1. *Silver iodate*. This may be obtained commercially or prepared as follows. Add a solution of potassium iodate in slight excess to a solution of silver nitrate filtering off the precipitate on a Buchner funnel. Wash the precipitate of silver iodate thoroughly with distilled water until no further change takes place on acidifying a sample of the filtrate and adding potassium iodide.

2. *Phosphoric acid*. About 3·4 M. Dilute 230 ml. of syrupy phosphoric acid to one litre with distilled water.

3. *Potassium iodide*. Solid.

4. *Sodium thiosulphate*. 0·1 N solution, standardized against potassium iodate (*see* p. 180).

Procedure

Measure the sample directly into a 100 ml. volumetric flask, dilute to about 60 ml. with distilled water and add 5 ml. of the phosphoric acid, followed by about 15–20 mg. of silver iodate for each mg. of chloride expected in the sample. Shake the mixture vigorously. Ascertain that a moderate excess of silver iodate is present; it settles more quickly than the chloride and does not react to light. If necessary add a further quantity of the iodate; at least 1 g. may be present before its volume affects the results significantly. If the solution foams badly add one drop of caprylic alcohol. Make up to the mark and filter through a Whatman No. 1 paper into a clean dry vessel. It may be necessary to return the first runnings to the filter or to use a double paper; ashless papers usually contain chloride and their use should be avoided.

Take a 20 ml. aliquot of the filtrate, add solid potassium iodide (about 1·0 g.) and titrate the liberated iodine with sodium thiosulphate.

If x be the volume in ml. of thiosulphate of normality n, used in the titration for a 20 ml. aliquot from 100 ml., the corrected chloride content is,

$$\text{Cl, mg.} = 35\cdot457 \left(0\cdot8369n . x - \frac{0\cdot00033}{n . x} \right).$$

For all values of x greater than 6, assuming n is about 0·1, the correction term is negligible, so that

$$\text{Cl, mg.} = 29\cdot67n . x.$$

METHOD REMOVING PROTEIN

In this method Somogyi's zinc hydroxide reagent is used to deproteinize the solution and after filtration a Volhard titration is carried out on an aliquot.

Reagents

1. *Somogyi's reagents.* A 5% w/v zinc sulphate solution and 0·3 N barium hydroxide made up separately.
2. *Silver nitrate.* A 0·02 N solution containing 3·398 g./l.
3. *Ammonium thiocyanate.* A solution containing 2 g./l.
4. *Indicator.* A saturated solution of ferric ammonium sulphate.
5. *Nitric acid.* Concentrated, blown free from oxides of nitrogen.

Procedure

Transfer the sample to a volumetric flask and add 5 ml. of the zinc sulphate solution followed by 5 ml. of the barium hydroxide solution; shake at intervals and preferably stand overnight. Make up to volume and filter or centrifuge. To an aliquot of the filtrate add 1 ml. of concentrated nitric acid and an excess of the standard silver nitrate (10 ml.); filter or preferably centrifuge, and wash the precipitate, adding the washings to the main supernatant. Keep the final volume below 30 ml. Titrate the excess of the silver nitrate with ammonium thiocyanate using 1 drop of the iron indicator and continuing the titration until a red colour persists for two minutes. Standardize the ammonium thiocyanate by titration against the 0·02 N silver nitrate solution.

If x is the titration for 5 ml. of 0·02 N silver nitrate with the thiocyanate and y ml. of the latter are required to titrate the excess after adding 10 ml. of the former to the sample, the chloride content of the sample (or aliquot) is

$$Cl, mg. = 0.71 \left(10 - \frac{5y}{x} \right).$$

SULPHATE

A really satisfactory volumetric method in the presence of chloride is still required; the method given by Robertson and Webb is rather less satisfactory than their methods for other ions. It depends upon the fact that rhodizonic acid reacts with barium ions to form a brilliant red compound, and that this colour is discharged when sufficient sulphate is added to precipitate the barium as sulphate. Dr Robertson finds Webb's later method more satisfactory (27); this method is similar to that of Sendroy for the estimation of chloride. Barium iodate is added to form the more insoluble sulphate and the liberated iodate estimated after the addition of iodide by titrating the iodine formed. Various factors affect the equilibrium in the solutions, and although Webb has given tables from which the appropriate conversion factors may be taken, it is better to run a control analysis with a solution containing sulphate and chloride at as close a value to the unknown as possible. If necessary a preliminary test analysis should be made.

Reagents

1. *Acetic acid.* 2% v/v.
2. *Barium iodate.* Pure solid.
3. *Potassium iodide.* Pure solid.
4. *Phosphoric acid.* 85% w/w.
5. *Sodium thiosulphate.* About 0·02 N accurately standardized (*see* p. 180).
6. *Starch indicator* (*see* p. 180).

Procedure

Transfer a measured quantity of the sample to a centrifuge tube and add a measured quantity of 0·2% acetic acid sufficient to bring the sulphate concentration between 0·25 and 0·65 mg. SO_4/ml. (If 1 ml. of sea water or body fluids with a similar concentration of sulphate is being used, 5 ml. is a suitable volume of acetic acid. Add about 40 mg. of solid barium iodate. Keep at constant temperature for four hours, shaking at frequent intervals. Centrifuge and pipette off an aliquot (2 or 5 ml.) of the supernatant. Add excess solid potassium iodide, a few drops of phosphoric acid, and titrate the liberated iodine with the sodium thiosulphate (*see* pp. 181 and 183–4). Repeat the procedure with the control solution of known sulphate content carried through along with the unknown. If the same solutions are used for the latter a factor to convert titration figure directly to sulphate content may be used.

Remarks

1. The acetic acid is added to prevent the precipitation of traces of barium carbonate or phosphate.

2. A mechanical shaker may be used but with solutions high in protein content the foaming may interfere with the subsequent analysis. The gentle mixing described was found adequate.

In this section references are given to the methods (not results) for the estimation of some of the major elements present in sea water and not dealt with in detail in other sections. The earlier literature may be obtained from these references.

REFERENCES

GENERAL

1. Barnes, H., 1949. 'Analytical Chemistry. 5. Analysis of sea water.' *Ann. Rept. Chem. Soc. (Lond.) for 1948*, **45**, 338–44. [Review.]
2. ——, 1954. 'Some tables for the ionic composition of sea water.' *J. exp. Biol.*, **31**, 582–8.
3. ——, 1955. 'The analysis of sea water.' A review. *Analyst*, **80**, 573–92.
4. Goldschmidt, V. M., 1933. 'Grundlagen der quantitativen geochemie.' *Fortschr. Min.*, **17**, 112–56. [Minor elements.]
5. ——, 1937. 'The principles of distribution of chemical elements in minerals and rocks.' *J. chem. Soc.*, 655–73. [Minor elements.]
6. Lyman, J., and Fleming, R. H., 1940. 'Composition of sea water.' *J. Mar. Res.*, **3**, 134–46. [The ionic composition.]
7. Miyake, Y., 1939. 'Chemical studies of the western Pacific Ocean. I. The chemical composition of the oceanic salt.' *Bull. chem. Soc. Japan*, **14**, 29–35.
8. Ramsay, J. A., 1950. 'The determination of sodium in small volumes of fluid by flame photometry.' *J. exp. Biol.*, **27**, 407–19.
9. ——, Brown, R. H. J., and Falloon, S. W. H. W., 1953. 'Simultaneous determination of sodium and potassium in small volumes of fluid by flame photometry.' *J. exp. Biol.*, **30**, 1–17.
10. ——, Falloon, S. W. H. W., and Machin, K. E., 1951. 'An integrating flame photometer for small quantities.' *J. sci. Instrum.*, **28**, 75–80.
11. Robertson, J. D., and Webb, D. A., 1939. 'The micro-estimation of sodium, potassium, calcium, magnesium, chloride and sulphate in sea water and body fluids of marine animals.' *J. exp. Biol.*, **16**, 155–77.
12. Rothschild, Lord, and Barnes, H., 1954. 'Constituents of bull seminal plasma.' *J. exp. Biol.*, **31**, 561–72.
13. Sverdrup, H. U., Johnson, M. W., and Fleming, R. H., 1942. *The Oceans*. Chapter 6, New York.
14. Thompson, T. G., and Robinson, R. J., 1932. 'Chemistry of the Sea. Physics of the earth. v.5. Oceanography', 95–203. *Bull. nat. Res. Coun., Wash.*, No. 85.
15. ——, and Wright, C. C., 1930. 'Ionic ratios of the waters of the North Pacific Ocean.' *J. Amer. chem. Soc.*, **52**, 915–21.

SODIUM

16. Robinson, R. J., and Knapman, F. W., 1941. 'The sodium-chlorinity ratio of ocean waters from the north-east Pacific.' *J. Mar. Res.*, **4**, 142–52.
    Thompson, T. G., and Robinson, R. J. [*See* reference 14 above.]
17. Webb, D. A., 1939. 'The sodium and potassium content of sea water.' *J. exp. Biol.*, **16**, 178–83.

POTASSIUM

Webb, D. A. [See reference 17 above.]

MAGNESIUM

Thompson, T. G., and Wright, C. C. [See reference 15 above.]

CALCIUM

18. Chow, T. G., and Thompson, T. G., 1955. 'Flame photometric determination of calcium in sea water.' *Analyt. Chem.* 27, 910–3.
19. Gripenberg, S., 1937. 'A simplified method for the determination of calcium in sea water.' *J. Cons. int. Explor. Mer,* 12, 284–92.
20. Kirk, P. L., and Moberg, E. G., 1933. 'Micro-determination of calcium in sea water.' *Industr. Engng. Chem. (Anal.),* 5, 95–7.
    Thompson, T. G., and Wright, C. C. [See reference 15 above.]

STRONTIUM

21. Chow, T. G., and Thompson, T. G., 1955. 'Flame photometric determination 388 of strontium in sea water.' *Analyt. Chem.,* 27, 18–21.
    Miyake, Y. [See reference 7 above.]
22. Smales, A. A., 1951. 'The determination of strontium in sea water by a combination of flame photometry and radio-chemistry.' *Analyt.,* 76, 348–55.
23. Webb, D. A., 1938. 'Strontium in sea water and its effect on calcium determinations.' *Nature, Lond.,* 142, 751–2.

SULPHATE

24. Bather, J. M., and Riley, J. P., 1954. 'The chemistry of the Irish Sea. 1. The sulphate-chlorinity ratio.' *J. Cons. int. Explor. Mer,* 20, 145–52.
25. Thompson, T. G., Johnston, W. R., and Wirth, H. E., 1931. 'The sulphate-chlorinity ratio in ocean waters.' *J. Cons. int. Explor. Mer,* 6, 246–51.
26. ——, Lang, J. W., and Anderson, L., 1927. 'The sulphate-chloride ratio of the waters of the north Pacific.' *Publ. Puget Sd. Mar. (biol.) Sta.,* 5, 277–93.
27. Webb, D. A., 1939. 'The micro-estimation of sulphates in sea water and the body fluids of marine animals.' *J. exp. Biol.,* 16, 438–45.

BROMIDE

28. Kolthoff, I. M., and Yutzy, H., 1937. 'Volumetric determination of bromide.' *Industr. Engng. Chem. (Anal.),* 9, 75–6.
29. Matida, Y., and Yamauchi, N., 1950. 'On the distribution of bromine in the ocean.' *J. Oceanogr. Soc. Japan,* 5, 111–15.
30. Szabó, Z. G., and Csányi, L., 1952. 'On the iodimetric determination of the bromide ion.' *Analyt. chim. acta,* 6, 208–16.
31. Thompson, T. G., and Korpi, E., 1942. 'The bromine-chlorinity ratio of sea water.' *J. Mar. Res.,* 5, 28–36.

BORON

32. Igelsrud, I., Thompson, T. G., and Zwicker, B. M. G., 1938. 'The boron content of sea water and of marine organisms.' *Amer. J. Sci.,* 35, 47–63.
    Miyake, Y. [See reference 7 above.]

33. Miyake, Y., 1939. 'Chemical studies of the western Pacific Ocean. VI. The vertical variation of minor constituents of the "Kurosio" region. Part 2.' *Bull. chem. Soc. Japan*, **14**, 467–71.
34. Harding, M. W., and Moberg, E. G., 1934. 'Determination and quantity of boron in sea water.' *5th Pacific Sci. Congr. Canada, 1933. Proc.* **3**, 2093–5.

FLUORINE

35. Anselm, C. D., and Robinson, R. J., 1951. 'The spectro-photometric determination of fluoride in sea water.' *J. Mar. Res.*, **10**, 203–4.
36. Beveridge, J. S., Hunter, G. J., and MacNulty, A. B., 1953. 'The determination of microgram quantities of fluoride. II. The determination of fluoride in waters and sewage effluent using the aluminium-haematoxylin complex.' *Analyt. chim. acta*, **9**, 330–7.
    Miyake, Y. [*See* reference 33 above.]
37. Matida, Y., 1956. 'On the source and fate of fluorine in water of Tokyo Bay.' *J. Oceanogr. Soc. Japan*, **10**, 71–5.
38. Thompson, T. G., and Taylor, H. J., 1933. 'Determination and occurrence of fluorides in sea water.' *Industr. Engng. Chem. (Anal.)*, **5**, 87–9.

IODINE

39. Sugawara, K., Koyama, T., and Terada, K., 1955. 'A new method of spectrophotometric determination of iodine in natural waters.' *Bull. chem. Soc. Japan*, **28**, 492–7.

18

TRACE METALS

The functions of the many metallic ions present in sea water at extremely low concentrations are largely unknown. Work on these 'trace' elements has been particularly concentrated on those few which have either been shown experimentally to be of importance in the growth of marine organisms (usually diatoms) or which, by analogy with other biological systems, might be expected to be so.

Little effort (with the exception of iron, see below) has so far been directed to ascertain in what state these metallic ions exist, whether as free ions, as ions absorbed or combined with colloidal organic matter or as ions complexed in inorganic cations. Until more is known, the investigator may evaporate the sea water, wet ash and determine the trace metal; in this case, the total concentration of all forms is determined. This is time-consuming and difficult on board ship. The alternative is to adopt a standard technique for its liberation before estimation. Co-precipitation with magnesium hydroxide by the addition of alkali may be used to concentrate the element (35). Most frequently the estimate is made on the basis of the amount that will react with a reagent selected for its analytical convenience.

IRON

Cooper (5, 6) has summarized the various forms in which iron may occur, namely:

1. Ionic iron: Fe^{++}, $FeOH^{++}$ and Fe^{+++} in true solution at equilibrium will amount to less than 10^{-8} μg.-atom/l, i.e. smaller concentrations than can be detected by analysis.
2. Dissolved inorganic complexes: ferri-fluoride, the most likely complex, is readily hydrolysable by sea water and there is no evidence of other inorganic complexes.
3. Dissolved crystalloidal or dispersed organic colloids.
4. Colloidal inorganic complexes: ferric hydroxide or ferric phosphate may be held in a dispersed state by mucilaginous or other protective colloids.
5. Particulate iron compounds: these include particulate ferric hydroxide and phosphate, terrigenous iron in mineral compounds, and organically bound iron in tissues or faecal pellets.

Since much of the iron is particulate, it is necessary when investigating the spatial distribution of iron to adopt an appropriate statistical design in planning the experiments and treating the results.

Three procedures have been adopted for analysis: Thompson and Bremner (8) evaporated the sample to dryness, ashed with sulphuric acid and estimated the iron with thiocyanate. The thiocyanate method is unreliable unless the conditions in sample and control (or calibration curve) are very carefully matched and the method is now rarely used. Cooper (2, 3, 5, 6) has used 2 : 2' dipyridyl (or 2 : 2' : 2" tripyridyl which is twice as sensitive) and either reagent could be used to replace the thiocyanate method after wet ashing. He determines what he calls the 'reducible' iron and 'total' iron: the former is the iron obtained after treating the sample with sodium sulphite and the latter is the iron liberated by treatment with bromine water under specified conditions.

Recently Lewis and Goldberg (6a) have measured the iron content of waters after separation on Millipore filters. The material passing the filter, that is $<5 \mu$, they term soluble iron; they found that this soluble fraction was far greater than that permissible as ionic iron on the basis of Cooper's calculations and they consider it is composed of soluble or colloidal iron complexes. Lewis and Goldberg use a modification of Cooper's method for the insoluble iron but use bathophenanthroline (4·7-diphenyl 1, 10-phenanthroline) for the smaller quantities of soluble iron.

THE 'REDUCIBLE' AND 'TOTAL' IRON (COOPER, 2, 5)

Reagents

1. *2 : 2'-dipyridyl* (or 2 : 2' : 2" tripyridyl). A 0·4% w/v solution in 0·2 N-HCl.

2. *Hydrochloric acid.* 4 N.

3. *Ammonium acetate.* 4 N, preserved with a few drops of toluene.

4. *Sodium sulphite.* A 10% w/v solution, freshly prepared.

5. *Bromine water.* A freshly prepared saturated solution.

6. *Ferrous ammonium sulphate.* Stock solution containing 100 mg. Fe/l. Dissolve 0·7023 g. $FeSO_4(NH_4)_2SO_4.6H_2O$ in distilled water containing 5 ml. of 4 N-HCl and make up to 1 litre: dilute as required.

Procedure ('reducible' iron)

Introduce 150 ml. of sea water into a 250 ml. flask and add 0·30 ml. of 4 N hydrochloric acid and 1·5 ml. of freshly prepared 10% sodium sulphite (final pH 2·8). After 18 hours add 0·4 ml. of 4 N ammonium acetate followed by 1·5 ml. of the dipyridyl reagent (final pH 5·0). Measure the transmittancy (Ilford 604 or at 522 mμ) after 24 hours. (Dr J. P. Riley suggests that these times may be reduced considerably.)

Procedure ('total' iron)

Treat 100 ml. sample of the sea water with 4 drops of 4 N hydrochloric acid and 1 ml. of bromine water; warm on the steam bath for 30 minutes in a fume chamber. Add distilled water to compensate for evaporation. Cool and treat as for 'reducible' iron.

Remarks

1. The maximum absorption is at about 522 mμ (7).

2. Buch (1) has made a detailed study of the reaction: the pH for complex formation should lie between 3 and 5: citrate buffers, which complex the iron, should be avoided: at high dilution ferric ions appear to give a colour and the estimation of ferrous iron should always be made in the presence of a reducing agent. The molar concentration of the dipyridyl should be at least twenty times that of the iron.

3. With moderate concentrations of iron, readings of transmittancy may be made within an hour, but, with the small quantities present in sea water, maximum colour development may require 24 hours.

4. Great care should be taken to prevent contamination of the samples during collection and manipulation.

5. There is no salt error.

6. The precision is stated to be ± 1 μg. Fe/l.

7. Ferri-fluoride in the amounts present does not affect the reduction of any ferric to ferrous ion under the conditions used.

8. According to Cooper's experiments the 'reducible' iron treatment sets free 25%, and the bromine treatment some 41% of the iron contained in Waksman's ferroligno-protein.

9. A separation of various particulate fractions should be possible by the use of selected filters. Tests should be made to ascertain whether iron complexes are adsorbed on the filter.

10. The method may be used for sea-water digests, for true total iron or for digests from plankton or other material (4). In these cases the solution should be first brought to pH 1–2 which can usually be done by dilution, and after transferring to a standard flask, the reducing agent is added. After standing for a few minutes, the pH should then be brought to 3–5 with the buffer and the dipyridyl reagent added (up to 100 μg. Fe, 1 ml. of a 0·4% solution is adequate). The solution is then made up to volume.

PARTICULATE IRON (LEWIS AND GOLDBERG, 6a)

Reagents

1. *2 : 2′ dipyridyl.* Dissolve 0·4 g. in 100 ml. of 0·2 N-HCl.
2. *Hydroxylamine hydrochloride.* 10% aqueous solution. To free this reagent from iron, dissolve 10 g. of the solid in 90 ml. of distilled water, add 4 ml. of the bathophenanthroline reagent (*see* below) and extract with two successive portions of isoamyl alcohol. Repeat if necessary.
3. *Acetic acid.* Glacial.
4. *Sodium acetate.* A 50% aqueous solution. To free this from iron dissolve 50 g. of reagent grade salt in water, add 2 ml. of the bathophenanthroline reagent and extract with isoamyl alcohol; any copper, as indicated by a red colour, should be extracted.
5. *Isoamyl alcohol.* Reagent grade.
6. *Hydrochloric acid.* 1·2 N. Dilute 10 ml. of concentrated acid to 100 ml. with distilled water.
7. *Perchloric acid.* 70% reagent grade. This may contain iron which cannot be removed. It is allowed for in the blank.
8. *Standard iron solution.* Stock, dissolve 0·3455 g. of ferric ammonium sulphate in 100 ml. of distilled water (adding 1·6 ml. of concentrated acid). This solution contains 400 μg. Fe/ml.

Procedure

Filter an appropriate quantity of water (about 1·2 litres) through the membrane filter (pore size 5 μ). Transfer the membrane filter (*see* pp. 247–9) to a 30 ml. Kjeldahl flask containing 5 ml. of the perchloric acid. (Warning! p. 157.) Heat until evolution of acid fumes ceases. Cool. Add 1 ml. of 1·2 N-HCl followed by 10 ml. of distilled water. Transfer solution and washings to a graduated flask (50 ml.) and add 1 ml. each of hydroxylamine hydrochloride, sodium acetate and dipyridyl reagents. Make up to volume. Determine the transmittancy (10 cm. cells) at 522 mμ or with a green filter (Ilford 604).

Remarks

1. The method was tested on haemin with recoveries of 97%.
2. A blank should be run; membrane may yield 2 μg. Fe.
3. Calibration curve is prepared by treating ferric solutions (0–40 μ) with 1 ml. each of 1·2 N hydrochloric acid, hydroxylamine and dipyridyl reagents, diluting to 50 ml. and measuring the transmittancies.

SOLUBLE IRON (LEWIS AND GOLDBERG, 6a)

Reagents

As for the particulate iron and
Bathophenanthroline. Dissolve 0·0334 g. in a mixture of 50 ml.
ethanol and 50 ml. water.

Procedure

Add 5 ml. of the perchloric acid to 100 ml. of the water passing the
membrane filter and evaporate to a thin paste (warning! p. 157).
Dissolve the residue in 100 ml. of water and boil. Cool, add 2 ml. of
hydroxylamine, followed by 0·4 ml. glacial acetic acid and sodium
acetate to give a pH of 4·0 (test). Add 4·0 ml. of the bathophenanthroline reagent and extract the coloured complex with 20 ml. of
isoamyl alcohol. Transfer the extract to a 25 ml. volumetric flask
and make up to volume. Determine the transmittancy at 533 mμ or
with a green filter (Ilford 604).

Remarks

1. There is no salt error.
2. Run blanks on the perchloric acid.
3. Calibration curve is run by taking known amounts of iron
(0–6 μg./100 ml.) through the whole procedure including extraction.

COPPER

This was first determined by Atkins (10, 11) who used sodium
diethyldithiocarbamate and compared his results with those obtained
by electro-deposition. A summary of the work on this element has
been given by Chow and Thompson (14). Copper has also been
determined with dithizone (13). To some extent the reagent is a
matter of personal choice: Chow and Thompson dislike the dithizone method; although some find the reagent somewhat capricious,
after a little experience it may be satisfactorily used for estimating
copper; there is no doubt, however, that more experience and care
with working conditions *are* necessary when using dithizone and
since for this element there is little advantage over the sodium
diethyldithiocarbamate method when combined with an extraction
technique, the latter will be given. Dr J. P. Riley (personal communication) has given details of a method using 2 : 2′-diquinolyl
and this will also be described; it may be used for sea water and for
samples of organisms, sediments and silicate rocks. The method is
specific for copper.

SODIUM DIETHYLDITHIOCARBAMATE METHOD
(11, 14, 15)

Reagent

Sodium diethyldithiocarbamate (SDDC). A 1% w/v aqueous solution. This solution is moderately stable, but should be renewed from time to time in order to obviate high blanks and to give full colour development.

Procedure

Measure out 500 ml. of sea water into a large separating funnel and add 2 ml. of the SDDC solution; shake and, after standing a few minutes, add 5 ml. of chloroform; shake vigorously. Allow the chloroform layer to settle and then run off into a dry cell. Measure the transmittancy at 440 mμ or with a violet filter (Ilford 601).

Remarks

1. Various solvents have been used for this extraction, but most commonly chloroform, carbon tetrachloride and xylene; the great advantage of chloroform is that it gives a very rapid and almost complete extraction of the yellow complex at one shaking and, being heavier than water, it is easily run off. Further, its considerable solubility in water allows say 5 ml. to be conveniently added from a burette and only a smaller quantity (3–4 ml.) to contain the yellow complex after shaking; a concentration is therefore obtained without the necessity of measuring out small quantities of extractant. Temperature conditions, however, must be kept relatively constant.

2. The colour is stable for at least an hour.

3. It is unlikely that any substance normally present in sea water will give any significant interference. In other materials, however, such as digests of organisms or muds the possibility of interference should be considered. If solutions containing appreciable quantities of iron, nickel or cobalt are to be dealt with, then 0·50 g. of disodium ethylenediamine tetra-acetic acid is first added to the water sample (500 ml.) and the solution allowed to stand for 30 minutes. 50 ml. of 20% w/v ammonium citrate solution (*p*H 9·0) are then added, followed by 10 ml. of SDDC and 10 ml. of chloroform. The solution is then extracted as before (15).

4. The chloroform extract may be freed from water by inserting a small roll of filter paper in the stem of the funnel before running off; in the case of small quantities, or in the presence of slime at the interface the chloroform layer may be centrifuged and then withdrawn by a fine-tipped pipette.

5. The optical cells should not be colder than the extract since water is then apt to separate whilst the transmittancy is being measured.

6. If the reagents are shaken with SDDC and chloroform to free from copper impurities before adding to the sample it must be remembered that the aqueous solution will be saturated with chloroform; the blank should be treated likewise to avoid volume errors.

7. Quantities of 1.0 μg. Cu/l. can be dealt with. 5 mg. of Cd, Co, Cr^{++}, Fe^{+++}, Pb, Mn, Ni, Sn^{++}, Th^{++}, Zn, do not interfere if complexing agents are added (see paragraph 3 above); bismuth may be eliminated by a back extraction of the extract with an equal volume of 1.0 N caustic soda (Jenkins, 15).

THE 2:2'-DIQUINOLYL METHOD (J. P. RILEY)

Reagents

1. *2 : 2'-Diquinolyl.* A 0.03% solution in hexyl alcohol; dissolve 0.03 g. of 2 : 2'-diquinolyl in 100 ml. of hexyl alcohol which has been redistilled from sodium hydroxide.

2. *Hydroxylamine hydrochloride solution.* Dissolve 25 g. of the solid in a minimum quantity of distilled water, filter and make up to 100 ml.

3. *Sodium acetate.* 1 N. Dissolve 136 g. of reagent grade hydrated sodium acetate in distilled water and make up to 1 litre.

4. *Hydroquinone solution.* A 1% w/v solution of hydroquinone in redistilled ethanol.

5. *Copper sulphate solution.* Dissolve 0.3927 g. $CuSO_4.5H_2O$ in distilled water and make up to 100 ml. This solution contains 1 g. Cu/l. Prepare suitable dilutions for calibration purposes.

Procedure

Transfer 500 ml. of sea water to a litre separating funnel, add 5 ml. of 25% hydroxylamine hydrochloride solution followed by 10 ml. of 1 N sodium acetate. The pH is about 4.5. Extract the solution with 8 ml. of 0.03% diquinolyl in hexyl alcohol. Run off the lower layer and re-extract with a further 3 ml. of the diquinolyl reagent after the addition of 2 ml. of the 25% hydroxylamine hydrochloride solution. Carry out a third extraction of the aqueous layer with a further 3 ml. of the diquinolyl reagent. Combine the hexyl alcohol extracts in a 10 ml. graduated flask containing 0.5 ml. of the hydroquinone solution and dilute to volume with hexyl alcohol. Measure the transmittancy at 540 mμ. Correct for a blank (distilled water) carried through the whole procedure. A calibration curve is obtained by carrying out the whole procedure on solutions of known copper content.

MANGANESE

The usual method for the estimation of small quantities of manganese depends upon its oxidation to permanganate; a number of reagents have been used for this purpose, most recently persulphates and periodates; the latter are more satisfactory. Thompson and Wilson (18) have estimated the total manganese present in sea water, after wet ashing, by the persulphate method. More recently Koroleff (17) has avoided wet ashing by co-precipitating the manganese by the addition of alkali. Harvey (16) has attempted to make a direct estimation by utilizing the catalytic action of manganese on the oxidation of tetra-base (tetramethyldiamino-diphenylmethane) with potassium periodate. Little further work has been done on this method.

OXIDATION OF TETRA-BASE METHOD (16)

Reagents

1. *Hydrochloric acid.* About 1·75 N.
2. *Ammonium acetate.* A 50% w/v aqueous solution.
3. *Potassium periodate.* A solution containing 0·23 g./l. A stock solution is made up and standardized by titration in alkaline solution with sodium arsenite after the addition of potassium iodide.
4. *Tetra-base* (tetramethyldiamino-diphenylmethane). A freshly prepared 0·25% solution in acetone.

Procedure

To 50 ml. of the sample add 1·5 ml. of the hydrochloric acid and allow to stand for three days. Then add 1·5 ml. of the ammonium acetate followed by 3·7 ml. of potassium periodate solution (0·85 mg.). Allow to stand for 10 minutes and pour into 4·5 ml. of the tetra-base solution. Transfer to optical cell and measure transmittancy immediately, using yellow filter (Ilford 606). The maximum colour is attained in 40 seconds. Run a blank.

AFTER CO-PRECIPITATION WITH ALKALI

In this technique alkali is added to the sea water, and the precipitate which contains the manganese is dealt with by the periodate method. A slightly modified method must be used in the presence of large quantities of organic matter.

Reagents

1. *Sodium periodate.* Pure solid.
2. *Periodate-sulphuric acid reagent.* Dilute one part of acid with

two parts of water and with this dilute acid make up a sodium periodate solution to contain 15 g./l.

3. *Potassium hydroxide.* 0·2 N solution free from manganese.

4. *Silver nitrate.* A 2 N and 0·2 N solution.

5. *Standard potassium permanganate solution.* Dissolve 57·5 mg. of $KMnO_4$ in water and add 1 ml. of 2 N sulphuric acid; reduce by the addition of 0·15 g. of sodium bisulphite. Boil the solution, cool and dilute to 200 ml. Dilute 1 ml. of this solution (containing 0·1 mg. Mn) to 60 ml. and heat to boiling with 10 ml. of sulphuric acid reagent and 2 ml. of silver nitrate (0·2 N) solution. Add exactly 50 mg. of sodium periodate and place in a boiling water bath for 30 minutes. Cool and dilute to exactly 100 ml. This standard solution contains 0·001 mg. Mn per ml. Dilute solutions of manganese salts, whether as Mn^{++} or $MnO_4,^-$ lose their strength very rapidly and should therefore be prepared fairly frequently.

Procedure

To 1 litre of the sample add 50 ml. of 0·2 N potassium hydroxide whilst mixing and let the precipitate settle for 12 hours. Remove the supernatant and dissolve the precipitate in 1·5 ml. of concentrated sulphuric acid. If the solution is colourless (absence of organic matter) precipitate the halide ions with 2 N silver nitrate avoiding too great an excess. Filter off the silver halides. Heat the filtrate to boiling with 10 ml. of sulphuric acid reagent, add 50 mg. of sodium periodate and heat on the water bath for 30 minutes; cool. Compare with standards or measure the transmittancy at 525 mμ or with a green filter (Ilford 604).

If organic matter is present the solution of the precipitates in acid must be heated to fuming in a platinum dish to remove excess acid and oxidize the organic matter; the salts should be fused. After cooling, dissolve the melt in 10 ml. of sulphuric acid reagent, heat to boiling, cool, filter. Dilute the filtrate to about 75 ml. and add 2 ml. of 0·2 N silver nitrate solution. Add as before 50 mg. of sodium periodate, heat on the water bath for half an hour and cool. Then proceed as in absence of organic matter (*see* above).

Remarks

1. The periodate method may be used for digests. The acidity should be adjusted to about 2 N which is optimal for the oxidation. 1 μg. manganese in 10 ml. is a convenient strength for measurement of transmittancies.

2. In the presence of much calcium the concentration of the latter should be reduced: in the presence of iron it is advisable to add phosphoric acid (S.G. 1·75) before the sulphuric acid.

3. Chlorides interfere and must be removed; if this has not been done in a wet ashing procedure by the sulphuric acid they must be precipitated as described above.

4. Common metals do not interfere except as self-colours.

SEPARATION ON A DITHIZONE ABSORBENT

Carritt (23) has recently experimented with a relatively simple method of separating the 'dithizone' reacting metals by passing the sample through a column containing dithizone held on a cellulose acetate support.

The Column Packing Material

Sieve a commercial granular cellulose acetate (Carritt used Fisher Scientific Co. No. C-215) through a set of well-cleaned standard sieves. Two grades gave satisfactory results, that passing 18 (1000 μ) and retained on 25 (750 μ) and that passing 25 and retained on 35 (500 μ). Treat 10 g. of this sieved material with 100 ml. of a carbon tetrachloride solution of dithizone 0·5 g./l. and, to evaporate the solvent, heat the slurry with constant agitation on a hot plate. Stop heating when the bulk of the product has passed from a deepish black-green to a light green.

The Column

Add and tamp into place 2 g. of untreated cellulose acetate held in place by a glass wool plug, followed by 3 g. of the dithizone-cellulose acetate. Pour 3 ml. of carbon tetrachloride into the top of the column and draw quickly into the packing to wet about three-quarters of its length.

Wash the column with 100 ml. of N hydrochloric acid and 250 ml. of metal-free water; it is then ready for use.

Use

Adjust the pH of the sample to 7·0 $\pm$0·1 and suck through the column under vacuum pump. A flow rate of 2 litres per hour is usual but up to 6 litres per hour has had no effect on recovery. The elements are removed from the column by 50 ml. of N hydrochloric acid (Pb, Zn, Cd, Mn^{++}) or 50 ml. of concentrated ammonia (Cu, Co).

Remarks

1. If the column is not wetted with carbon tetrachloride it gives no recovery of trace metals and the dithizone is rapidly stripped from the support.

2. Carritt analysed elements from the column polarographically (except for manganese). The effluent is treated with 0·5 ml. of concentrated sulphuric acid and heated to fuming, 1 ml. of nitric acid added and the residue evaporated to dryness. Clearly standard methods may be applied to the residue. The ammonia effluent was first evaporated to remove most of the ammonia before adding the acid.

3. Recovery tests were made and indicated satisfactory results, although in some cases the concentrations used were greater than those normally occurring in sea water.

4. Care should be taken when adjusting the pH not to make the solution alkaline, since in this case loss of manganese will take place by oxidation.

5. Recovery of 10 μg. zinc and copper was obtained from 10 litres.

6. Rapid fluctuations in pressure during elutriation should be avoided; a large free volume is inserted between column and pump. Capacity of column is 3 mg. elements.

7. Columns can only be used again after hydrochloric acid elutriation.

DITHIZONE

Some workers find this very versatile reagent difficult to use, and the following notes are therefore included.

Dithizone, diphenylthiocarbazone, a violet-black solid, is appreciably soluble in many organic solvents and in alkaline aqueous solution. Solutions in chloroform or carbon tetrachloride are almost invariably used in analytical work. In these solvents dilute solutions are green; when more concentrated they appear green in reflected light and red in transmitted light. If a solution of dithizone in any of these organic solvents is shaken with an aqueous solution of many metallic ions it reacts to give a metal dithizonate, also soluble in the organic solvent. These metal-dithizonates are, like the reagent itself, more soluble in chloroform than in carbon tetrachloride.

Of all the procedures that have been used with this reagent for estimating traces of metal ions, the 'colorimetric' method is now almost invariably employed. Since dithizone itself is strongly coloured the excess base is usually removed for visual comparison; this method is not entirely satisfactory since there is a tendency to remove some of the metal dithizonates on 'washing' the extract with ammonia. With an absorptiometer or spectrophotometer a so-called mixed colour method is used; in this the transmittancy is measured in the presence of the excess dithizone at the appropriate wave-length (or with the appropriate filter) at either the metal dithizonate or the unchanged dithizone absorption maximum.

It should be stressed that the basis of most of the procedures is still empirical, although Irving and co-workers (24, 25, 26, 27; *see also* 28) have recently made some theoretical studies. The *exact* instructions should be followed in using published methods. Among the factors affecting dithizone systems are:

1. The acidity of the aqueous solution.
2. The concentration of dithizone.
3. The relative volumes of reagent and aqueous solution which influence the partition of the various components between the two phases.
4. The time and vigour of shaking (whose effect may differ considerably with the particular solvent, 19, 20).
5. The solvent used for the reagent.
6. The presence of complex-forming substances in the aqueous solution.

Preparation and Storage of Dithizone Solutions (H. Barnes, 19, 20)

Dithizone is easily oxidized to diphenylthiocarbodiazone and in some solvents this oxidation takes place readily in strong light (possibly interaction with decomposition products of the solvent or contained impurities under the action of light). This oxidation product, unlike dithizone, is insoluble in alkaline aqueous solution but soluble in organic solvents to give a yellow solution. When purifying dithizone, it is best to weigh out the quantity required for a strong stock solution and to take this through the purification procedure, running the purified product into a volumetric flask in which it may be stored. The commercial product is first dissolved in chloroform and shaken with dilute ammonia in a large separating funnel: the impurities, which remain in the organic phase colouring it yellow, are discarded. This extraction is repeated with further additions of chloroform until no yellow colour appears in the extract but only the slight green tint of dithizone itself. More chloroform is then added followed by acid. Some workers add hydrochloric acid, but the use of a strong solution of sulphur dioxide will be found to give a solution with less tendency to oxidize on storage. The acid precipitates the dithizone in the aqueous layer, from which it is extracted with pure organic solvent. The organic layer, containing the purified dithizone, is run off directly into a volumetric flask and then more solvent added and the shaking repeated. This is continued with successive small portions of solvent until a negligible quantity of reagent remains in the aqueous layer. The stock solution, now in the standard flask, is made up to volume with the solvent and covered with a small quantity of sulphur dioxide solution or aqueous hydroxylamine hydrochloride to prevent air oxidation during subsequent manipulation. Both stock and working solutions should be kept in the refrigerator when not in use. Dithizone solutions and extracts should not be exposed to bright sunlight.

Recovery of Chloroform from Waste Dithizone Extracts

Various methods have been used for the recovery. Mullin and Riley (29) have recently discussed this problem and they find the most satisfactory method is as follows.

First distil the contaminated chloroform through a layer of 10% aqueous sodium sulphite. Shake the distillate with either a portion of 10% sulphite or preferably a 3% hydroxylamine hydrochloride solution, until the extract is colourless. Redistil from lime or active charcoal. With heavily contaminated residues repeat the distillation. The same method may be employed for the recovery of chloroform from 8-hydroxy-quinoline extracts.

Procedure for Dithizone Estimations (H. Barnes, 19, 20)

In the direct mixed colour method the solution containing the trace metal is transferred to a separating funnel and brought to the appropriate pH; a complexing agent may then be added. The pH and complexing agent are selected according to the metal to be estimated and the presence of interfering elements. A known volume of the dithizone in the organic solvent is then added and the funnel shaken uniformly for a fixed time. After allowing the two layers to separate, the organic layer—chloroform or carbon tetrachloride—is run off, with a small roll of filter paper in the stem of the funnel, into the optical cell. The transmittancy is measured with the appropriate filter. Since most metal dithizonates are red, a green filter (Ilford 604) is used. The literature (24, 28) should be consulted for the appropriate wave-length if a spectrophotometer is to be used. The process is repeated using distilled water for the blank. When working with digests the blank should be taken through the whole procedure. Traces of oxidizing agents will react with the dithizone; it is necessary to remove such oxidizing substances.

Irving and co-workers have developed an alternative method termed 'reversion', and this eliminates the necessity to have the conditions for the blank identical with those for the estimation (26). The procedure described above is the first stage; a portion of the organic layer is then withdrawn and its transmittancy measured at the maximum absorption of dithizone, (600 mμ) or with a yellow filter. A second portion is then withdrawn and shaken with a reversion reagent which decomposes the metal dithizonate, liberating dithizone in equivalent quantity and returning the metal ion to the aqueous layer. The transmittancy of the organic layer is measured. The increase is the equivalent dithizone liberated and the calibration curve is set up in terms of this absorption. The reversion blank should be determined. The reversion reagent will depend upon the metal; for lead and bismuth 2 N acid may be used; for other metals, which only slowly return to the aqueous phase under these conditions, e.g. silver and mercury, other reagents are necessary. 2 : 3 dimercaptopropanol (BAL) is an excellent reversion reagent.

REFERENCES

IRON

1. Buch, K., 1942. 'Analytisk bestämning av extremt låga järnkoncentrationer med α : α′ : dipyridyl.' *Medd. finska Kemistsamf.*, N:o. 1–2, 1–18.
2. Cooper, L. H. N., 1935. 'Iron in the sea and in marine plankton.' *Proc. roy. Soc.*, Ser. B, **118**, 419–38.
3. ——, 1937. 'Some conditions governing the solubility of iron.' *Proc. roy. Soc.*, Ser. B, **124**, 299–307.
4. ——, 1939. 'Phosphorus, nitrogen, iron and manganese in marine zooplankton.' *J. Mar. biol. Ass. U.K.*, **23**, 387–90.
5. ——, 1948a. 'The distribution of iron in the waters of the western English Channel.' *J. Mar. biol. Ass. U.K.*, **27**, 279–313.
6. ——, 1948b. 'Some considerations on the distribution of iron in the sea.' *J. Mar. biol. Ass. U.K.*, **27**, 314–21.
6a. Lewis, G. E., and Goldberg, E. D., 1954. 'Iron in marine waters.' *J. Mar. Res.*, **13**, 183–97.
7. Moss, M. L., and Mellon, M. G., 1942. 'Colorimetric determination of iron with 2 : 2′ dipyridyl and with 2 : 2′ : 2″ terpyridyl.' *Industr. Engng. Chem. (Anal.)*, **4**, 862.
8. Thompson, T. G., and Bremner, R. W., 1935a. 'The determination of iron in sea water.' *J. Cons. int. Explor. Mer*, **10**, 33–8.
9. ——, ——, 1935b. 'The occurrence of iron in the waters of the north-Pacific Ocean.' *J. Cons. int. Explor. Mer*, **10**, 39–47.

COPPER

10. Atkins, W. R. G., 1932. 'The copper content of sea water.' *J. Mar. biol. Ass. U.K.*, **18**, 193–8.
11. ——, 1933. 'A rapid estimation of the copper content of sea water.' *J. Mar. biol. Ass. U.K.*, **19**, 63–6.
12. Barnes, H., 1946. 'The estimation in sea water solutions of microquantities of mercury in the presence of copper by means of dithizone.' *J. Mar. biol. Ass. U.K.*, **26**, 303–11.
13. Buch, K., 1944. 'Dithizonmetod för bestämning av zink och koppar i naturliga vatten.' *Medd. finska Kemistsamf.*, N:o 1–2, 25–37.
14. Chow, T. G., and Thompson, T. G., 1952. 'The determination and distribution of copper in the sea. Part I. The spectrophotometric determination of copper in sea water.' *J. Mar. Res.*, **11**, 124–38.
15. Jenkins, E. N., 1954. 'The absorptiometric determination of traces of copper in highly purified water.' *Analyst*, **79**, 209–16.

238   APPARATUS AND METHODS OF OCEANOGRAPHY

MANGANESE

16. Harvey, H. W., 1949. 'On manganese in sea and fresh waters.' *J. Mar. biol. Ass. U.K.*, **28**, 155–64.
17. Koroleff, F., 1947. 'Determination of manganese in natural waters.' *Acta chem. scand.*, **1**, 503–6.
18. Thompson, T. G., and Wilson, T. L., 1935. 'The occurrence and determination of manganese in sea water.' *J. Amer. chem. Soc.*, **57**, 233–6.

DITHIZONE

19. Barnes, H., 1947. 'The determination of mercury by means of dithizone.' *Analyst*, **72**, 469–72.
20. ——, 1951. 'The determination of zinc by dithizone.' *Analyst*, **76**, 220–3.
21. Buch, K., 1944. 'Dithizonmetoden för bestämning av zink och koppar i naturliga vatten.' *Medd. finska Kemistsamf.*, N : o. 1–2, 25–37.
22. ——, and Koroleff, F., 1945. 'Jämviksstudier rörande blyoch alkalidithizonater.' *Medd. finska Kemistsamf.*, N : o. 3–4, 98–110.
23. Carritt, D. E., 1953. 'Separation and concentration of trace metals from natural waters.' *Analyt. Chem.*, **25**, 1927–8.
24. Irving, H. M. N. H., and Risdon, E. J., 1949. 'Studies with dithizone. Part I. The determination of traces of mercury.' *J. chem. Soc.*, 541–7.
25. ——, Cooke, S. J. H., Wordger, S. C., and Williams, R. J. P. 'Studies with dithizone. Part II. Dithizone as a monobasic acid.' *J. chem. Soc.*, 1847–55.
26. ——, ——, and Andrew, G., 1949. 'The absorptiometric determination of traces of metals. Reversion: a new procedure.' *J. chem. Soc.*, 537–41.
27. ——, and Williams, R. J. P., 1949. 'Metal complexes and partition equilibria.' *J. chem. Soc.*, 1841–7.
28. Koroleff, F., 1950. *Determination of traces of heavy metals in sea water by means of dithizone.* Thesis, University of Helsingfors, Helsingfors.
29. Mullin, J. B., and Riley, J. P., 1955. 'Recovery of chloroform used in dithizone extraction.' *Analyst*, **80**, 316–7.

GENERAL

The following general references to trace element estimations will be found useful.

30. Allport, N. L., 1945. *Colorimetric Analysis.* Chapman and Hall, Ltd., London, 452 pp.
    [An excellent practical book of selected modern methods for metallic and acidic radicals and substances of biochemical importance.]
31. Anon., 1934. *Bibliography of the More Important Heavy Metals occurring in Food and Biological Material* (1921–33). Compiled for the Society of Public Analysts and other Analytical Chemists. W. Heffer & Sons, Ltd., Cambridge, England. 30 pp.
32. ——, 1948–53. *Bibliography of the Literature on the Minor Elements and their relation to Plant and Animal Nutrition.* Compiled and published by the Chilean Nitrate Educational Bureau, Inc., New York. Vol. I (1948), 1037 pp.; Vol. II (1952), 152 pp.; Vol. III (1953), 117 pp.

33. Anon., 1948. *Bibliography of Standard, Tentative and recommended or recognized Methods of Analysis*. Compiled under the authority of the Analytical Methods Committee of the Society of Public Analysts, and other Analytical Chemists. W. Heffer & Sons, Ltd., Cambridge, England, 221 pp.

34. Block, R. J., 1952. *Paper Chromatography. A Laboratory Manual*. Academic Press, Inc. Publishers, New York, 195 pp.

35. Ishibashi, M., 1953. 'Studies on minute elements in sea water.' *Rec. oceanogr. Wks. Jap.*, New Ser., **1**, 88–92.

[V, Cr, Co, Ni, As, Se, Mo, W are co-precipitated by the addition of various reagents and after treatment of the precipitate the element is determined by standard methods.]

36. Mellon, M. G. (Ed.), 1950. *Analytical Absorption Spectroscopy*. John Wiley and Sons, Inc., New York. Second printing 1953, 618 pp.

[Excellent account of general principles and instruments. Few practical analytical details of procedures are given.]

37. Middleton, G., and Stuckey, R. E., 1953. 'The preparation of biological material for the determination of trace metals. Part I. A critical review of existing techniques.' *Analyst*, **78**, 532–42.

[This is an excellent review with very full bibliography.]

38. ——, ——, 1954. 'The preparation of biological material for the determination of trace metals. Part II. A method for the destruction of organic matter in biological material.' *Analyst*, **79**, 138–42.

[Nitric acid is the only reagent used in any quantity; the maximum temperature attained does not exceed 350°C. and the mineral constituents are obtained in acid solution with small quantities of other reagents.]

39. Sandell, E. B., 1944. *Colorimetric Determination of Traces of Metals*. Interscience Publishers, Inc., New York, 487 pp.

[Only metals are dealt with and particular emphasis is given to dithizone techniques. Useful discussion of separation and general principles of trace-element analysis, with necessary practical details. General discussion of colorimetric reagents is included.]

40. Snell, F. D., and Snell, C. T., 1948–54. *Colorimetric Methods of Analysis*. Vol. I (1948), 239 pp.; Vol. II (1949), 950 pp.; Vol. III (1953), 606 pp.; Vol. IV (1954), 676 pp. D. van Nostrand Co. Inc., New York.

[A comprehensive text-book.]

41. Stiles, W., 1946. *Trace Elements in Plants and Animals*. Cambridge University Press, Cambridge, England. 189 pp.

42. Strafford, N., Wyatt, P. F., and Kershaw, F. G., 1945. 'A scheme for the photometric determination of minute amounts of arsenic, copper, lead, zinc and iron (with certain other metals) in organic compounds, e.g. medicinal.' *Analyst*, **70**, 232–46.

43. Various Authors, 1945. 'Symposium on trace metals in soils.' *Soil Sci.*, **60**, 497 pp.

44. Vinograd, A. P., 1934. 'Geochemistry of the scattered rare elements in sea water.' *Usekhi Khimi*, **13**, 3–24 (in Russian).

45. Weil, B. H., Murray, P. E., Reed, G. W., and Ingols, R. S. *Bibliography on Water and Sewage Analysis*. Georgia Institute of Technology, Atlanta, Georgia. Spec. Report No. 28.

46. Williams, T. I., 1946. *An Introduction to Chromatography*. Blackie and Son, Ltd., London. 100 pp.

19

PLANKTON PIGMENTS

The major pigments of phytoplankton are chlorophylls (two-thirds) accompanied by carotenoids, including carotenes, other polythene hydrocarbons and xanthophylls (21, 22, 23, 25). It is a simple matter to extract these pigments and to measure the transmittancy of the resultant solution either at a selected wave-length or with an appropriate filter. When the object of such measurements is to estimate the standing crop of phytoplankton the following limitations of the method must, however, be borne in mind (7). First, the relative pigment composition of the various phytoplankton groups is by no means constant and any estimate of the standing crop based on one pigment, or group of pigments, may be biased by the presence or absence of certain species or groups. The method is, therefore, at its best in making comparisons of plankton populations within a limited area at the same time; under these circumstances its composition is likely to be similar from place to place, varying only in total quantity. Comparisons between different places or times are less reliable. Secondly, if the results are to be translated into numbers of organisms or living organic matter the pigment estimations must be calibrated against counts in pure cultures; if the plankton is very mixed, conversion of pigment values to other parameters can only be approximate.

SINGLE TRANSMITTANCY MEASUREMENTS

Reagents

1. *Acetone.* 90% v/v aqueous solution. Reagent grade acetone should be distilled over an aqueous solution of mixed sodium sulphite and sodium carbonate.
2. *Magnesium carbonate.* Reagent grade fine powder.

Procedure

Filter an appropriate quantity (usually 0·5–5 litres) of the water sample through a fine paper, membrane or other filter. Transfer the filter to a stoppered vessel and add an appropriate amount of solvent (usually 5 ml. is adequate) followed by 0·1 g. magnesium carbonate powder. Shake and allow to stand in the dark for 18–24 hours. Pour into a tube and centrifuge. Transfer some of the supernatant to an optical cell and measure the transmittancy with a red filter (Ilford 608) or at 663 mμ, setting the instrument against pure solvent.

Remarks

1. 80% acetone and extraction over shorter periods have been used in the estimation (13). However, 90% acetone is a better solvent for all plankton pigments and the longer standing is essential for complete extraction.

2. Filtration even on the finest papers will undoubtedly lead to a loss of some of the smaller organisms and, if these make up a considerable proportion of the phytoplankton, this will vitiate the result; in general, however, about 90–95% of the phytoplankton will be retained on a Whatman No. 42 paper (12).

3. This method, using a red filter, estimates largely the chlorophylls. In Harvey's original technique (13), the colour of the extract was compared with artificial standards of potassium chromate and nickel sulphate. One 'Harvey unit' consisted of 1 ml. of a solution of 25 mg. K_2CrO_4 and 430 mg. of $NiSO_4.6H_2O$ in one litre of distilled water. Atkins and Parke (3) have pointed out that it is better to dissolve nickel wire in sulphuric acid for the second component of this artificial standard because the water of crystallization in nickel sulphate is variable. Various comparisons have been made between Harvey units and chlorophyll solutions (2, 3, 4, 12, 19); 1 unit equivalent to 0·3 μg. chlorophyll seems to be the best available estimate. The Harvey unit is not strictly a chlorophyll unit and transmittancies are best compared with a calibration curve prepared from pure chlorophyll (19, 27).

4. The magnesium carbonate (not used by some workers) should be added to prevent the development of acidity, with resultant changes in pigment composition.

5. Atkins and Parke (3) have given some data for the chlorophyll content of a number of organisms obtained from pure cultures and counted before pigment extraction.

TABLE I

Number of cells giving 1 mg. chlorophyll (3).

Coscinodiscus centralis	74×10^3
Thalassiosira gravida	123×10^6
Nitzschia closterium var. minutissima	743×10^6
Dicrateria inornata	563×10^6
Hemiselmis rufescens	3260×10^6
Chlamydomonas I	202×10^6
Chlamydomonas III	109×10^6
Chlorella I	2400×10^6
Gymnodinium sp.	58×10^6

6. Attention should be drawn to the fact that direct filtration separates both living material and the detritus and that the latter contains considerable quantity of chlorophyll. Krey (16) and Gillbricht (8) have considered this question and given values for the chlorophyll content of the various fractions separated by filtration (*see also* Gorshkova, 11, and Fox, 6). There is an increased tendency to try to determine the living content of the micro-plankton by chemical methods (Aleem, 1; Krey, 15).

ESTIMATION OF SEVERAL PIGMENTS

When a spectrophotometer is available, transmittancy measurements at several wave-lengths may be made on the same sample. If the absorption curves for the constituent components are known, then, by solving a set of simultaneous equations, the concentrations of the several components may be determined. Measurements are required at the same number of wave-lengths as the number of components which it is desired to compute, and each measurement should be made where the absorption of one of the components is high. In the case of plankton extracts, substances other than the chlorophylls and carotenoids frequently give high absorption values in the range 320–430 mμ and this region should not be used.

There is a considerable literature on plant pigments; Richards and Richards and Thompson (17, 18) have summarized and extended the pertinent data for marine plankton. Their data are set out in Tables 40–45 (pp. 319–24).

Procedure

The pigments may be extracted as described above.

Richards and Thompson, however, recommend the use of a Foerst centrifuge. Add 0·1 g. of the powdered magnesium carbonate to a 1- or 2-litre sample; shake and pass through a Foerst Plankton Centrifuge. (Drs Creitz and Richards report that separation on molecular filters gives quantitative separation for particles greater than 0·8 μ.) Transfer the residue to an ordinary centrifuge tube with a little water and centrifuge at high speed for 3 minutes. Pour off the supernatant and dry the residue in a vacuum desiccator. Failure to dry the plankton sample thoroughly will lead to turbidities and incorrect estimates of the quantity of chlorophyll. Add 5 ml. or the appropriate quantity of aqueous acetone (90%), stopper, shake and allow to stand for 18–24 hours. Again centrifuge and then transfer a suitable quantity of the supernatant to an optical cell (1, 5 or 10 cm. length). Measure the transmittancies at 665, 645, 630, 510, and 480 mμ in a spectrophotometer; a red-sensitive photocell should be used for the readings at the first three wave-lengths and a blue-sensitive tube for those at 510 and 480 mμ. A check at 750 mμ is suggested (Drs Creitz and Richards personal communication) for turbidity since at this wave-length the pigments have very little absorption.

Calculations

For the estimation of the chlorophylls, we have

$$A_{665}=0 \cdot 0667C_a+0 \cdot 0065C_b+0 \cdot 0011C_c,$$
$$A_{645}=0 \cdot 0164C_a+0 \cdot 0456C_b+0 \cdot 0044C_c,$$
$$A_{630}=0 \cdot 0119C_a+0 \cdot 0127C_b+0 \cdot 0104C_c,$$

where A_λ is the calculated absorbancy at the wave-lengths indicated, C_a, and C_b are the concentrations of chlorophylls a and b in mg./l., and C_c is that for chlorophyll c expressed in m S.P.U./l (see p. 244).

$$C_a=15 \cdot 6A_{665}-2 \cdot 0A_{645}-0 \cdot 8A_{630},$$
$$C_b=25 \cdot 4A_{645}-4 \cdot 4A_{665}-10 \cdot 3A_{630},$$
$$C_c=109A_{630}-12 \cdot 5A_{665}-28 \cdot 7A_{645}.$$

The results should be multiplied by the appropriate factor, taking into account the volume of solvent used and that of the original water sample.

The concentrations of the carotenoid components are obtained by first subtracting the contribution of the chlorophylls to give the residual absorbancies; then,

$$A_{\text{resid. } 510}=A_{510}-0 \cdot 0026C_a-0 \cdot 0035C_b-0 \cdot 0021C_c$$
$$=0 \cdot 45C_{nac}+0 \cdot 169C_{ac},$$
$$A_{\text{resid. } 480}=A_{480}-0 \cdot 0019C_a-0 \cdot 0136C_b-0 \cdot 0054C_c$$
$$=0 \cdot 203C_{nac}+0 \cdot 249C_{ac}.$$

Where C_{nac} and C_{ac} are the respective concentrations of the non-astacin type and astacin type carotenoids in m S.P.U./l.; solving, we have

$$C_{ac}=2(4 \cdot 45A_{\text{resid. } 510}-A_{\text{resid. } 480}),$$
$$C_{nac}=7 \cdot 6(A_{\text{resid. } 480}-1 \cdot 49A_{\text{resid. } 510}).$$

Remarks

1. Calculation of the individual components of the carotenoid fraction was found impracticable since too many equations must be

solved and the errors are cumulative: furthermore, the type of carotenoid components depend upon the species present.

2. The absorption spectra of the common components are given in Tables 40–45. For chlorophylls and β-carotene the values are given as logarithmic values of the absorbancy index.

$$\log E = \log \frac{A}{b.c} = \log \frac{A}{c} \qquad \text{(since } b=1 \text{ cm. path).}$$

For the other components they are expressed in terms of the yellow maximum which was arbitrarily assigned the value 2·400.

In calculating the concentrations, the absorbancy indices are used for chlorophylls a and b and β-carotene. Chlorophyll c and xanthophylls are expressed in so-called specified pigment units (S.P.U.) which are defined so that one such unit in a litre of 90% acetone has, at the wave-length of maximum absorption, the absorbancy shown in Table 44. These absorbancies were chosen equal (or nearly so) to the absorbancy indices of corresponding maxima in the spectra of related compounds (21–23) so that the S.P.U. represents a specific but undetermined weight of pigment which should be about 1 g. For those pigments whose absorbancy indices are unknown the S.P.U. has been used instead of the gram in calculating the specified absorbancy index. Since the xanthophyllic components are not separated, average values for their absorbancy index should be calculated.

These are given as follows:

at 420 mμ $A^{\text{S.P.U.}}_{1\,\text{cm.}}$ Total non-astacin carotenoids$=171$,

at 450 mμ $A^{\text{S.P.U.}}_{1\,\text{cm.}}$ Total non-astacin carotenoids$=246$,

at 480 mμ $A^{\text{S.P.U.}}_{1\,\text{cm.}}$ Total non-astacin carotenoids$=203$,

at 510 mμ $A^{\text{S.P.U.}}_{1\,\text{cm.}}$ Total non-astacin carotenoids$=\ \ 45$.

For the astacin pigments a value of 251 in S.P.U. at 474 mμ is used; these values are those used in preceding equations.

REFERENCES

1. Aleem, A. A., 1955. 'Measurement of plankton populations by triphenyltetrazolium chloride.' *Kiel. Meeresforsch.*, **11**, 160–73.
2. Atkins, W. R. G., and Jenkins, P. G., 1953. 'Seasonal changes in the phytoplankton during the year 1951–2 as indicated by spectrophotometric chlorophyll estimations.' *J. Mar. biol. Ass. U.K.*, **31**, 495–508.
3. ——, and Parke, M., 1951. 'Seasonal changes in the phytoplankton as indicated by chlorophyll estimations.' *J. Mar. biol. Ass. U.K.*, **29**, 609–18.

4. Fleming, R. H., 1939. 'Composition of plankton and units for reporting populations and production.' *Proc. 6th Pac. Sci. Cong.*, **3**, 535–40.

5. Fox, D. L., 1947. 'Carotenoid and indolic biochromes of animals.' *Ann. Rev. Biochem.*, 443–70.

6. ——, 1953. *Animal Biochromes and Structural Colours.* University Press, Cambridge, 379 pp.

7. Gardiner, A. C., 1943. 'Measurement of phytoplankton population by the pigment extraction method.' *J. Mar. biol. Ass. U.K.*, **25**, 739–44.

8. Gillbricht, M., 1951. 'Untersuchungen zur Produktions-biologie des Planktons in der Kieler Bucht.' *Kiel. Meeresforsch.*, **8**, 173–91.

9. Goodwin, T. W., 1950. 'Carotenoids and reproduction.' *Biol. Rev.*, **25**, 391–413.

10. ——, 1952. *The Comparative Biochemistry of the Carotenoids.* Chapman and Hall, Ltd., London, 356 pp.

11. Gorschkova, T., 1938. 'Organisches Stoff in den Sedimenten des Motovskij Busens.' *Trans. Inst. Mar. Fish. Oceanog. U.S.S.R.*, **5**, 71–84.

12. Graham, H. W., 1943. 'Chlorophyll content of marine plankton.' *J. Mar. Res.*, **5**, 153–60.

13. Harvey, H. W., 1934. 'Measurement of phytoplankton population.' *J. Mar. biol. Ass. U.K.*, **19**, 761–73.

14. Kalle, K., 1951. 'Meereskundlich-chemische Untersuchungen mit Hilfe des Pulfrich-Photometers von Zeiss. VII. Mitteilung. Die Mikrobestimmungen des Chlorophylls und der Eigenfluoreszenz des Meerwassers.' *Dtsch. hydrogr. Z.*, **4**, 92–6.

15. Krey, J., 1939. 'Die Bestimmung des Chlorophylls in Meerwasser-Schöpfproben.' *J. Cons. int. Explor. Mer*, **14**, 201–9.

16. ——, 1952. 'Die Untersuchung des Eiweissgehaltes in kleinen Planktonproben.' *Kiel. Meeresforsch.*, **8**, 164–72.

17. Richards, F. A., 1952. 'The estimation and characterization of plankton populations by pigment analysis. I. The absorption spectra of some pigments occurring in diatoms, dinoflagellates and brown algae.' *J. Mar. Res.*, **11**, 147–55.

18. —— with Thompson, T. G., 1952. 'The estimation and characterization of plankton populations by pigment analysis. II. A spectrographic method for the estimation of plankton pigments.' *J. Mar. Res.*, **11**, 156–72.

19. Riley, G. A., 1938. 'The measurement of phytoplankton.' *Int. Rev. Hydrobiol.*, **36**, 371–3.

20. Steele, C. C., 1937. 'Recent progress in determining the chemical structure of chlorophyll.' *Chem. Rev.*, **20**, 1–40.

21. Strain, H. H., 1938. *Leaf Xanthophylls.* Publ. Carneg. Instn, No. 490, 159 pp.

22. ——, and Manning, W. M., 1942. 'Chlorofucins (Chlorophyll *c*) a green pigment of diatoms and algae.' *J. biol. Chem.*, **144**, 625–36.

23. ——, ——, and Hardin, G., 1944. 'Xanthophylls and carotenes of diatoms, brown algae, dinoflagellates and sea anemones.' *Biol. Bull., Woods Hole*, **86**, 169–89.

24. Tucker, A., 1949. 'Pigment extraction as a method of quantitative analysis of phytoplankton.' *Trans. Amer. micr. Soc.*, **68**, 21–33.

25. Whitford, L. A., 1947. 'A study of some algal pigments.' *J. Elisha Mitchell sci. Soc.*, **63**, 155–62.

26. Zscheile, F. P., Jr., 1934. 'A quantitative spectro photo-electrical analytical method applied to solutions of chlorophyll a and b. *J. phys. Chem.*, **38**, 95–102.

27. ——, Comar, C. L., and Mackinney, G., 1942. 'Inter-laboratory comparison of absorption spectra by the photoelectric spectro-photometric method. Determination on chlorophyll and Weigert's solutions.' *Plant Physiol.*, **17**, 666–70.

28. ——, and Polgar, A., 1943. 'Cis-trans isomerisation and spectral characteristics of carotenoids and some related compounds.' *J. Amer. chem. Soc.*, **65**, 1522–8.

20

FILTRATION

Suspended matter, finely particulate and colloidal, organic and inorganic is present to some extent in sea water from all localities (2, 5). Recent work has stressed the importance of some knowledge of this leptopel, as it has been termed, for both oceanographical and marine biological studies. Leptopel ranges in size from small colloidal micelles to visible particulate matter. These studies are of importance in any consideration of:

1. Regeneration of plant nutrients from decaying organic matter.
2. The physical and chemical characters of sediments, and the chemical and biochemical reactions occurring within them.
3. The direct utilization of suspended matter by 'filter' feeding organisms.
4. The optical properties of sea water.

Separation of the Leptopel

The leptopel may be separated by filtration. Filter papers are not satisfactory for critical work since only an approximate figure can be given for their pore size. Membrane filters are available with a stated maximum pore size (3) and more recently so-called molecular filters and absorption materials have been introduced into this type of work (5, 6, 7, 8). Molecular filters are composed of incompletely cross-linked high polymer molecules of partially substituted cellulose acetate and can be prepared with a uniform pore size ranging from 0·5 to 5000 μ. These molecular filters are anisomorphous; the upper surface has a uniform pore size but the body of the filter which supports this upper layer is much more porous, and the overall flow rate is, therefore, more rapid than with papers or adsorptive powders: dependent on the pore size 1 litre will pass through in 5–30 minutes. In use they are generally mounted in a holder which is fastened on to a coarse filter.

Use of the Filter for Microscopic Examination of Plankton (5)

To a freshly collected litre of sea water add 40 ml. of potassium iodide solution saturated with iodine to kill and fix the organisms. Stand for 1 hour and then pass through the selected molecular filter. Gradually wash off excess fixative with graded dilutions of sea and distilled water from 5 to 100%. Add 20 ml. of Fast Green (5) and leave in contact with membrane for 30 minutes. Suck through excess dye and again wash with distilled water. Dehydrate the organisms with successive washes of 5, 10, 25, 50, 75, 90 and 100% v/v distilled ethanol-water mixtures sucking through as rapidly as possible to avoid dissolution of the membrane. Render the water-free membrane transparent with cedar wood oil by drawing through it serial dilutions of 10, 25, 50 and 100% cedar wood oil in ethanol. The membrane may then be mounted directly in Canada balsam. All reagents should be passed through a molecular filter before use.

These filters may be used to separate the inorganic particles, which may also be examined under the microscope or submitted to chemical tests whilst still on the filter or after further treatment. Since the filters are ashless, ignition of the filter disc and particulate matter will give the total ash content of the sample. The filters are not only ashless but have a weight of about 95 mg. reproducible to ± 0.2 mg. after repeated washing and drying at about 100°C.

Collection by Adsorption (6)

Instead of using ultra-filter membranes the finely suspended matter may be quantitatively removed by passing through a thin layer of adsorptive inorganic material.

Fox *et al.* (6) have found that a mixture of pure powdered magnesium oxide and silica in equal parts by weight (Hyflo-Supercell) is very effective.

It is necessary to use sufficient absorbent for the amount of material in suspension and a layer of the mixture (1–2 g.) is best packed 6–8 mm. deep in a standard sinter glass crucible. The crucible is prepared as follows.

Fit the sinter glass crucible into a standard adaptor and attach to a suction flask. To prevent the pores of the sinter glass from becoming clogged, lay a disc of Whatman No. 50 filter paper over the sinter glass, pour on water and fit smoothly. A layer or circle of fibre glass is then laid on and sucked into place to prevent contamination of the adsorbent by organic matter from the filter paper. Prepare a suspension of the adsorbent in distilled water, pour on to the fibre glass and allow to settle. Draw through the water to pack the adsorbent in position. Do *not* suck dry until ready for use.

Water samples should be collected in water-repellent plastic bottles, primed if necessary with a little adsorbent suspension. 0·1 g./l. of mercuric chloride may be added as preservative.

REFERENCES

1. American Public Health Association and others, 1955. *Standard Methods for the Examination of Water, Sewage and Industrial Wastes.* Amer. Publ. Health Ass. Inc., New York, 10th Ed., 1955, 522 pp. *See* pp. 395–404.
2. Armstrong, F. A. J., and Atkins, W. R. G., 1950. 'The suspended matter of sea water.' *J. Mar. biol. Ass. U.K.*, **29**, 139–43.
3. Ferry, J. D., 1936. 'Ultrafilter membranes and ultrafiltration. *Chem. Rev.*, **18**, 373–455.
4. Fox, D. L., 1950. 'Comparative metabolism of organic debris by inshore animals.' *Ecology*, **31**, 100–8.
5. ——, Isaacs, J. D., and Corcoran, E. F., 1952. 'Marine leptopel, its recovery measurement and distribution.' *J. Mar. Res.*, **11**, 29–46.
6. ——, Oppenheimer, C. H., and Kittredge, J. S., 1953. 'Micro-filtration in marine research. II. Retention of colloidal micelles by adsorptive filters and by filter feeding invertebrates; proportions of dispersed to organic matter and to organic solutes.' *J. Mar. Res.*, **12**, 233–43.
7. Goetz, A., and Tsuneishi, N., 1951. 'The application of molecular filter membranes to the bacteriological analysis of water.' *J. Amer. Wat. Wks. Ass.*, **43**, 943–69.
8. Goldberg, E. D., Baker, M., and Fox, D. L., 1952. 'Micro-filtration in marine research. I. Marine sampling with the molecular filter.' *J. Mar. Res.*, **11**, 194–204.
9. Jerlov, N. G., 1951. 'Optical measurement of particle distribution in the sea.' *Tellus*, **3**, 122–8.

21

THE PHYSICAL AND CHEMICAL
EXAMINATION OF SEDIMENTS

The complete description of a sediment sample involves not only chemical and physical analysis but also a complete mineralogical examination including the determination of the component minerals —their size, shape and quantity. This has been stressed by Professor K. O. Emery who points out that the examination of a sediment should not, as is so often the case, be restricted to a mechanical (particle size) analysis; much more is required as geological investigations cease to be merely descriptive. It will not be possible to deal with all the appropriate methods; they have, in any case, been dealt with in a comprehensive manner in a number of text-books on sediment and soil analysis. Some of these are listed on p. 267, together with a number of recent papers to which Professor Emery has drawn attention.

Nevertheless, the particle size composition of recent sediments and a number of chemical properties, e.g. organic matter and calcium carbonate content, appear to be of direct importance in some current biological problems. After discussion with a number of workers many of whom favour the inclusion, an outline of the methods used is given.

GRADE SCALES

A sediment usually contains a continuous size-frequency distribution of particles. For convenience and descriptive purposes this may be divided into a set of grades or class intervals defined by certain size limits. The choice of such grades is arbitrary but an attempt may be made to form natural groups which to some extent correspond to certain properties of a sediment. No grade scale is universally recognized.

The Atterberg scale (4) was an attempt to base the class intervals on the physical properties of size groups; it was adopted by the International Commission on Soil Science and is widely used by European workers. The class interval was based on the unit value 2 mm. and involved a fixed ratio of 10 for each successive grade. Each of these major grades was divided into two sub-grades chosen at the geometric mean of the grade limits; thus the 20–2 mm. grade is split at 6·32 mm. rounded to 6·00. The scale is given in Table I.

TABLE I

Atterberg's size classification

Grade limits, (diameter, mm.)	Name	Character
2000–200	Blocks ⎫	Not water
200–20	Cobbles ⎬	holding
20–2	Pebbles ⎭	
2–0·2	Coarse sand ⎱	Water holding
0·2–0·02	Fine sand ⎰	
0·02–0·002	Silt	Microscopic particles
Below 0·002	Clay	Brownian movement

This scale has not been adopted by the U.S. Bureau of Soils and is rarely used by American workers. They prefer the Udden scale as modified by Wentworth (Table II). This is based on a fixed geometric interval, each size group limit being twice the one below; closer intervals are obtained by using the ratio $\sqrt{2}$ or $4\sqrt{2}$ instead of 2.

TABLE II

Udden-Wentworth size classification

Grade limits (diameter, mm.)	Name
Above 256	Boulders
256–64	Cobbles
64–4	Pebbles
4–2	Granules
2–1	Very coarse sand
1–0·5	Coarse sand
0·5–0·25	Medium sand
0·25–0·125	Fine sand
0·125–0·0625	Very fine sand
0·0625–0·0039	Silt
Below 0·0039	Clay

The sieve openings of the A.S.T.M. sieves (*see* p. 254) comply with the Udden-Wentworth Scale.

Other grade scales, for example that of Robinson (15), are based directly on the settling velocity or its logarithmic value; an advantage of these is that no difficulties are introduced in view of the irregular shape of the particles. Unequal geometric intervals may be converted into equal arithmetic intervals of a transformed value, thus Krumbein (10, 11; *see also* Inman, 9) has applied a logarithmic transformation to the Wentworth and Atterberg scales giving the so-called ϕ and ζ scales (Table III), where

$$\phi = -\log_2 d$$

and

$$\zeta = 0\cdot301 - \log_{10} d,$$

where d is the diameter in millimetres.

TABLE III

Phi and zeta grade scales

Wentworth grades, mm.	ϕ	Atterberg grades, mm.	ζ
32	−5	2000	−3
16	−4	200	−2
8	−3	20	−1
4	−2	2	0
2	−1	0·2	+1
1	0	0·02	+2
1/2	+1	0·002	+3
1/4	+2	0·0002	+4
1/8	+3		
1/16	+4		
1/32	+5		
1/64	+6		
1/128	+7		
1/256	+8		
1/512	+9		
1/1024	+10		

It cannot be too strongly emphasized that grade scales are arbitrary; the limits chosen for a grade and the descriptive terminology are matters of convenience and mutual agreement. When using the results of a mechanical analysis to study the continuous distribution function, class intervals are again purely arbitrary but convenient units are desirable: the Atterberg and Wentworth grade scales are sufficiently flexible for both purposes.

THE PRINCIPLES OF MECHANICAL ANALYSIS

For a normal sediment the various size groups are separated by different methods. The coarser material is separated by sieving and the size may be expressed in terms of the mesh size of the sieves. The mesh sizes which correspond to the Wentworth grades in the A.S.T.M. sieves are shown in heavy type (Table V). The finer particles are separated by the settling velocities either by direct pipetting or by decantation. Since the particles are not spheres the results are expressed in terms of spherical particles which would settle at the observed velocity.

SIEVES AND SIEVING

Coarse materials such as sands are usually analysed by sieving. For convenience the line between coarse and fine sediments may be taken at a particle size of 1/16 mm., i.e. the lower limit of sand in Wentworth's classification.

Sieves are usually made from wire cloth with definitely spaced openings. However, there are several types in use with both square and round holes; neither is in point of fact capable of sharply differentiating particle sizes since the shape and manner of passing through the openings plays an important part. It is, therefore, necessary to use standard sieves.

Tyler Sieve Series

This is a standard American series. The series is based on the size of the opening in 200-mesh cloth namely 0·0029 in. and the scale consists of sieves whose openings are in a fixed ratio of $\sqrt{2}$. The main series is shown in Table IV. Intermediate sieves can be obtained.

TABLE IV

Tyler Standard Screen Scale Sieves

Mesh no.	Opening		Wire diameter in.
	mm.	in.	
—	26·67	1·050	0·148
—	22·43	0·883	0·135
—	18·85	0·742	0·135
—	15·85	0·624	0·120
—	13·33	0·525	0·105
—	11·20	0·441	0·105
—	9·423	0·371	0·092
2½	7·925	0·312	0·088
3	6·680	0·263	0·070
3½	5·613	0·221	0·065
4	4·699	0·185	0·065
5	3·962	0·156	0·044
6	3·327	0·131	0·036
7	2·794	0·110	0·0328
8	2·362	0·093	0·032
9	1·981	0·078	0·033
10	1·651	0·065	0·035
12	1·397	0·055	0·028
14	1·168	0·046	0·025
16	0·991	0·0390	0·0235
20	0·833	0·0328	0·0172
24	0·701	0·0276	0·0141
28	0·589	0·0232	0·0125
32	0·495	0·0195	0·0118
35	0·417	0·0164	0·0122
42	0·351	0·0138	0·0100
48	0·295	0·0116	0·0092
60	0·246	0·0097	0·0070
65	0·208	0·0082	0·0072
80	0·175	0·0069	0·0056
100	0·147	0·0058	0·0042
115	0·124	0·0049	0·0038
150	0·104	0·0041	0·0026
170	0·088	0·0035	0·0024
200	0·074	0·0029	0·0021

The U.S. Series of Sieves

This series, recommended by the U.S. National Bureau of Standards and adopted by the A.S.T.M., differs only slightly from the Tyler Series. The sieve with a millimetre opening is adopted as standard and the size again changes by $\sqrt{2}$ (Table V).

TABLE V

U.S. Series, A.S.T.M. Standards

Mesh no.	Opening mm.	in. (app.)	Wire diameter mm.
3½	5·66	0·233	1·28– 1·90
4	4·76	0·187	1·14 –1·68
5	4·00	0·157	1·00 –1·47
6	3·36	0·132	0·87 –1·32
7	2·83	0·111	0·80 –1·20
8	2·38	0·0937	0·74 –1·10
10	2·00	0·0787	0·68 –1·00
12	1·68	0·0661	0·62 –0·90
14	1·41	0·0555	0·56 –0·80
16	1·19	0·0469	0·50 –0·70
18	1·00	0·0394	0·43 –0·62
20	0·84	0·0331	0·38 –0·55
25	0·71	0·0280	0·33 –0·48
30	0·59	0·0232	0·29 –0·42
35	0·50	0·0197	0·26 –0·37
40	0·42	0·0165	0·23 –0·33
45	0·35	0·0138	0·20 –0·29
50	0·297	0·0117	0·170–0·253
60	0·250	0·0098	0·149–0·220
70	0·210	0·0083	0·130–0·187
80	0·177	0·0070	0·114–0·154
100	0·149	0·0059	0·096–0·125
120	0·125	0·0049	0·079–0·103
140	0·105	0·0041	0·063–0·087
170	0·088	0·0035	0·054–0·073
200	0·074	0·0029	0·045–0·061
230	0·062	0·0024	0·039–0·052
270	0·053	0·0021	0·035–0·046
325	0·044	0·0017	0·031–0·040
400	0·037	0·0015	0·023–0·035

The British I.M.M. Sieve Series (Table VI)

This was developed on the theory that the diameter of the wire should be equal to the size of the opening in order to prevent the wires from shifting; this is not necessary with modern sieves.

TABLE VI
I.M.M. Sieve Series

Mesh no.	Opening	
	mm.	in. (app.)
5	2·540	0·1000
8	1·574	0·0620
10	1·270	0·0500
12	1·056	0·0416
16	0·792	0·0312
20	0·635	0·0250
25	0·508	0·0200
30	0·422	0·0166
35	0·416	0·0164
40	0·317	0·0125
50	0·254	0·0100
60	0·211	0·0083
70	0·180	0·0071
80	0·157	0·0062
90	0·139	0·0055
100	0·127	0·0050
120	0·107	0·0042
150	0·084	0·0033
200	0·063	0·0025

The series is, however, widely used although it has been to some extent superseded by the British Engineering Standards Association Series (Table VII).

TABLE VII
The B.E.S.A. Sieve Series

Mesh no.	Opening		Wire diameter in.	Equivalent Tyler mesh no.
	mm.	in.		
5	3·353	0·1320	0·068	6
6	2·812	0·1107	0·056	7
7	2·410	0·0949	0·048	8
8	2·057	0·0810	0·044	9
10	1·676	0·0660	0·034	10
12	1·405	0·0553	0·028	12
14	1·204	0·0474	0·024	14
16	1·003	0·0395	0·023	16
18	0·853	0·0336	0·022	20
22	0·699	0·0275	0·018	24
25	0·599	0·0236	0·0164	28
30	0·500	0·0197	0·0136	32
36	0·422	0·0166	0·0112	35
44	0·353	0·0139	0·0088	42
52	0·295	0·0116	0·0076	48
60	0·251	0·0099	0·0068	60
72	0·211	0·0083	0·0056	65
85	0·178	0·0070	0·0048	80
100	0·152	0·0060	0·0040	100
120	0·124	0·0049	0·0034	115
150	0·104	0·0041	0·0026	150
170	0·0889	0·0035	0·0024	170
200	0·0762	0·0030	0·0020	200
240	0·0660	0·0026	0·0016	250

The openings follow closely the Tyler Series.

Sieving Efficiency

The material on the sieve must be moved about in order to get it to pass through the meshes; this may be done by hand or by a mechanical shaker or vibrator. Normally, sieves are provided with flanges and a set may be mounted one above the other with the coarsest at the top and a retaining vessel at the bottom; the whole set is shaken together. A simple shaker may be easily constructed. There has been some work on the efficiency of sieving and its variation with the type of motion in respect to the duration of sieving. When an automatic shaker is used a time of 10 minutes is usually given. If in doubt about the completeness of sieving the sieve should be shaken over a sheet of glazed paper.

Usually a sample of 25 g. is adequate. After shaking, the contents of each sieve are transferred to a sheet of glazed paper if necessary brushing down the meshes with a camel-hair brush, and then transferred to receptacles for weighing.

EXPRESSION OF RESULTS

Although parts of the analysis are always made on the air-dry material, the results are usually expressed in terms of oven-dry (105° C.) material. A separate estimation of the factor required for this conversion is made by drying a sample of the thoroughly mixed material to constant weight at 105° C.

LOSS ON ACID TREATMENT

This gives the content of salts and carbonate.

Reagents

1. *About 2 N hydrochloric acid.* 75 ml. of concentrated hydrochloric acid diluted to 1 litre with distilled water.

2. *About 0·2 N hydrochloric acid.* Dilute the above 2 N acid tenfold.

Procedure

Transfer 10 g. of the air-dry sediment to a 250 ml. beaker and add 100 ml. of 2 N hydrochloric acid; allow to stand for 1 hour. (If the sediment contains more than 2% calcium carbonate add more acid; an additional quantity of 1 ml. of 2 N hydrochloric acid for each additional 1% calcium carbonate is required.) Filter off the residue on a No. 44 Whatman filter paper (previously dried and weighed in a weighing bottle at 105° C.), and wash with successive portions of 40 ml., 20 ml. and 20 ml. of 0·2 N hydrochloric acid; wash with distilled water until the filtrate is almost neutral. Drain, transfer the filter paper and contents to the weighing bottle and dry at 105° C. for 24 hours. Calculate the loss on an oven-dry basis.

THE MECHANICAL ANALYSIS OF A SEDIMENT

For many purposes it is not necessary to set up the complete size-frequency curve for the sediment, but only to grade it. The following method, recommended by the International Society of Soil Science is based on Atterberg's Scale (*see*, however, Remarks) and separates the grades according to Table VIII.

TABLE VIII

(From Piper, 2)

Fraction	Maximum diameter mm.	Upper limit definition	Equivalent settling velocity at 20° C. cm./sec.
Stones	>2·0	—	—
Coarse Sand	2·0	2 mm. round-holed sieve	347
Fine Sand	0·2	70-mesh I.M.M. sieve	3·47
Silt	0·02	Sedimentation velocity 10 cm./4·8 min.	0·0347
Clay	0·002	Sedimentation velocity 10 cm./8 hrs.	0·00347

Apparatus

1. *Shaking machine.* An end-over-end shaking machine working at about 15 revolutions per minute is to be preferred. If only a limited number of samples are to be analysed and a machine is not available a bicycle wheel driven by a suitably geared electric motor may be used: bottles containing soil suspensions may be conveniently attached to the spokes.

2. *A motor dispersion unit.* An ordinary electrical stirrer (1/50 h.p.) fitted with a stainless steel double-bladed propeller is suitable. A unit may be constructed from a stand on which the motor is mounted and whose recessed base holds a 600 ml. beaker. A set of baffle plates should be available, which fit into the beaker and tend to oppose the mass rotation of the fluid and to break up the particles.

3. *Sieves.* A 2 mm. round-holed sieve and a No. 70 I.M.M. sieve (0·180 mm. openings, equivalent to No. 85 B.E.S.A. sieve=No. 80 Tyler sieve, *see* Tables IV, V, VI and VII) are required. The metal gauze should be stretched lightly over the supporting frame, which conveniently tapers in its lower part. Sieves should always be carefully handled to avoid undue wear; the meshes, which are easily strained, should be examined from time to time under a microscope.

4. *Sedimentation cylinder.* Gas jars, (graduate cylinders), 40 cm. high, about 6·5 cm. internal diameter and capable of holding at least 1250 ml. liquid are used: the 1250 ml. level should not be less than 25 mm. nor more than 75 mm. from the top of the cylinder. If many samples are to be analysed as a routine procedure the cylinders should be matched with the shaking device; otherwise it may be necessary to use separate containers for shaking the suspension.

5. *Suction regulating device.* In taking a suspension from a sedimentation cylinder a suction pump should be used, and to ensure a steady gentle suction of the pipette, it is best to insert an aspirator between the pump and pipette; the aspirator is first evacuated and then after shutting off from the pump is used to suck off the suspension.

The pipettes should be fitted, at the appropriate height, to a cork block which will rest across the top of the sedimentation cylinder.

6. *Pipettes.* These should have long stems and deliver 20 ml. at 20°C. For the first sample (silt+clay) the lower stem should be 39 cm. long with a mark 28 cm. from the tip. For the second sample (clay) the lower stem should be 32 cm. long with a mark at 22 cm. from the tip.

Reagents

1. *About 2 N hydrochloric acid.* 75 ml. of concentrated hydrochloric acid diluted to 1 litre with distilled water.

2. *About 0·2 N hydrochloric acid.* Dilute the above 2 N acid tenfold.

3. *Sodium hexametaphosphate* $(NaPO_3)_6$. 6·2 g./l. aqueous solution.

4. *Hydrogen peroxide.* 6% aqueous solution.

Procedure

If a sub-sample from a larger quantity of material is to be analysed the primary sample should first be thoroughly mixed in any convenient way.

1. *Hydrogen peroxide treatment.* Transfer 25 g. of air-dry sediment to an 800 ml. beaker and add 50–60 ml. of 6% hydrogen peroxide; allow to stand overnight and then heat gently on the water bath. If the sediment contains large quantities of organic matter repeat the heating with extra additions of hydrogen peroxide until there is no further reaction. Only rarely is a third addition of hydrogen peroxide necessary. If the sediment contains manganese dioxide (which decomposes the hydrogen peroxide before it reacts with the humic material) add 100 ml. of water and 0·5–2·0 g. of sodium bisulphite and boil down to about 50 ml. before peroxide treatment.

2. *Acid treatment and washing.* When the contents of the beaker are cold, rub down the sides and add 25 ml. of 2 N hydrochloric acid

(if the sediment contains more than 2% calcium carbonate add an extra 2·5 ml. of 2 N acid for each 1%). Thoroughly rub the soil and acid together with a rubber pestle or rubber-covered stirring rod; repeat at intervals. Ensure that the solution is still acid. Transfer the soil on to a filter paper (Whatman No. 50 hardened paper) on a Buchner funnel and wash under gentle suction with four 50 ml. portions of 0·2 N hydrochloric acid, draining the filter between each addition. Wash the residue thoroughly with-distilled water.

3. *Separation of the coarse stones.* Wash the soil from the filter paper on to a 2 mm. round-holed sieve, collecting the washings in a 600 ml. beaker. 200–250 ml. of distilled water should be used, the last traces of sediment from the paper and funnel being removed by a jet of water and a camel-hair brush. Allow the sieve to drain and dry; transfer the coarse stones to a weighed crucible and dry overnight in an oven at 105°C.; cool in a desiccator and weigh. This gives the coarse stone fraction.

4. *First dispersion.* Add 10 ml. of the sodium hexametaphosphate solution to the contents of the beaker, place the baffle plates in position and stir mechanically for 10–15 minutes. Pass the suspension through a 70-mesh I.M.M. sieve into the dispersion bottle or sedimentation cylinder.

5. *Coarse sand fraction.* Allow the material on the 70-mesh sieve to dry; rub lightly and sieve until no more material passes through, collecting anything which passes through the sieve. Transfer the residue on the sieve to a weighed crucible, dry in the oven overnight at 105°C.; cool in a desiccator and weigh. This gives the coarse sand fraction.

6. *Second dispersion.* Shake the suspension passing the 70-mesh I.M.M. sieve on the mechanical shaker for 12–16 hours to complete dispersion.

7. *Silt and clay.* Stand the sedimentation cylinder on the bench (or transfer from shaking bottle to sedimentation cylinder), dilute to the 1250 ml. mark and take the temperature. From Table IX determine the appropriate time at which to take the sediment samples. Stir the suspension steadily but completely with a paddle made from a horizontal brass plate pierced with holes and attached to a long handle. Prepare the 39 cm. pipette and cork block for use at 28 cm. level. Pipette and cylinders should be matched for the two levels (with 1250 ml. of liquid) when a large number of samples are to be analysed; note, the level changes for the second sample due to the withdrawal of the first. Just before the required time, carefully lower the pipette into the suspension with its top closed and fill by gentle suction from the evacuated aspirator; remove the pipette from the suspension, adjust to the mark and deliver the sample into a

weighed crucible. Dry overnight at 105°C.; cool in a desiccator and weigh; this gives the silt and clay.

Leave the sedimentation cylinder to stand as far as possible under uniform temperature conditions; and withdraw a sample at the appropriate time for the clay fraction; treat this as for the silt+clay fraction. If 25 g. of sediment are taken, and the volume of suspension is 1250 ml. then

% silt=(weight of first pipette sample
—weight of second pipette sample)×250,

and

% clay=weight of second pipette sample×250.

TABLE IX

(From Piper, 2)

The time of sedimentation at different temperatures.
International system

Tempera-ture °C.	Fine sand decantation. Depth 10 cm.		First pipette sample. Depth 28 cm.		Second pipette sample			
					Depth 22 cm.		Depth 28 cm.	
	mins.	secs.	mins.	secs.	hrs.	mins.	hrs.	mins.
8	6	40	18	45	24	30	—	—
9	6	30	18	0	23	15	—	—
10	6	20	17	30	23	0	—	—
11	6	10	17	0	22	15	—	—
12	6	0	16	30	21	45	—	—
13	5	50	16	15	21	15	—	—
14	5	40	15	45	20	30	—	—
15	5	30	15	15	20	0	—	—
16	5	20	15	0	19	30	24	45
17	5	10	14	30	19	0	24	15
18	5	0	14	15	18	30	23	30
19	5	0	13	45	18	0	23	0
20	4	48	13	30	17	30	22	30
21	4	40	13	15	17	15	22	0
22	4	30	13	0	16	45	21	30
23	4	30	12	30	—	—	21	0
24	4	20	12	15	—	—	20	30
25	4	15	12	0	—	—	20	0
26	4	10	11	45	—	—	19	30
27	4	5	11	30	—	—	19	0
28	4	0	11	15	—	—	18	30
29	3	55	11	0	—	—	18	15
30	3	50	10	45	—	—	17	45
31	3	45	10	30	—	—	17	30
32	3	40	10	15	—	—	17	0
33	3	35	10	0	—	—	16	45

This value should be corrected for the sodium hexametaphosphate used in the dispersion process and still remaining in solution; note that the second pipette must be adjusted for the change in level due to withdrawal of the first sample.

8. *Fine sand.* After withdrawing the second pipette sample carefully siphon off the suspension to within 3–4 cm. of the bottom of the cylinder using an upturned siphon. Transfer the residue to a tall 500 ml. beaker marked at 10 cm. from the bottom and add any fine sand which passed the 70-mesh sieve when the coarse sand was separated (*see* p. 259). Stand for 10–15 minutes and pour off three-quarters of the supernatant, disturbing the sediment as little as possible. Then reduce the turbidity by filling to the 10 cm. mark, standing for 10–15 minutes and carefully pouring off the supernatant; repeat. Determine the temperature and find the appropriate settling time from Table IX. Fill the beaker to the 10 cm. mark, stir and, after the appropriate time interval, pour off the supernatant without losing any of the material on the bottom of the beaker. Repeat until a negligible amount of material remains in suspension; for the last few decantations the time intervals should come at the mid-point of pouring off. When decantation is complete, transfer the residual fine sand to a weighed crucible, dry in the oven overnight at 105° C.; cool and weigh as fine sand.

Remarks

1. If 25 g. were taken the weight of stones, coarse and fine sand, should be multiplied by four to obtain the percentage.

2. The summation should approximate to 100%.

3. Sodium hexametaphosphate is one of the best dispersing agents. Formerly N sodium hydroxide was used; if the polyphosphate is not available add 10 ml. of N sodium hydroxide (p. 259).

4. For the possibility of dispersing without removing electrolytes or organic matter Reference 18 should be consulted.

5. Professor Emery has pointed out that for many purposes the separation given by the above technique is too coarse. The following fractions are separated in routine analyses in his laboratory:

$$
\left.\begin{array}{l}
2\text{–}1 \text{ mm.} \\
1\text{–}0{\cdot}5 \\
0{\cdot}5\text{–}0{\cdot}25
\end{array}\right\} \text{Sand}
$$

$$
\left.\begin{array}{l}
0{\cdot}25\ \text{–}0{\cdot}125 \\
0{\cdot}125\text{–}0{\cdot}062
\end{array}\right\} \text{Fine sand}
$$

$$\left.\begin{array}{l} 0\cdot062-0\cdot031 \\ 0\cdot031-0\cdot016 \\ 0\cdot016-0\cdot008 \\ 0\cdot008-0\cdot004 \end{array}\right\} \text{Silt}$$

$$\left.\begin{array}{l} 0\cdot004-0\cdot002 \\ 0\cdot002-0\cdot001 \end{array}\right\} \text{Clay}$$

The sand fractions correspond to the Wentworth grades but further sub-fractions are separated in the finer groups on the same scale.

The following Table X is provided for those who wish to make closer separations based on the Wentworth Scale.

TABLE X

Settling times at 20°C.

Diameter mm.	Velocity cm./sec.	Height cm.	Hrs.	Mins.	Secs.
0·0625	0·347	20	0	0	58
0·0442	0·174	20	0	1	56
0·0312	0·0869	10	0	1	56
0·0221	0·0435	10	0	3	52
0·0156	0·0217	10	0	7	44
0·0110	0·0109	10	0	15	—
0·0078	0·00543	10	0	31	—
0·0055	0·00272	10	1	1	—
0·0039	0·00136	10	2	3	—
0·00276	0·00068	10	4	5	—
0·00195	0·00034	10	8	10	—
0·00138	0·000168	10	16	21	—
0·00098	0·000085	5	16	21	—
0·00069	0·000043	5	32	42	—
0·00049	0·000021	5	65	25	—

THE EMERY RAPID METHOD FOR SANDS (5)

When a large number of coarse sands have to be analysed this method may be used in preference to sieving. Once the settling tube has been calibrated an analysis takes only about 5 minutes.

Apparatus (Fig. 43)

A glass tube, 142 cm. long and 2·1 cm. internal diameter, is joined to a shorter tube (15 cm. long and 0·7 cm. internal diameter) graduated in millimetres and fitted with a stop-cock. The bore of the cock should be 6 mm. to prevent any blocking.

Calibration

A sample of sand whose percentage size distribution is known is required. This may be obtained by sieving a series of sands, weighing the fractions and recombining for the calibration sample.

Allow about 3 g. of the calibration sample to fall through the settling tube (*see* Procedure, below).

Take the total height after settlement. Calculate the cumulative height for each size fraction assuming the percentage by volume (here expressed as height) is the same as the percentage by weight. Allow the sample to sediment a second time; take the time required for the volume to reach the cumulative height of each size fraction as calculated. In running an unknown the height reached in these times gives the relative quantities of the stated fractions.

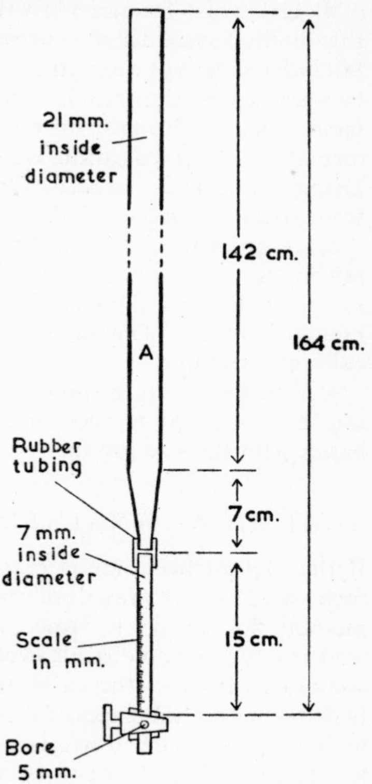

Procedure

Fill the settling tube with distilled water. Introduce about 3 g. of the sample into a 10 cm. length of glass tubing, fill with water and, closing the ends with the fingers, shake to detach air bubbles.

Release the suspension into the settling tube and start stop-watch. Read the height of the sand at the time intervals required for the cumulative fractions to settle as determined in the calibration. If required intermediate readings may be taken in order to establish more points on the sedimentation curve. During the run, tap the measuring tube lightly to prevent sudden compaction of the sand and to give a flat top to the sand column.

Fig. 43. Essential features of Emery's settling tube. (Redrawn from Emery, K. O., *J. sediment. Petrol*, 1938.)

Remarks

1. Emery found the maximum deviation between replicates to be 3% compared with 1% for sieving method.

2. The method requires a little practice particularly the technique of introducing the sample.

3. The amount of sample affects the results in a complex way; an effort should be made to use samples of similar size so that the results

may be comparable. Variations in final height between 4 and 6 cm. give an error of only 2%.

4. Grain-size fractions less than 0·06 mm. cannot be analysed by this method since density currents are set up and the particles do not fall independent of each other. The coarse fraction of a sediment can be analysed by the settling tube after it has been separated by sedimentation. In this case take a weighed quantity (wet to prevent the formation of lumps), transfer to a cylinder and make up to 11 cm. Disperse and allow to settle for 2 minutes; remove the supernatant. Repeat several times. Collect the sand residue for analysis.

5. In order to find the median diameter of a sand sample take the settling time of the mid-point of the sand column. This is best done by interpolation, taking readings every 10 seconds in addition to the regular readings. The median diameter is then read from a size-time calibration graph.

6. The temperature should be kept constant (preferably by working in a constant temperature room) since the temperature effect varies with the size group.

CHEMICAL ANALYSIS: CALCIUM CARBONATE

If the highest accuracy is required Hutchinson and MacLennan's method (2) which was developed for soils should be used. In this method the carbonate is decomposed by cold dilute hydrochloric acid and the carbon dioxide evolved *in vacuo* is absorbed in standard sodium hydroxide; the carbonate is then precipitated with barium hydroxide and the excess alkali back-titrated. Ferrous chloride is used to prevent decarboxylation in certain organic and manganiferous sediments. For consistent results a reasonably high vacuum is necessary.

HUTCHINSON AND MACLENNAN'S METHOD

Apparatus

This is shown in Fig. 44, and consists of a separating funnel (A) whose stem projects to the bottom of a 150 ml., round-bottomed flask. The exit from this flask (B) passes via a tube (C), to (D), a large (1000 ml.) Buchner flask connected to the vacuum pump.

Reagents

1. *Hydrochloric acid.* 100 ml. of concentrated acid diluted to 2 litres.

2. *Hydrochloric acid-ferrous chloride.* Dissolve 3 g. of ferrous chloride ($FeCl_2 . 4H_2O$) in 100 ml. of the above acid just before use.

3. *Barium chloride.* 150 g. $BaCl_2.2H_2O$ per litre.
4. *Standard hydrochloric acid.* 0·1 N.
5. *Standard sodium hydroxide.* 0·1 N.
6. *Indicator.* Thymolphthalein or phenolphthalein.

Procedure (Fig. 44)

If necessary grind the sediment to homogenize; weigh out an amount containing between 0·15 and 0·2 g. of calcium carbonate and transfer to the 150 ml. round-bottomed flask.

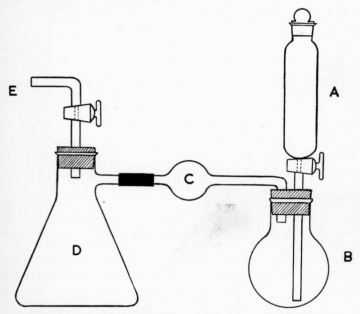

FIG. 44. Apparatus for estimation of carbonates by Hutchinson and MacLennan's method.

Pipette 50 ml. of 0·1 N sodium hydroxide (carbonate free) into the 1000 ml. flask, add 4–5 drops of thymolphthalein (or phenolphthalein) indicator and close the flasks tightly. Evacuate the system by pump as completely as possible and then close all cocks. Transfer 50 ml. of the acid-ferrous chloride solution to the separating funnel and slowly add this into flask (B), avoiding too vigorous a reaction at the start. Close the cock of the funnel leaving a little acid in it to act as a seal.

After a few minutes gently shake the flask; repeat this shaking during 20 minutes to ensure complete decomposition of the carbonate.

Connect the top of the funnel to a supply of carbon-dioxide-free air and gradually draw it in until the vacuum is destroyed. The air is drawn in through the acid soil mixture and helps to sweep out the carbon dioxide. Shake the flask at intervals for a further 20 minutes. Disconnect the litre flask, washing its stopper with carbon-dioxide-free distilled water and add 10 ml. of the barium chloride solution. Titrate the contents of the flask with 0·1 N hydrochloric acid until the indicator just goes colourless. Repeat without the soil for a blank. Then

$$\% \ CaCO_3 = \frac{(\text{ml. HCl for blank} - \text{ml. HCl for sample})}{\text{Weight of sediment taken}} \times 0.5.$$

RAPID DIRECT TITRATION METHOD

If an approximate estimate only is required (to the nearest 1%) a direct titration may be used.

Reagents

1. *Hydrochloric acid.* 1·0 N.
2. *Sodium hydroxide.* 1·0 N.
3. *Indicator.* Bromothymol blue.

Procedure

Weigh out 5 g. of sediment and transfer to a tall 150 ml. beaker. Add rapidly 100 ml. of the N hydrochloric acid, cover with a clock glass and stir vigorously several times during a period of 1 hour.

Allow to settle and pipette off 20 ml. of the supernatant fluid. Transfer to a titration flask, add 6–8 drops of bromothymol blue and titrate with N sodium hydroxide; add more indicator if there is any tendency to fading near the end-point. Carry out a blank estimation.

$$\% \ CaCO_3 = (\text{blank} - \text{titration}) \times 5.$$

Note. The inaccuracy of the titration method is due to attack of non-calcareous matter by the acid and adsorption of hydrogen ions on the colloidal fraction. A method in which these effects are minimized has been developed by Gripenberg (20) and modified by Koczy and Titze (21).

ORGANIC CONTENT

There has been relatively little work on the methods of estimation of the organic matter of marine sediments, and it is, therefore, hardly possible to recommend a relatively simple technique. Clearly, dry combustion if the appropriate precautions are taken (*see* Wright, 3) will give the carbon content, but the method requires considerable apparatus and technical skill; there is also the uncertainty in the conversion factor for carbon to organic matter and when calcareous sediments are dealt with a correction must be applied for the inorganic carbon content. Many workers are content with determining the loss on ignition of the oven-dry sediment. In noncalcareous sediments this may give at least comparable values in similar sediments; the values so obtained will include some bound water. The titration method of Walkley and Black (23, 24) has been much used as a rapid method for soils but is sensitive to the presence of chloride. A study of this method suitably modified for marine sediments and eliminating any interference of chloride would be valuable.

REFERENCES

GENERAL

1. Krumbein, W. C., and Pettijohn, F. J., 1938. *Manual of Sedimentary Petrography*. Appleton-Century-Crofts, Inc., New York, 549 pp.
2. Piper, C. S., 1942. *Soil and Plant Analysis*. The University of Adelaide, Adelaide. Reprinted 1950, by Interscience Publishers Inc., New York, 368 pp.
3. Wright, C. H., 1934. *Soil Analysis. A handbook of physical and chemical methods.* Thomas Murby and Co., London, 2nd Ed., 1939. 276 pp.

ANALYSIS OF PARTICLE SIZE COMPOSITION

4. Atterberg, A., 1905. 'Die rationelle Klassifikation der Sande und Kiese.' *Chem. Ztg.*, **29**, 195–8.
5. Emery, K. O., 1938. 'A rapid method for the mechanical analysis of sands.' *J. sediment. Petrol.*, **8**, 105–11.
6. ——, 1955. 'Marine beach gravels.' *J. Geol.*, **63**, 39–49.
7. ——, and Gould, H. R., 1948. 'A code for expressing grain size distribution.' *J. sediment. Petrol.*, **18**, 14–23.
8. ——, and Stevenson, R. E., 1950. 'Laminated beach sand.' *J. sediment. Petrol.*, **20**, 220–3.
9. Inman, D. L., 1952. 'Measures for describing the size distribution of sediments.' *J. sediment. Petrol.*, **22**, 125–45.
10. Krumbein, W. C., 1934. 'Size frequency distributions of sediments.' *J. sediment. Petrol.*, **4**, 65–77.
11. ——, 1936. 'The application of logarithmic moments to size frequency distributions of sediments.' *J. sediment. Petrol.*, **6**, 35–47.
12. ——, 1941. 'Measurement and geological significance of shape and roundness of sedimentary particles.' *J. sediment. Petrol.*, **11**, 64–72.
13. Rittenhouse, G., 1939. 'The pipette method modified for mass production.' *Rept. Comm. Sediments* (1938–9), 88–102.
14. ——, 1943. 'A visual method of estimating two-dimensional sphericity.' *J. sediment. Petrol.*, **13**, 79–81.

15. Robinson, G. W., 1924. 'The forms of mechanical composition curves of soils, clays and other granular substances.' *J. agric. Sci.*, **14**, 626–33.
16. Sherman, I., 1951. 'A rapid substitute for textural analysis.' *J. sediment. Petrol.*, **21**, 173–7.
17. Sherzer, W. H., 1910. 'Criteria for the recognition of various types of sand grains.' *Bull. geol. Soc. Amer.*, **21**, 625–33.
18. Tchillingarian, G., 1952. 'Study of the dispersing agents.' *J. sediment. Petrol.*, **22**, 229–33.
19. Wentworth, C. K., 1922. 'A scale of grade and class terms for elastic sediments.' *J. Geol.*, **30**, 377–92.

CALCIUM CARBONATE

20. Gripenberg, S., 1953. 'Acidimetric carbonate analysis.' *Göteborgs Vetensk Samh. Handl.*, Ser. B., **6**, No. 9, 32 pp.
21. Koczy, F. F., and Titze, H., 1956. 'Eine rasche Präzisionbestimmung von Kalk in kleinen Sedimentmengen.' *Z. anal. Chem.*, **150**, 100–10.

ORGANIC

22. Allison, L. E., 1935. 'Organic carbon by reduction of chromic acid.' *Soil Sci.*, **40**, 311–20.
23. Walkley, A., 1935. 'An examination of methods for determining organic carbon and nitrogen in soils.' *J. agric. Sci.*, **25**, 598–609.
24. ——, and Black, I. A. 1934. 'An examination of the Degtjareff method for determining soil organic matter, and a proposed modification of the chromic acid titration method.' *Soil Sci.*, **37**, 29–38.

APPENDIX

Publications on analytical work continue unabated. Some are directly relevant to sea-water analysis, others are of less direct interest but should be taken into account. In view of delays during publication it is not possible to be completely up to date in any text. The following reference list (complete up to July 1958) is, therefore, appended.

CHLORINITY: SECTION 4

Christie, A. A., and Newman, O. F., 1955. 'The use of a magnetic stirrer in the determination of the salinity of sea water.' *J. Cons. int. Explor. Mer*, **21**, 1–5.
Honma, M., 1955. 'Flame photometric determination of chloride in sea water.' *Analyt. Chem.*, **27**, 1656–9.
Kalle, K., 1955. 'Ein kreisförmiger Rechenschieber zur Bestimmung des Salzgehaltes bei der Cl'-Titration des Meerwassers.' *Dtsch. hydrogr. Z.*, **8**, 29–30.
Japan, Maritime Safety Board, 1957. 'On the accuracy of determination of end point in the titration of chlorinity of sea water.' *Hydrogr. Bull.*, Publ. 981, **53**, 38–43.
Marvin, K. T., 1957. 'A device for rapid conversion of titration values to salinity.' *Limnol. and Oceanogr.*, **2**, 371–4.
Proctor, C. M., 1956. 'Chlorinity titration.' *Trans. Amer. Geophys. Union*, **37**, 31–7.
Van Landingham, J. W., 1957. 'A modification of the Knudsen method for salinity determination.' *J. Cons. int. Explor. Mer*, **22**, 174–9.

NITROGEN: SECTIONS 6–9

Fukai, R., 1955. 'Critical studies on the analytical methods for minor chemical constituents of sea water. Part 3. Remarks on the method of estimation of nitrate-nitrogen by means of reduced strychnine reagent.' *J. Oceanogr. Soc. Japan*, **11**, 19–23.
Isaeva, A. B., 1956. 'K metodike opredeleniya nitratov o morskoi vode difenilaminnym metodom pri pomoshchi fotoelektricheskogo kolorimetra. (A method of determining nitrates in sea water . . . by means of a photoelectric colorimeter.)' *Trudy Inst. Okeanol.*, **19**, 304–11.
Marvin, K. T., 1955. 'Notes on the precision of a modified routine nitrate-nitrite analysis.' *J. Mar. Res.*, **14**, 79–87.
Morgan, G. B., Lackey, J. B., and Gilcreas, F. W., 1957. 'Quantitative determination of organic nitrogen in water, sewage and industrial wastes.' *Analyt. Chem.*, **29**, 833–5.
Riley, J. P., and Sinhaseni, P., 1957. 'The determination of ammonia and total ionic inorganic nitrogen in sea water.' *J. Mar. biol. Ass. U.K.*, **36**, 161–8.
Ungar, J., 1956. 'Determination of nitrates in aqueous solution.' *J. appl. Chem.*, **6**, 245–7.

Vatova, A., 1956. 'Elektrophotometrische Nitratbestimmung im Meerwasser mit dem Photometer "Elko II".' *Dtsch. hydrogr. Z.*, **9**, 194–8.
——, 1956. 'Il dosaggio dell' azote nitrico nell' acqua di mare con l'elettrofotometro Elko II.' *Nova Thal.*, **2** (5), 5–25.

PHOSPHORUS: SECTIONS 10 AND 11

Fukai, R., 1954. 'Critical studies on the analytical methods for minor chemical constituents in sea water. Part I. On the estimation of phosphate phosphorus.' *J. Oceanogr. Soc. Japan*, **10**, 110–20.
Ishibashi, M., and Tabushi, M., 1957. 'Zur Bestimmung von 2–50 μg. Phosphor in 100–1000 ml. Seewasser.' *Jap. Analyst. Univ. Kyoto*, **6**, 7–11.
Murphy, J., and Riley, J. P., 1956. 'The storage of sea-water samples, for the determination of dissolved inorganic phosphate.' *Analyt. chim. acta*, **14**, 318–19.
——, ——, 1958. 'A single-solution method for the determination of phosphate in sea water.' *J. Mar. biol. Ass. U.K.*, **37**, 9–14.
Rhodes, D. N., 1955. 'Micro-determination of phosphorus.' *Nature, Lond.*, **176**, 215–16.
Suryanarayana Rao, S. V., 1957. 'Preliminary observations on the total phosphorus content of the inshore waters of the Malabar coast off Calicut.' *Proc. Ind. Acad. Sci.*, B. **45**, 77–85.
Takedo, I., 1956. 'Organic phosphorus in Pacific waters off the eastern shore of northern Honshu.' *J. Chem. Soc. Japan*, **77**, 1208–12.
Tamaka, M., and Kanamori, S., 1956. 'Colorimetric determination of phosphorus in organic matter.' *Analyt. chim. acta*, **14**, 263–5.

SILICON: SECTION 12

Fukai, R., 1954. 'Critical studies on the analytical methods for minor chemical constituents in sea water. Part II. Some notes on the determination of silicate.' *J. Oceanogr. Soc. Japan*, **10**, 206–8.
Vatova, A., 1956. 'Il dosaggio dei silicati nell' acqua di mare con l'elettrofotometro Elko II.' *Nova Thal.*, **2** (6), 3–20.

CARBON: SECTION 13

el Wakeel, S. K., and Riley, J. P., 1957. 'The determination of organic carbon in marine muds.' *J. Cons. int. Explor. Mer*, **22**, 180–3.

OXYGEN: SECTION 14

Allen, J. A., 1955. 'Solubility of oxygen in water.' *Nature, Lond.*, **175**, 83.
Buchoff, L. S., Ingber, N. M., and Brady, J. H., 1955. 'Colorimetric determination of low concentrations of dissolved oxygen in water.' *Analyt. Chem.*, **27**, 1401–4.
Føyn, E., 1955. 'Continuous oxygen recording.' *Rept. Norweg. Fish. Mar. Investg.*, **11**, No. 3, 8 pp.
Freier, R., and Resch, G., 1956. 'Determination of oxygen dissolved in water.' *Z. anal. Chem.*, **148**, 427–34.
Gameson, A. L. H., and Robertson, K. G., 1955. 'The solubility of oxygen in pure water and sea water.' *J. appl. Chem.*, **5**, 502.
Kurshun, M. A., and Gel'man, N. E., 1946. 'Apparatus for direct microdetermination of oxygen.' *Zavofskaia Laboratoriia*, **12**, 500–2; RT-1020, Bibl. Transl. Rus, Sci. and Tech. Lit., No. 7.

Oulman, C. S., and Baumann, E. R., 1956. 'A colorimetric method for determining dissolved oxygen.' *Sewage and Ind. Wastes*, **28**, 1461–5.
Potter, E. C., 1957. 'The microdetermination of dissolved oxygen in water. I. The nature of the problem.' *J. appl. Chem.*, **7**, 285–96.
——, 1957. 'The microdetermination of dissolved oxygen in water. II. The design of water-sampling vessels.' *J. appl. Chem.*, **7**, 297–308.
——, and White, J. F., 1957. 'The microdetermination of dissolved oxygen in water. III. Titimetric determination of iodine in submicrogramme amounts.' *J. appl. Chem.*, **7**, 309–16.
——, ——, 1957. 'The microdetermination of dissolved oxygen in water. IV. Test of Winkler's reaction to below 0·001 p.p.m. of dissolved oxygen.' *J. appl. Chem.*, **7**, 317–27.
Truesdale, G. A., and Gameson, A. L. H., 1957. 'The solubility of oxygen in saline water.' *J. Cons. int. Explor. Mer*, **22**, 163–6.

CONSERVATIVE AND TRACE ELEMENTS: SECTIONS 16 AND 17

Armstrong, F. A. J., 1957. 'The iron content of sea water.' *J. Mar. biol. Ass. U.K.*, **36**, 509–17.
Bather, J. M., and Riley, J. P., 1954. 'The chemistry of the Irish Sea, Part I. The sulphate-chlorinity ratio.' *J. Cons. int. Explor. Mer*, **20**, 145–52.
Bowen, H. J. M., 1956. 'Strontium and barium in sea water and marine organisms.' *J. Mar. biol. Ass. U.K.*, **35**, 451–60.
Carlisle, D. B., and Hummerstone, L. G., 1958. 'Niobium in sea water.' *Nature, Lond.*, **181**, 1002–3.
Carpenter, J. H., 1957. 'The determination of calcium in natural waters.' *Limnol. and Oceanogr.*, **2**, 271–80.
Ishibashi, M., Shigematsu, T., and Nakagawa, Y., 1953. 'Determination of selenium in sea water.' *Rec. oceanogr. Wks. Japan*, **1**, 44–8.
——, ——, ——, 1956. 'On the amount of beryllium in sea water.' *Bull. Inst. chem. Res., Kyoto Univ.*, **34**, 210–13.
Jentoft, R. E., and Robinson, R. J., 1956. 'The potassium chlorinity ratio of ocean water.' *J. Mar. Res.*, **15**, 170–80.
Mullin, J. B., and Riley, J. P., 1956. 'The occurrence of cadmium in sea water and in marine organisms and sediments.' *J. Mar. Res.*, **15**, 103–22.
Odum, H. T., 1957. 'Strontium in natural waters.' *Publ. Inst. Mar. Sci.*, **4**, 22–37.
Smales, A. A., Mapper, D., and Wood, A. J., 1957. 'The determination by radioactivation, of small quantities of nickel, cobalt and copper in rocks, marine sediments and meteorites.' *Analyst*, **82**, 75–88.
——, and Webster, R. K., 1957. 'The determination of rubidium in sea water by the stable isotope dilution method.' *Geochim. et Cosmochim. acta*, **11**, 139.
Sporek, K. F., 1956. 'The gravimetric determination of potassium in sea water as the potassium tetraphenylboron salt.' *Analyst*, **81**, 540–3.
Swan, E. F., 1956. 'The meaning of strontium-calcium ratios.' *Deep-Sea Res.*, **4**, 71.
Wilson, K. G., and Arons, A. B., 1955. 'Osmotic pressures of sea-water solutions computed from experimental vapor pressure lowering.' *J. Mar. Res.*, **14**, 195–8.

Yamagata, N., 1957. 'Separation of a trace amount of calcium by ion exchange chromatography. A preliminary study for the determination of calcium in sea water.' *J. chem. Soc. Japan*, **78**, 513–17.

PIGMENTS: SECTION 19

Creitz, G. I., and Richards, F. A., 1955. 'The estimation and characterization of plankton populations by pigment analysis. III. A note on the use of "millipore" membrane filters in the estimation of plankton pigments.' *J. Mar. Res.*, **14**, 211–16.

Duxbury, A. C., and Yentsch, C. S., 1956. 'Plankton pigment nomographs.' *J. Mar. Res.*, **15**, 92–101.

Orr, W. L., and Grady, J. R., 1957. 'Determination of chlorophyll derivatives in marine sediments.' *Deep-Sea Res.*, **4**, 263–71.

FILTRATION: SECTION 20

Connor, R. M., 1957. 'Comparison of fermentation tube and membrane filter techniques for estimating coliform densities in sea water. I. Preliminary report.' *Appl. Microbiol.*, **5**, 141–4.

EXAMINATION OF SEDIMENTS: SECTION 21

Japan, Maritime Safety Board, 1957. 'Grain-analysis of sandy sediments (especially about Emery-tube analysis).' *Hydrogr. Bull.*, Publ. 981, **54**, 1–7.

del Riego, A. F., 1956. 'El contenido en carbono orgánico en los sedimentos de la riá de Vigo. Algunos datos sobre la relación carbono-nitrógeno.' *Bol. Inst. Españ. Ocean.*, **78**, 27 pp.

Turekian, K. K., 1956. 'Rapid technique for determination of carbonate content of deep-sea cores.' *Bull. Amer. Ass. Petrol. Geol.*, **40**, 2507–9.

Young, R. S., 1955. 'Size grading and analysis.' *J. Chem. Educ.*, **32**, 326–8.

TABLES

		page
1.	Logarithms	274
2.	Antilogarithms	276
3.	Limits for normal deviate	278
4.	Percentage of observations exceeding normal deviate	278
5.	t table	279
6.	Variance ratio, 1% points	280
7.	Variance ratio, 5% points	282
8.	Corrections for constant glass errors	284
9.	Factors for calibrating glassware	285
10.	Symbols recommended by the Chemical Society	286
11.	Collected conversion factors	290
12.	Atomic weights	291
13.	Molecular and equivalent weights, common substances	292
14.	Preparation of acids and alkalis of approximate strength	293
15.	Transmission data, Ilford standard filters	294
16.	Transmission data, Ilford bright filters	295
17.	Conversion, transmission (T) to absorption ($A = \log_{10} 1/T$)	296
18.	Saturation values of oxygen in sea water, mg. atom/litre (Fox)	300
19.	Saturation values of oxygen in sea water, ml. (S.T.P.)/litre (Fox)	301
20.	Saturation values of oxygen in sea water, mg. atom/litre (Truesdale, Downing and Lowden)	302
21.	Saturation values of oxygen in sea water, ml. (S.T.P.)/litre (Truesdale, Downing and Lowden)	303
22.	Depth coefficient (ΔpH) of pH	304
23.	Temperature coefficient of pH and chlorinity	304
24.	pHs of N.B.S. standards, 0°–95°C.	305
25.	First apparent dissociation constant (K'_1) for carbon dioxide	306
26.	Second apparent dissociation constant (K'_2) for carbon dioxide	306
27.	Correction factor (γ) excess base	307
28.	Values of the factor P_{CO_2}/A'	308
29.	Values of the factor CO_2/A'	309
30.	Solubility of carbon dioxide in sea water	310
31.	Activity of water in sea water	310
32.	Ionic ratios in sea water	311
33.	Ionic concentrations in sea water (g./Kg.)	312
34.	Ionic concentrations in sea water (g./l.)	313
35.	Ionic concentrations in sea water (mg.-ions/Kg.)	314
36.	Ionic concentrations in sea water (mg.-ions/l.)—molarity	315
37.	Ionic concentrations in sea water (g./Kg. water)	316
38.	Ionic concentrations in sea water (mg.-ions/Kg. water)—molality	317
39.	Vapour pressure, osmotic equivalence, sea water	318
40.	Absorption spectra, chlorophylls a and c	319
41.	Specific absorption coefficients—carotene	320
42.	Absorption spectra of diatom xanophylls in 90% alcohol	321
43.	Absorbancies of various pigments	322
44.	Specific and specified absorption coefficients	323
45.	Relative absorption spectrum, astacin-type pigment	324

TABLE 1

LOGARITHMS

	0	1	2	3	4	5	6	7	8	9	1	2	3	4	5	6	7	8
10	0000	0043	0086	0128	0170	0212	0253	0294	0334	0374	4	8	12	17	21	25	29	33
11	0414	0453	0492	0531	0569	0607	0645	0682	0719	0755	4	8	11	15	19	23	26	30
12	0792	0828	0864	0899	0934	0969	1004	1038	1072	1106	3	7	10	14	17	21	24	28
13	1139	1173	1206	1239	1271	1303	1335	1367	1399	1430	3	6	10	13	16	19	23	26
14	1461	1492	1523	1553	1584	1614	1644	1673	1703	1732	3	6	9	12	15	18	21	24
15	1761	1790	1818	1847	1875	1903	1931	1959	1987	2014	3	6	8	11	14	17	20	22
16	2041	2068	2095	2122	2148	2175	2201	2227	2253	2279	3	5	8	11	13	16	18	21
17	2304	2330	2355	2380	2405	2430	2455	2480	2504	2529	2	5	7	10	12	15	17	20
18	2553	2577	2601	2625	2648	2672	2695	2718	2742	2765	2	5	7	9	12	14	16	19
19	2788	2810	2833	2856	2878	2900	2923	2945	2967	2989	2	4	7	9	11	13	16	18
20	3010	3032	3054	3075	3096	3118	3139	3160	3181	3201	2	4	6	8	11	13	15	17
21	3222	3243	3263	3284	3304	3324	3345	3365	3385	3404	2	4	6	8	10	12	14	16
22	3424	3444	3464	3483	3502	3522	3541	3560	3579	3598	2	4	6	8	10	12	14	15
23	3617	3636	3655	3674	3692	3711	3729	3747	3766	3784	2	4	6	7	9	11	13	15
24	3802	3820	3838	3856	3874	3892	3909	3927	3945	3962	2	4	5	7	9	11	12	14
25	3979	3997	4014	4031	4048	4065	4082	4099	4116	4133	2	3	5	7	9	10	12	14
26	4150	4166	4183	4200	4216	4232	4249	4265	4281	4298	2	3	5	7	8	10	11	13
27	4314	4330	4346	4362	4378	4393	4409	4425	4440	4456	2	3	5	6	8	9	11	13
28	4472	4487	4502	4518	4533	4548	4564	4579	4594	4609	2	3	5	6	8	9	11	12
29	4624	4639	4654	4669	4683	4698	4713	4728	4742	4757	1	3	4	6	7	9	10	12
30	4771	4786	4800	4814	4829	4843	4857	4871	4886	4900	1	3	4	6	7	9	10	11
31	4914	4928	4942	4955	4969	4983	4997	5011	5024	5038	1	3	4	6	7	8	10	11
32	5051	5065	5079	5092	5105	5119	5132	5145	5159	5172	1	3	4	5	7	8	9	11
33	5185	5198	5211	5224	5237	5250	5263	5276	5289	5302	1	3	4	5	6	8	9	10
34	5315	5328	5340	5353	5366	5378	5391	5403	5416	5428	1	3	4	5	6	8	9	10
35	5441	5453	5465	5478	5490	5502	5514	5527	5539	5551	1	2	4	5	6	7	9	10
36	5563	5575	5587	5599	5611	5623	5635	5647	5658	5670	1	2	4	5	6	7	8	10
37	5682	5694	5705	5717	5729	5740	5752	5763	5775	5786	1	2	3	5	6	7	8	9
38	5798	5809	5821	5832	5843	5855	5866	5877	5888	5899	1	2	3	5	6	7	8	9
39	5911	5922	5933	5944	5955	5966	5977	5988	5999	6010	1	2	3	4	5	7	8	9
40	6021	6031	6042	6053	6064	6075	6085	6096	6107	6117	1	2	3	4	5	6	8	9
41	6128	6138	6149	6160	6170	6180	6191	6201	6212	6222	1	2	3	4	5	6	7	8
42	6232	6243	6253	6263	6274	6284	6294	6304	6314	6325	1	2	3	4	5	6	7	8
43	6335	6345	6355	6365	6375	6385	6395	6405	6415	6425	1	2	3	4	5	6	7	8
44	6435	6444	6454	6464	6474	6484	6493	6503	6513	6522	1	2	3	4	5	6	7	8
45	6532	6542	6551	6561	6571	6580	6590	6599	6609	6618	1	2	3	4	5	6	7	8
46	6628	6637	6646	6656	6665	6675	6684	6693	6702	6712	1	2	3	4	5	6	7	7
47	6721	6730	6739	6749	6758	6767	6776	6785	6794	6803	1	2	3	4	5	5	6	7
48	6812	6821	6830	6839	6848	6857	6866	6875	6884	6893	1	2	3	4	4	5	6	7
49	6902	6911	6920	6928	6937	6946	6955	6964	6972	6981	1	2	3	4	4	5	6	7
50	6990	6998	7007	7016	7024	7033	7042	7050	7059	7067	1	2	3	3	4	5	6	7
51	7076	7084	7093	7101	7110	7118	7126	7135	7143	7152	1	2	3	3	4	5	6	7
52	7160	7168	7177	7185	7193	7202	7210	7218	7226	7235	1	2	2	3	4	5	6	7
53	7243	7251	7259	7267	7275	7284	7292	7300	7308	7316	1	2	2	3	4	5	6	6
54	7324	7332	7340	7348	7356	7364	7372	7380	7388	7396	1	2	2	3	4	5	6	6

TABLE 1—*continued*

LOGARITHMS

0	1	2	3	4	5	6	7	8	9	1	2	3	4	5	6	7	8	9
7404	7412	7419	7427	7435	7443	7451	7459	7466	7474	1	2	2	3	4	5	5	6	7
7482	7490	7497	7505	7513	7520	7528	7536	7543	7551	1	2	2	3	4	5	5	6	7
7559	7566	7574	7582	7589	7597	7604	7612	7619	7627	1	2	2	3	4	5	5	6	7
7634	7642	7649	7657	7664	7672	7679	7686	7694	7701	1	1	2	3	4	4	5	6	7
7709	7716	7723	7731	7738	7745	7752	7760	7767	7774	1	1	2	3	4	4	5	6	7
7782	7789	7796	7803	7810	7818	7825	7832	7839	7846	1	1	2	3	4	4	5	6	6
7853	7860	7868	7875	7882	7889	7896	7903	7910	7917	1	1	2	3	4	4	5	6	6
7924	7931	7938	7945	7952	7959	7966	7973	7980	7987	1	1	2	3	3	4	5	6	6
7993	8000	8007	8014	8021	8028	8035	8041	8048	8055	1	1	2	3	3	4	5	5	6
8062	8069	8075	8082	8089	8096	8102	8109	8116	8122	1	1	2	3	3	4	5	5	6
8129	8136	8142	8149	8156	8162	8169	8176	8182	8189	1	1	2	3	3	4	5	5	6
8195	8202	8209	8215	8222	8228	8235	8241	8248	8254	1	1	2	3	3	4	5	5	6
8261	8267	8274	8280	8287	8293	8299	8306	8312	8319	1	1	2	3	3	4	5	5	6
8325	8331	8338	8344	8351	8357	8363	8370	8376	8382	1	1	2	3	3	4	4	5	6
8388	8395	8401	8407	8414	8420	8426	8432	8439	8445	1	1	2	2	3	4	4	5	6
8451	8457	8463	8470	8476	8482	8488	8494	8500	8506	1	1	2	2	3	4	4	5	5
8513	8519	8525	8531	8537	8543	8549	8555	8561	8567	1	1	2	2	3	4	4	5	5
8573	8579	8585	8591	8597	8603	8609	8615	8621	8627	1	1	2	2	3	4	4	5	5
8633	8639	8645	8651	8657	8663	8669	8675	8681	8686	1	1	2	2	3	4	4	5	5
8692	8698	8704	8710	8716	8722	8727	8733	8739	8745	1	1	2	2	3	4	4	5	5
8751	8756	8762	8768	8774	8779	8785	8791	8797	8802	1	1	2	2	3	3	4	5	5
8808	8814	8820	8825	8831	8837	8842	8848	8854	8859	1	1	2	2	3	3	4	5	5
8865	8871	8876	8882	8887	8893	8899	8904	8910	8915	1	1	2	2	3	3	4	4	5
8921	8927	8932	8938	8943	8949	8954	8960	8965	8971	1	1	2	2	3	3	4	4	5
8976	8982	8987	8993	8998	9004	9009	9015	9020	9025	1	1	2	2	3	3	4	4	5
9031	9036	9042	9047	9053	9058	9063	9069	9074	9079	1	1	2	2	3	3	4	4	5
9085	9090	9096	9101	9106	9112	9117	9122	9128	9133	1	1	2	2	3	3	4	4	5
9138	9143	9149	9154	9159	9165	9170	9175	9180	9186	1	1	2	2	3	3	4	4	5
9191	9196	9201	9206	9212	9217	9222	9227	9232	9238	1	1	2	2	3	3	4	4	5
9243	9248	9253	9258	9263	9269	9274	9279	9284	9289	1	1	2	2	3	3	4	4	5
9294	9299	9304	9309	9315	9320	9325	9330	9335	9340	1	1	2	2	3	3	4	4	5
9345	9350	9355	9360	9365	9370	9375	9380	9385	9390	1	1	2	2	3	3	4	4	5
9395	9400	9405	9410	9415	9420	9425	9430	9435	9440	0	1	1	2	2	3	3	4	4
9445	9450	9455	9460	9465	9469	9474	9479	9484	9489	0	1	1	2	2	3	3	4	4
9494	9499	9504	9509	9513	9518	9523	9528	9533	9538	0	1	1	2	2	3	3	4	4
9542	9547	9552	9557	9562	9566	9571	9576	9581	9586	0	1	1	2	2	3	3	4	4
9590	9595	9600	9605	9609	9614	9619	9624	9628	9633	0	1	1	2	2	3	3	4	4
9638	9643	9647	9652	9657	9661	9666	9671	9675	9680	0	1	1	2	2	3	3	4	4
9685	9689	9694	9699	9703	9708	9713	9717	9722	9727	0	1	1	2	2	3	3	4	4
9731	9736	9741	9745	9750	9754	9759	9763	9768	9773	0	1	1	2	2	3	3	4	4
9777	9782	9786	9791	9795	9800	9805	9809	9814	9818	0	1	1	2	2	3	3	4	4
9823	9827	9832	9836	9841	9845	9850	9854	9859	9863	0	1	1	2	2	3	3	4	4
9868	9872	9877	9881	9886	9890	9894	9899	9903	9908	0	1	1	2	2	3	3	4	4
9912	9917	9921	9926	9930	9934	9939	9943	9948	9952	0	1	1	2	2	3	3	4	4
9956	9961	9965	9969	9974	9978	9983	9987	9991	9996	0	1	1	2	2	3	3	3	4

TABLE 2

ANTILOGARITHMS

	0	1	2	3	4	5	6	7	8	9	1	2	3	4	5	6	7	8
·00	1000	1002	1005	1007	1009	1012	1014	1016	1019	1021	0	0	1	1	1	1	2	2
·01	1023	1026	1028	1030	1033	1035	1038	1040	1042	1045	0	0	1	1	1	1	2	2
·02	1047	1050	1052	1054	1057	1059	1062	1064	1067	1069	0	0	1	1	1	1	2	2
·03	1072	1074	1076	1079	1081	1084	1086	1089	1091	1094	0	0	1	1	1	1	2	2
·04	1096	1099	1102	1104	1107	1109	1112	1114	1117	1119	0	1	1	1	1	2	2	2
·05	1122	1125	1127	1130	1132	1135	1138	1140	1143	1146	0	1	1	1	1	2	2	2
·06	1148	1151	1153	1156	1159	1161	1164	1167	1169	1172	0	1	1	1	1	2	2	2
·07	1175	1178	1180	1183	1186	1189	1191	1194	1197	1199	0	1	1	1	1	2	2	2
·08	1202	1205	1208	1211	1213	1216	1219	1222	1225	1227	0	1	1	1	1	2	2	2
·09	1230	1233	1236	1239	1242	1245	1247	1250	1253	1256	0	1	1	1	1	2	2	2
·10	1259	1262	1265	1268	1271	1274	1276	1279	1282	1285	0	1	1	1	1	2	2	2
·11	1288	1291	1294	1297	1300	1303	1306	1309	1312	1315	0	1	1	1	2	2	2	2
·12	1318	1321	1324	1327	1330	1334	1337	1340	1343	1346	0	1	1	1	2	2	2	2
·13	1349	1352	1355	1358	1361	1365	1368	1371	1374	1377	0	1	1	1	2	2	2	3
·14	1380	1384	1387	1390	1393	1396	1400	1403	1406	1409	0	1	1	1	2	2	2	3
·15	1413	1416	1419	1422	1426	1429	1432	1435	1439	1442	0	1	1	1	2	2	2	3
·16	1445	1449	1452	1455	1459	1462	1466	1469	1472	1476	0	1	1	1	2	2	2	3
·17	1479	1483	1486	1489	1493	1496	1500	1503	1507	1510	0	1	1	1	2	2	2	3
·18	1514	1517	1521	1524	1528	1531	1535	1538	1542	1545	0	1	1	1	2	2	2	3
·19	1549	1552	1556	1560	1563	1567	1570	1574	1578	1581	0	1	1	1	2	2	3	3
·20	1585	1589	1592	1596	1600	1603	1607	1611	1614	1618	0	1	1	1	2	2	3	3
·21	1622	1626	1629	1633	1637	1641	1644	1648	1652	1656	0	1	1	2	2	2	3	3
·22	1660	1663	1667	1671	1675	1679	1683	1687	1690	1694	0	1	1	2	2	2	3	3
·23	1698	1702	1706	1710	1714	1718	1722	1726	1730	1734	0	1	1	2	2	2	3	3
·24	1738	1742	1746	1750	1754	1758	1762	1766	1770	1774	0	1	1	2	2	2	3	3
·25	1778	1782	1786	1791	1795	1799	1803	1807	1811	1816	0	1	1	2	2	2	3	3
·26	1820	1824	1828	1832	1837	1841	1845	1849	1854	1858	0	1	1	2	2	3	3	3
·27	1862	1866	1871	1875	1879	1884	1888	1892	1897	1901	0	1	1	2	2	3	3	3
·28	1905	1910	1914	1919	1923	1928	1932	1936	1941	1945	0	1	1	2	2	3	3	4
·29	1950	1954	1959	1963	1968	1972	1977	1982	1986	1991	0	1	1	2	2	3	3	4
·30	1995	2000	2004	2009	2014	2018	2023	2028	2032	2037	0	1	1	2	2	3	3	4
·31	2042	2046	2051	2056	2061	2065	2070	2075	2080	2084	0	1	1	2	2	3	3	4
·32	2089	2094	2099	2104	2109	2113	2118	2123	2128	2133	0	1	1	2	2	3	3	4
·33	2138	2143	2148	2153	2158	2163	2168	2173	2178	2183	0	1	1	2	2	3	3	4
·34	2188	2193	2198	2203	2208	2213	2218	2223	2228	2234	1	1	2	2	3	3	4	4
·35	2239	2244	2249	2254	2259	2265	2270	2275	2280	2286	1	1	2	2	3	3	4	4
·36	2291	2296	2301	2307	2312	2317	2323	2328	2333	2339	1	1	2	2	3	3	4	4
·37	2344	2350	2355	2360	2366	2371	2377	2382	2388	2393	1	1	2	2	3	3	4	4
·38	2399	2404	2410	2415	2421	2427	2432	2438	2443	2449	1	1	2	2	3	3	4	4
·39	2455	2460	2466	2472	2477	2483	2489	2495	2500	2506	1	1	2	2	3	3	4	5
·40	2512	2518	2523	2529	2535	2541	2547	2553	2559	2564	1	1	2	2	3	4	4	5
·41	2570	2576	2582	2588	2594	2600	2606	2612	2618	2624	1	1	2	2	3	4	4	5
·42	2630	2636	2642	2649	2655	2661	2667	2673	2679	2685	1	1	2	2	3	4	4	5
·43	2692	2698	2704	2710	2716	2723	2729	2735	2742	2748	1	1	2	3	3	4	4	5
·44	2754	2761	2767	2773	2780	2786	2793	2799	2805	2812	1	1	2	3	3	4	4	5
·45	2818	2825	2831	2838	2844	2851	2858	2864	2871	2877	1	1	2	3	3	4	5	5
·46	2884	2891	2897	2904	2911	2917	2924	2931	2938	2944	1	1	2	3	3	4	5	5
·47	2951	2958	2965	2972	2979	2985	2992	2999	3006	3013	1	1	2	3	3	4	5	
·48	3020	3027	3034	3041	3048	3055	3062	3069	3076	3083	1	1	2	3	4	4	5	
·49	3090	3097	3105	3112	3119	3126	3133	3141	3148	3155	1	1	2	3	4	4	5	

TABLE 2—continued

ANTILOGARITHMS

0	1	2	3	4	5	6	7	8	9	1	2	3	4	5	6	7	8	9
3162	3170	3177	3184	3192	3199	3206	3214	3221	3228	1	1	2	3	4	4	5	6	7
3236	3243	3251	3258	3266	3273	3281	3289	3296	3304	1	2	2	3	4	5	5	6	7
3311	3319	3327	3334	3342	3350	3357	3365	3373	3381	1	2	2	3	4	5	5	6	7
3388	3396	3404	3412	3420	3428	3436	3443	3451	3459	1	2	2	3	4	5	6	6	7
3467	3475	3483	3491	3499	3508	3516	3524	3532	3540	1	2	2	3	4	5	6	6	7
3548	3556	3565	3573	3581	3589	3597	3606	3614	3622	1	2	2	3	4	5	6	7	7
3631	3639	3648	3656	3664	3673	3681	3690	3698	3707	1	2	3	3	4	5	6	7	8
3715	3724	3733	3741	3750	3758	3767	3776	3784	3793	1	2	3	3	4	5	6	7	8
3802	3811	3819	3828	3837	3846	3855	3864	3873	3882	1	2	3	4	4	5	6	7	8
3890	3899	3908	3917	3926	3936	3945	3954	3963	3972	1	2	3	4	5	5	6	7	8
3981	3990	3999	4009	4018	4027	4036	4046	4055	4064	1	2	3	4	5	6	6	7	8
4074	4083	4093	4102	4111	4121	4130	4140	4150	4159	1	2	3	4	5	6	7	8	9
4169	4178	4188	4198	4207	4217	4227	4236	4246	4256	1	2	3	4	5	6	7	8	9
4266	4276	4285	4295	4305	4315	4325	4335	4345	4355	1	2	3	4	5	6	7	8	9
4365	4375	4385	4395	4406	4416	4426	4436	4446	4457	1	2	3	4	5	6	7	8	9
4467	4477	4487	4498	4508	4519	4529	4539	4550	4560	1	2	3	4	5	6	7	8	9
4571	4581	4592	4603	4613	4624	4634	4645	4656	4667	1	2	3	4	5	6	7	9	10
4677	4688	4699	4710	4721	4732	4742	4753	4764	4775	1	2	3	4	5	7	8	9	10
4786	4797	4808	4819	4831	4842	4853	4864	4875	4887	1	2	3	4	6	7	8	9	10
4898	4909	4920	4932	4943	4955	4966	4977	4989	5000	1	2	3	5	6	7	8	9	10
5012	5023	5035	5047	5058	5070	5082	5093	5105	5117	1	2	4	5	6	7	8	9	11
5129	5140	5152	5164	5176	5188	5200	5212	5224	5236	1	2	4	5	6	7	8	10	11
5248	5260	5272	5284	5297	5309	5321	5333	5346	5358	1	2	4	5	6	7	9	10	11
5370	5383	5395	5408	5420	5433	5445	5458	5470	5483	1	3	4	5	6	8	9	10	11
5495	5508	5521	5534	5546	5559	5572	5585	5598	5610	1	3	4	5	6	8	9	10	12
5623	5636	5649	5662	5675	5689	5702	5715	5728	5741	1	3	4	5	7	8	9	10	12
5754	5768	5781	5794	5808	5821	5834	5848	5861	5875	1	3	4	5	7	8	9	11	12
5888	5902	5916	5929	5943	5957	5970	5984	5998	6012	1	3	4	5	7	8	10	11	12
6026	6039	6053	6067	6081	6095	6109	6124	6138	6152	1	3	4	6	7	8	10	11	13
6166	6180	6194	6209	6223	6237	6252	6266	6281	6295	1	3	4	6	7	9	10	11	13
6310	6324	6339	6353	6368	6383	6397	6412	6427	6442	1	3	4	6	7	9	10	12	13
6457	6471	6486	6501	6516	6531	6546	6561	6577	6592	2	3	5	6	8	9	11	12	14
6607	6622	6637	6653	6668	6683	6699	6714	6730	6745	2	3	5	6	8	9	11	12	14
6761	6776	6792	6808	6823	6839	6855	6871	6887	6902	2	3	5	6	8	9	11	13	14
6918	6934	6950	6966	6982	6998	7015	7031	7047	7063	2	3	5	6	8	10	11	13	15
7079	7096	7112	7129	7145	7161	7178	7194	7211	7228	2	3	5	7	8	10	12	13	15
7244	7261	7278	7295	7311	7328	7345	7362	7379	7396	2	3	5	7	8	10	12	13	15
7413	7430	7447	7464	7482	7499	7516	7534	7551	7568	2	3	5	7	9	10	12	14	16
7586	7603	7621	7638	7656	7674	7691	7709	7727	7745	2	4	5	7	9	11	12	14	16
7762	7780	7798	7816	7834	7852	7870	7889	7907	7925	2	4	5	7	9	11	13	14	16
7943	7962	7980	7998	8017	8035	8054	8072	8091	8110	2	4	6	7	9	11	13	15	17
8128	8147	8166	8185	8204	8222	8241	8260	8279	8299	2	4	6	8	9	11	13	15	17
8318	8337	8356	8375	8395	8414	8433	8453	8472	8492	2	4	6	8	10	12	14	15	17
8511	8531	8551	8570	8590	8610	8630	8650	8670	8690	2	4	6	8	10	12	14	16	18
8710	8730	8750	8770	8790	8810	8831	8851	8872	8892	2	4	6	8	10	12	14	16	18
8913	8933	8954	8974	8995	9016	9036	9057	9078	9099	2	4	6	8	10	12	15	17	19
9120	9141	9162	9183	9204	9226	9247	9268	9290	9311	2	4	6	8	11	13	15	17	19
9333	9354	9376	9397	9419	9441	9462	9484	9506	9528	2	4	7	9	11	13	15	17	20
9550	9572	9594	9616	9638	9661	9683	9705	9727	9750	2	4	7	9	11	13	16	18	20
9772	9795	9817	9840	9863	9886	9908	9931	9954	9977	2	5	7	9	11	14	16	18	20

TABLE 3

Table of limits for the deviate, d, corresponding
to a given percentage.

(Calculated from Table 2 in R. A. Fisher and F. Yates, *Statistical Tables for Biological,
Agricultural and Medical Research*, Oliver and Boyd, London and Edinburgh, 1938.
Third Edition 1948.)

Percentage	±d	Percentage	±d	Percentage	±d
99·99	3·89	85	1·44	40	0·52
99·9	3·29	80	1·28	35	0·45
99	2·58	75	1·15	30	0·39
98	2·33	70	1·04	25	0·32
97	2·17	65	0·93	20	0·25
96	2·05	60	0·84	15	0·19
95	1·96	55	0·76	10	0·13
92	1·75	50	0·67	5	0·06
90	1·64	45	0·60	0	0·00

TABLE 4

Table of the percentage of observations exceeding
a given normal deviate, d.

(Calculated from Table 2 in R. A. Fisher and F. Yates, *Statistical Tables for Biological,
Agricultural and Medical Research*, Oliver and Boyd, London and Edinburgh, 1938.
Third Edition 1948.)

d	Percentage	d	Percentage	d	Percentage
4·0	0·003	1·0	15·9	−1·1	86·43
3·5	0·023	0·9	18·4	−1·2	88·49
3·2	0·069	0·8	21·2	−1·3	90·32
3·0	0·135	0·7	24·2	−1·4	91·92
2·8	0·256	0·6	27·4	−1·5	93·32
2·6	0·466	0·5	30·9	−1·6	94·52
2·5	0·621	0·4	34·5	−1·7	95·54
2·4	0·820	0·3	38·2	−1·8	96·41
2·3	1·07	0·2	42·1	−1·9	97·13
2·2	1·39	0·1	46·0	−2·0	97·72
2·1	1·79	0·0	50·0	−2·1	98·21
2·0	2·28	−0·1	54·0	−2·2	98·61
1·9	2·87	−0·2	57·9	−2·3	98·93
1·8	3·59	−0·3	61·8	−2·4	99·180
1·7	4·46	−0·4	65·5	−2·5	99·379
1·6	5·48	−0·5	69·1	−2·6	99·534
1·5	6·68	−0·6	72·6	−2·8	99·744
1·4	8·08	−0·7	75·8	−3·0	99·865
1·3	9·68	−0·8	78·8	−3·2	99·931
1·2	11·51	−0·9	81·6	−3·5	99·977
1·1	13·57	−1·0	84·1	−4·0	99·997

TABLE 5

Percentage of trials in which a given estimated deviate, *t*, is exceeded.

(Calculated from Table 3 in R. A. Fisher and F. Yates, *Statistical Tables for Biological, Agricultural and Medical Research*. Oliver & Boyd, London and Edinburgh, 1938. Third Edition 1948.)

Degrees of freedom	Percentage of trials in which deviate is exceeded							
	50	25	10	5	2·5	1·0	0·5	0·1
1	1·00	2·41	6·31	12·71	25·45	63·66	127·32	636·62
2	0·82	1·60	2·92	4·30	6·20	9·92	14·09	31·60
3	0·76	1·42	2·35	3·18	4·18	5·84	7·45	12·94
4	0·74	1·34	2·13	2·78	3·50	4·60	5·60	8·61
5	0·73	1·30	2·01	2·57	3·16	4·03	4·77	6·86
6	0·72	1·27	1·94	2·45	2·97	3·71	4·32	5·96
7	0·71	1·25	1·89	2·36	2·84	3·50	4·03	5·40
8	0·71	1·24	1·86	2·30	2·75	3·35	3·83	5·04
9	0·70	1·23	1·83	2·26	2·68	3·25	3·69	4·78
10	0·70	1·22	1·81	2·23	2·63	3·17	3·58	4·59
11	0·70	1·21	1·80	2·20	2·59	3·11	3·50	4·44
12	0·70	1·21	1·78	2·18	2·56	3·05	3·43	4·32
13	0·69	1·20	1·77	2·16	2·53	3·01	3·37	4·22
14	0·69	1·20	1·76	2·14	2·51	2·98	3·32	4·14
15	0·69	1·20	1·75	2·13	2·49	2·95	3·29	4·07
16	0·69	1·19	1·74	2·12	2·47	2·92	3·25	4·01
17	0·69	1·19	1·74	2·11	2·46	2·90	3·22	3·96
18	0·69	1·19	1·73	2·10	2·44	2·88	3·20	3·92
19	0·69	1·19	1·73	2·09	2·43	2·86	3·17	3·88
20	0·69	1·18	1·72	2·09	2·42	2·84	3·15	3·85
22	0·69	1·18	1·72	2·07	2·40	2·82	3·12	3·79
24	0·68	1·18	1·71	2·06	2·39	2·80	3·09	3·75
26	0·68	1·17	1·71	2·06	2·38	2·78	3·07	3·71
28	0·68	1·17	1·70	2·05	2·37	2·76	3·05	3·67
30	0·68	1·17	1·70	2·04	2·36	2·75	3·03	3·65
40	0·68	1·17	1·68	2·02	2·33	2·70	2·97	3·55
50	0·68	1·16	1·68	2·01	2·31	2·68	2·93	3·50
60	0·68	1·16	1·67	2·00	2·30	2·66	2·91	3·46
∞	0·67	1·15	1·64	1·96	2·24	2·58	2·81	3·29

TABLE 6

Variance-ratio table, 1% points giving the values of the ratio exceeded by pure chance in 1% of trials.

(From G. W. Snedecor, *Statistical Methods*, Iowa State College Press, Ames, Iowa, U.S.A., 1950.)

	Degrees of freedom of numerator									
	1	2	3	4	5	6	7	8	9	10
1	4,052	4,999	5,403	5,625	5,764	5,859	5,928	5,982	6,022	6,056
2	98·49	99·00	99·17	99·25	99·30	99·33	99·34	99·36	99·38	99·40
3	34·12	30·82	29·46	28·71	28·24	27·91	27·67	27·49	27·34	27·23
4	21·20	18·00	16·69	15·98	15·52	15·21	14·98	14·80	14·66	14·54
5	16·26	13·27	12·06	11·39	10·97	10·67	10·45	10·27	10·15	10·05
6	13·74	10·92	9·78	9·15	8·75	8·47	8·26	8·10	7·98	7·87
7	12·25	9·55	8·45	7·85	7·46	7·19	7·00	6·84	6·71	6·62
8	11·26	8·65	7·59	7·01	6·63	6·37	6·19	6·03	5·91	5·82
9	10·56	8·02	6·99	6·42	6·06	5·80	5·62	5·47	5·35	5·26
10	10·04	7·56	6·55	5·99	5·64	5·39	5·21	5·06	4·94	4·85
11	9·65	7·20	6·22	5·67	5·32	5·07	4·88	4·74	4·63	4·54
12	9·33	6·93	5·95	5·41	5·06	4·82	4·65	4·50	4·39	4·30
13	9·07	6·70	5·74	5·20	4·86	4·62	4·44	4·30	4·19	4·10
14	8·86	6·51	5·56	5·03	4·69	4·46	4·28	4·14	4·03	3·94
15	8·68	6·36	5·42	4·89	4·56	4·32	4·14	4·00	3·89	3·80
16	8·53	6·23	5·29	4·77	4·44	4·20	4·03	3·89	3·78	3·69
17	8·40	6·11	5·18	4·67	4·34	4·10	3·93	3·79	3·68	3·59
18	8·28	6·01	5·09	4·58	4·25	4·01	3·85	3·71	3·60	3·51
19	8·18	5·93	5·01	4·50	4·17	3·94	3·77	3·63	3·52	3·43
20	8·10	5·85	4·94	4·43	4·10	3·87	3·71	3·56	3·45	3·37
21	8·02	5·78	4·87	4·37	4·04	3·81	3·65	3·51	3·40	3·31
22	7·94	5·72	4·82	4·31	3·99	3·76	3·59	3·45	3·35	3·26
23	7·88	5·66	4·76	4·26	3·94	3·71	3·54	3·41	3·30	3·21
24	7·82	5·61	4·72	4·22	3·90	3·67	3·50	3·36	3·25	3·17
25	7·77	5·57	4·68	4·18	3·86	3·63	3·46	3·32	3·21	3·13
26	7·72	5·53	4·64	4·14	3·82	3·59	3·42	3·29	3·17	3·09
27	7·68	5·49	4·60	4·11	3·79	3·56	3·39	3·26	3·14	3·06
28	7·64	5·45	4·57	4·07	3·76	3·53	3·36	3·23	3·11	3·03
29	7·60	5·42	4·54	4·04	3·73	3·50	3·33	3·20	3·08	3·00
30	7·56	5·39	4·51	4·02	3·70	3·47	3·30	3·17	3·06	2·98
40	7·31	5·18	4·31	3·83	3·51	3·29	3·12	2·99	2·88	2·80
50	7·17	5·06	4·20	3·72	3·41	3·18	3·02	2·88	2·78	2·70
60	7·08	4·98	4·13	3·65	3·34	3·12	2·95	2·82	2·72	2·63
70	7·01	4·92	4·08	3·60	3·29	3·07	2·91	2·77	2·67	2·59
80	6·96	4·88	4·04	3·56	3·25	3·04	2·87	2·74	2·64	2·55
100	6·90	4·82	3·98	3·51	3·20	2·99	2·82	2·69	2·59	2·51
150	6·81	4·75	3·91	3·44	3·14	2·92	2·76	2·62	2·53	2·44
200	6·76	4·71	3·88	3·41	3·11	2·90	2·73	2·60	2·50	2·41
∞	6·64	4·60	3·78	3·32	3·02	2·80	2·64	2·51	2·41	2·32

Degrees of freedom of denominator

TABLE 6—*continued*

Variance-ratio table, 1% points giving the values of the ratio exceeded
by pure chance in 1% of trials.

			Degrees of freedom of numerator							
12	16	20	24	30	40	50	60	75	100	∞
6,106	6,169	6,208	6,234	6,258	6,286	6,302	6,313	6,323	6,334	6,366
99·42	99·44	99·45	99·46	99·47	99·48	99·48	99·48	99·49	99·49	99·50
27·05	26·83	26·69	26·60	26·50	26·41	26·35	26·32	26·27	26·23	26·12
14·37	14·15	14·02	13·93	13·83	13·74	13·69	13·65	13·61	13·57	13·46
9·89	9·68	9·55	9·47	9·38	9·29	9·24	9·20	9·17	9·13	9·02
7·72	7·52	7·39	7·31	7·23	7·14	7·09	7·06	7·02	6·99	6·88
6·47	6·27	6·15	6·07	5·98	5·90	5·85	5·82	5·78	5·75	5·65
5·67	5·48	5·36	5·28	5·20	5·11	5·06	5·03	5·00	4·96	4·86
5·11	4·92	4·80	4·73	4·64	4·56	4·51	4·48	4·45	4·41	4·31
4·71	4·52	4·41	4·33	4·25	4·17	4·12	4·08	4·05	4·01	3·91
4·40	4·21	4·10	4·02	3·94	3·86	3·80	3·78	3·74	3·70	3·60
4·16	3·98	3·86	3·78	3·70	3·61	3·56	3·54	3·49	3·46	3·36
3·96	3·78	3·67	3·59	3·51	3·42	3·37	3·34	3·30	3·27	3·16
3·80	3·62	3·51	3·43	3·34	3·27	3·21	3·18	3·14	3·11	3·00
3·67	3·48	3·36	3·29	3·20	3·12	3·07	3·05	3·00	2·97	2·87
3·55	3·37	3·25	3·18	3·10	3·01	2·96	2·93	2·89	2·86	2·75
3·45	3·27	3·16	3·08	3·00	2·92	2·86	2·83	2·79	2·76	2·65
3·37	3·19	3·07	3·00	2·91	2·83	2·78	2·75	2·71	2·68	2·57
3·30	3·12	3·00	2·92	2·84	2·76	2·70	2·67	2·63	2·60	2·49
3·23	3·05	2·94	2·86	2·77	2·69	2·63	2·61	2·56	2·53	2·42
3·17	2·99	2·88	2·80	2·72	2·63	2·58	2·55	2·51	2·47	2·36
3·12	2·94	2·83	2·75	2·67	2·58	2·53	2·50	2·46	2·42	2·31
3·07	2·89	2·78	2·70	2·62	2·54	2·48	2·45	2·41	2·37	2·26
3·03	2·85	2·74	2·66	2·58	2·49	2·44	2·40	2·36	2·33	2·21
2·99	2·81	2·70	2·62	2·54	2·45	2·40	2·36	2·32	2·29	2·17
2·96	2·77	2·66	2·58	2·50	2·41	2·36	2·33	2·28	2·25	2·13
2·93	2·74	2·63	2·55	2·47	2·38	2·33	2·29	2·25	2·21	2·10
2·90	2·71	2·60	2·52	2·44	2·35	2·30	2·26	2·22	2·18	2·06
2·87	2·68	2·57	2·49	2·41	2·32	2·27	2·23	2·19	2·15	2·03
2·84	2·66	2·55	2·47	2·38	2·29	2·24	2·21	2·16	2·13	2·01
2·66	2·49	2·37	2·29	2·20	2·11	2·05	2·02	1·97	1·94	1·81
2·56	2·39	2·26	2·18	2·10	2·00	1·94	1·91	1·86	1·82	1·68
2·50	2·32	2·20	2·12	2·03	1·93	1·87	1·84	1·79	1·74	1·60
2·45	2·28	2·15	2·07	1·98	1·88	1·82	1·79	1·74	1·69	1·53
2·41	2·24	2·11	2·03	1·94	1·84	1·78	1·74	1·70	1·65	1·49
2·36	2·19	2·06	1·98	1·89	1·79	1·73	1·69	1·64	1·59	1·43
2·30	2·12	2·00	1·91	1·83	1·72	1·66	1·62	1·56	1·51	1·33
2·28	2·09	1·97	1·88	1·79	1·69	1·62	1·58	1·53	1·48	1·28
2·18	1·99	1·88	1·79	1·69	1·59	1·52	1·47	1·41	1·36	1·00

TABLE 7

Variance-ratio table, 5% points giving the values of the ratio exceeded
by pure chance in 5% of trials.

(From G. W. Snedecor, *Statistical Methods*, Iowa State College Press, Ames, Iowa,
U.S.A., 1950.)

		Degrees of freedom of numerator								
	1	2	3	4	5	6	7	8	9	10
1	161	200	216	225	230	234	237	239	241	242
2	18·51	19·00	19·16	19·25	19·30	19·33	19·36	19·37	19·38	19·39
3	10·13	9·55	9·28	9·12	9·01	8·94	8·88	8·84	8·81	8·78
4	7·71	6·94	6·59	6·39	6·26	6·16	6·09	6·04	6·00	5·96
5	6·61	5·79	5·41	5·19	5·05	4·95	4·88	4·82	4·78	4·74
6	5·99	5·14	4·76	4·53	4·39	4·28	4·21	4·15	4·10	4·06
7	5·59	4·74	4·35	4·12	3·97	3·87	3·79	3·73	3·68	3·63
8	5·32	4·46	4·07	3·84	3·69	3·58	3·50	3·44	3·39	3·34
9	5·12	4·26	3·86	3·63	3·48	3·37	3·29	3·23	3·18	3·13
10	4·96	4·10	3·71	3·48	3·33	3·22	3·14	3·07	3·02	2·97
11	4·84	3·98	3·59	3·36	3·20	3·09	3·01	2·95	2·90	2·86
12	4·75	3·88	3·49	3·26	3·11	3·00	2·92	2·85	2·80	2·76
13	4·67	3·80	3·41	3·18	3·02	2·92	2·84	2·77	2·72	2·67
14	4·60	3·74	3·34	3·11	2·96	2·85	2·77	2·70	2·65	2·60
15	4·54	3·68	3·29	3·06	2·90	2·79	2·70	2·64	2·59	2·55
16	4·49	3·63	3·24	3·01	2·85	2·74	2·66	2·59	2·54	2·49
17	4·45	3·59	3·20	2·96	2·81	2·70	2·62	2·55	2·49	2·45
18	4·41	3·55	3·16	2·93	2·77	2·66	2·58	2·51	2·46	2·41
19	4·38	3·52	3·13	2·90	2·74	2·63	2·55	2·48	2·43	2·38
20	4·35	3·49	3·10	2·87	2·71	2·60	2·52	2·45	2·40	2·35
21	4·32	3·47	3·07	2·84	2·68	2·57	2·49	2·42	2·37	2·32
22	4·30	3·44	3·05	2·82	2·66	2·55	2·47	2·40	2·35	2·30
23	4·28	3·42	3·03	2·80	2·64	2·53	2·45	2·38	2·32	2·28
24	4·26	3·40	3·01	2·78	2·62	2·51	2·43	2·36	2·30	2·26
25	4·24	3·38	2·99	2·76	2·60	2·49	2·41	2·34	2·28	2·24
26	4·22	3·37	2·98	2·74	2·59	2·47	2·39	2·32	2·27	2·22
27	4·21	3·35	2·96	2·73	2·57	2·46	2·37	2·30	2·25	2·20
28	4·20	3·34	2·95	2·71	2·56	2·44	2·36	2·29	2·24	2·19
29	4·18	3·33	2·93	2·70	2·54	2·43	2·35	2·28	2·22	2·18
30	4·17	3·32	2·92	2·69	2·53	2·42	2·34	2·27	2·21	2·16
40	4·08	3·23	2·84	2·61	2·45	2·34	2·25	2·18	2·12	2·07
50	4·03	3·18	2·79	2·56	2·40	2·29	2·20	2·13	2·07	2·02
60	4·00	3·15	2·76	2·52	2·37	2·25	2·17	2·10	2·04	1·99
70	3·98	3·13	2·74	2·50	2·35	2·23	2·14	2·07	2·01	1·97
80	3·96	3·11	2·72	2·48	2·33	2·21	2·12	2·05	1·99	1·95
100	3·94	3·09	2·70	2·46	2·30	2·19	2·10	2·03	1·97	1·92
150	3·91	3·06	2·67	2·43	2·27	2·16	2·07	2·00	1·94	1·89
200	3·89	3·04	2·65	2·41	2·26	2·14	2·05	1·98	1·92	1·87
∞	3·84	2·99	2·60	2·37	2·21	2·09	2·01	1·94	1·88	1·83

Degrees of freedom of denominator

TABLE 7—*continued*

Variance-ratio table, 5% points giving the values of the ratio exceeded by pure chance in 5% of trials.

			Degrees of freedom of numerator							
12	16	20	24	30	40	50	60	75	100	∞
244	246	248	249	250	251	252	252	253	253	254
19·41	19·43	19·44	19·45	19·46	19·47	19·47	19·48	19·48	19·49	19·50
8·74	8·69	8·66	8·64	8·62	8·60	8·58	8·57	8·57	8·56	8·53
5·91	5·84	5·80	5·77	5·74	5·71	5·70	5·69	5·68	5·66	5·63
4·68	4·60	4·56	4·53	4·50	4·46	4·44	4·43	4·42	4·40	4·36
4·00	3·92	3·87	3·84	3·81	3·77	3·75	3·74	3·72	3·71	3·67
3·57	3·49	3·44	3·41	3·38	3·34	3·32	3·30	3·29	3·28	3·23
3·28	3·20	3·15	3·12	3·08	3·05	3·03	3·00	3·00	2·98	2·93
3·07	2·98	2·93	2·90	2·86	2·82	2·80	2·79	2·77	2·76	2·71
2·91	2·82	2·77	2·74	2·70	2·67	2·64	2·62	2·61	2·59	2·54
2·79	2·70	2·65	2·61	2·57	2·53	2·50	2·49	2·47	2·45	2·40
2·69	2·60	2·54	2·50	2·46	2·42	2·40	2·38	2·36	2·35	2·30
2·60	2·51	2·46	2·42	2·38	2·34	2·32	2·30	2·28	2·26	2·21
2·53	2·44	2·39	2·35	2·31	2·27	2·24	2·22	2·21	2·19	2·13
2·48	2·39	2·33	2·29	2·25	2·21	2·18	2·16	2·15	2·12	2·07
2·42	2·33	2·28	2·24	2·20	2·16	2·13	2·10	2·09	2·07	2·01
2·38	2·29	2·23	2·19	2·15	2·11	2·08	2·06	2·04	2·02	1·96
2·34	2·25	2·19	2·15	2·11	2·07	2·04	2·02	2·00	1·98	1·92
2·31	2·21	2·15	2·11	2·07	2·02	2·00	1·98	1·96	1·94	1·88
2·28	2·18	2·12	2·08	2·04	1·99	1·96	1·95	1·92	1·90	1·84
2·25	2·15	2·09	2·05	2·00	1·96	1·93	1·92	1·89	1·87	1·81
2·23	2·13	2·07	2·03	1·98	1·93	1·91	1·89	1·87	1·84	1·78
2·20	2·10	2·04	2·00	1·96	1·91	1·88	1·86	1·84	1·82	1·76
2·18	2·09	2·02	1·98	1·94	1·89	1·86	1·84	1·82	1·80	1·73
2·16	2·06	2·00	1·96	1·92	1·87	1·84	1·82	1·80	1·77	1·71
2·15	2·05	1·99	1·95	1·90	1·85	1·82	1·80	1·78	1·76	1·69
2·13	2·03	1·97	1·93	1·88	1·84	1·80	1·78	1·76	1·74	1·67
2·12	2·02	1·96	1·91	1·87	1·81	1·78	1·77	1·75	1·72	1·65
2·10	2·00	1·94	1·90	1·85	1·80	1·77	1·75	1·73	1·71	1·64
2·09	1·99	1·93	1·89	1·84	1·79	1·76	1·74	1·72	1·69	1·62
2·00	1·90	1·84	1·79	1·74	1·69	1·66	1·64	1·61	1·59	1·51
1·95	1·85	1·78	1·74	1·69	1·63	1·60	1·58	1·55	1·52	1·44
1·92	1·81	1·75	1·70	1·65	1·59	1·56	1·53	1·50	1·48	1·39
1·89	1·79	1·72	1·67	1·62	1·56	1·53	1·50	1·47	1·45	1·35
1·88	1·77	1·70	1·65	1·60	1·54	1·51	1·48	1·45	1·42	1·32
1·85	1·75	1·68	1·63	1·57	1·51	1·48	1·45	1·42	1·39	1·28
1·82	1·71	1·64	1·59	1·54	1·47	1·44	1·41	1·37	1·34	1·22
1·80	1·69	1·62	1·57	1·52	1·45	1·42	1·39	1·35	1·32	1·19
1·75	1·64	1·57	1·52	1·46	1·40	1·35	1·32	1·28	1·24	1·00

TABLE 8

Corrections for constant glass errors.

(From E. J. Conway, *Microdiffusion Analysis and Volumetric Error*. Crosby Lockwood & Son Ltd., London, 1947.)

Temp. °C	s	a	g	f
10	0·027	0·109	0·026	0·064
11	0·037	0·109	0·023	0·058
12	0·048	0·109	0·021	0·051
13	0·060	0·108	0·018	0·045
14	0·073	0·108	0·016	0·038
15	0·087	0·107	0·013	0·032
16	0·103	0·107	0·010	0·026
17	0·120	0·107	0·008	0·019
18	0·138	0·106	0·005	0·013
19	0·157	0·106	0·003	0·006
20	0·177	0·105	0·000	0·000
21	0·198	0·105	−0·003	−0·006
22	0·220	0·105	−0·005	−0·013
23	0·244	0·104	−0·008	−0·019
24	0·268	0·104	−0·010	−0·026
25	0·293	0·103	−0·013	−0·032
26	0·319	0·103	−0·016	−0·038
27	0·346	0·103	−0·018	−0·045
28	0·374	0·102	−0·021	−0·051
29	0·403	0·102	−0·023	−0·058
30	0·433	0·101	−0·026	−0·064

TABLE 9

Factors for calibrating glassware.

(From E. J. Conway, *Microdiffusion Analysis and Volumetric Error*. Crosby Lockwood & Son Ltd., London, 1947.)

Temp. °C	α	β	γ	δ	ε
10	0·136	0·162	0·226	−0·026	−0·090
11	0·146	0·169	0·227	−0·023	−0·081
12	0·157	0·178	0·229	−0·021	−0·072
13	0·168	0·186	0·231	−0·018	−0·063
14	0·181	0·197	0·235	−0·016	−0·054
15	0·194	0·207	0·239	−0·013	−0·045
16	0·210	0·220	0·246	−0·010	−0·036
17	0·227	0·235	0·254	−0·008	−0·027
18	0·244	0·249	0·262	−0·005	−0·018
19	0·263	0·265	0·271	−0·003	−0·009
20	0·282	0·282	0·282	0·000	0·000
21	0·303	0·300	0·294	0·003	0·009
22	0·325	0·320	0·307	0·005	0·018
23	0·348	0·340	0·321	0·008	0·027
24	0·372	0·362	0·336	0·010	0·036
25	0·396	0·383	0·351	0·013	0·045
26	0·422	0·406	0·368	0·016	0·054
27	0·449	0·431	0·386	0·018	0·063
28	0·476	0·455	0·404	0·021	0·072
29	0·505	0·482	0·424	0·023	0·081
30	0·534	0·508	0·444	0·026	0·090

TABLE 10

SYMBOLS RECOMMENDED BY THE CHEMICAL SOCIETY

(From *J. chem. Soc.*, 1944, pp. 717–23).

(Where two or more symbols separated by commas or semicolons are given for a quantity, these symbols are to be regarded as alternatives for which no preference is expressed. On the other hand, where two symbols are separated by a dotted line, the former is the first preference.)

1. To be printed in Black Italic.

Certain important physical constants.

F Faraday's constant.
J Mechanical equivalent of heat.
N Avogadro's number.
R $\begin{cases} \text{Gas constant per mol.} \\ \text{Rydberg's constant.} \end{cases}$

c Velocity of light *in vacuo*.
e Electronic charge (charge equal and opposite in sign to that of an electron).
g Acceleration due to gravity (standard value, if variation from standard is significant).
h Planck's constant.
k Boltzmann's constant.
m Rest mass of an electron.

2. To be printed in Ordinary Italic when not Greek.

General Physics and Chemistry.

Length . . . . . } *l*	
mean free path of molecules . . } *l*	
height . . . . . *h*	
diameter, distance . . . . *d*	
diameter of molecules . . . σ	
radius . . . . . *r*	
Mass . . . . . *m*	
molecular weight . . . . *M*	
atomic weight . . . . *A*	
atomic number . . . . *Z*	
gram-equivalent weight . . . *Z, J*	
Time . . . . . *t*	
time interval, especially half- or mean-life . *r*	
frequency . . . . . ν	
Velocity . . . . . *v; c*, (*u, v, w*)	
of ions . . . . . *u* (with subscript)	
angular . . . . . ω	
Acceleration . . . . *f . . . a*	
due to gravity (as variable) . . *g*	
Force . . . . . *F*, (*x, y, z*)	
Moment of inertia . . . . *I*	
Pressure . . . . . *p, P*	
especially osmotic . . . . Π	

Volume	.	.	.	.	v, V
Density	.	.	.	.	$\rho \ldots d$
Compressibility	.	.	.	.	$\varkappa \ldots K$
Viscosity	.	.	.	.	η
Fluidity	.	.	.	.	ϕ

Surface area	.	.	.	.	$A \ldots s$
Angle of contact	.	.	.	.	θ
Surface tension	.	.	.	.	$\gamma \ldots \sigma$
Parachor	.	.	.	.	$[P]$
Surface concentration excess	.	.	.	Γ

Number of mols	.	.	.	.	n
Concentration, mol. fraction	.	.	.	N, x
in other terms	.	.	.	c, C
Solubility	.	.	.	.	s
Diffusion coefficient	.	.	.	.	D

Chemical equilibrium constant (products/reactants)	K
solubility product	.	.	.	.	$K_s \ldots L$
Velocity constant of chemical reaction	.	k
Number of molecular collisions per second	.	Z
Partition function	.	.	.	.	f

| Efficiency, of any process | . | . | . | n |
| Wave function | . | . | . | . | ψ |

Heat and Thermodynamics

Temperature, on absolute scale, (°K)	.	.	T
on other scales	.	.	$\theta \ldots t$
Thermal conductivity	.	.	.	k

Energy (general symbol)	.	.	.	E
Work done by or on a system	.	.	$w \ldots W$
Heat entering a system	.	.	.	q
Specific heat (at constant pressure and volume)	c_p and c_v
molecular heat (at constant pressure and volume)	C_p and C_v
Ratio of specific heats	.	.	.	γ
Latent heat, per g.	.	.	.	l
per mol.	.	.	.	L

Intrinsic energy	.	.	.	.	$U \ldots E$
Enthalpy, total heat, or heat content	.	.	H
Entropy	.	.	.	.	S
Free energy (Helmholtz)	.	.	.	$A \ldots F$
Thermodynamic potential, Gibbs function, free energy (G. N. Lewis)	.	.	.	G

| Vapour pressure constant | . | . | . | i |

Chemical potential	.	.	.	.	μ
Activity	.	.	.	.	a
coefficient (for molar concentration)	.	f
Osmotic coefficient	.	.	.	.	g
Van't Hoff's factor	.	.	.	.	i

Electricity

Quantity of electricity . . .	Q
especially electrostatic charge . .	e
Potential (difference) . . .	$\left.\vphantom{\begin{array}{c}a\\b\end{array}}\right\}V$
Volta potential	
Electrokinetic potential . . .	ζ
especially electromotive force of voltaic cells	E
Potential gradient, in electric field . .	X
Electronic exit work function . . .	ϕ
Current	I
Resistance	R
specific resistance . . .	$\rho \ldots r$
specific conductance . . .	$\varkappa \ldots \sigma$
Inductance, self	L
mutual	M
Electrostatic capacity	C
Dielectric constant	ε
Dipole moment	τ

Electrochemistry

Degree of electrolytic dissociation . .	α
Valency of an ion	z
Ionic strength	I
Equivalent conductance . . .	Λ
equivalent ionic conductance, 'mobility' .	l (with subscript)
Transport number	T (with subscript) . . .
	n (with subscript)
Single electrode potential . . .	e (with subscript),
	E (with subscript)
Electrolytic polarization, overvoltage . .	$\eta \ldots \pi$

Magnetism

Magnetic field strength . . .	H
flux	ϕ
permeability . . .	μ
susceptibility—volume . .	$\varkappa$
mass . .	χ
moment	M
induction	B

Optics

Wave-length	λ
Wave number	ν
Intensity of light	I
Refractive index	n (with subscript)
	$\ldots \mu$ (with subscript)
specific refraction	r (with subscript)
molecular refraction . . .	$[R]$ (with subscript)
Molar extinction coefficient . . .	ε
Angle of (optical) rotation . . .	α
specific rotation	$[\alpha]$
Specific magnetic rotation . . .	ω

3. To be printed in Roman when not Greek.

Examples of Mathematical Constants and Operators.

Base of natural logarithms . . .	e
Ratio of circumference to diameter . .	π
Differential	d
partial	∂
Increment	Δ
very small increment . . .	δ
Sum	Σ
Product	Π
Function	f, ϕ
*Ampere (in sub-units) . . .	a.
Volt	v.
Ohm	Ω
Watt	W.
Farad	F.
Henry	H.
Centigrade	C.
Fahrenheit	F.
Kelvin	K.
Ångström unit.	A.
micron	μ
metre	m.
gram	g.
Litre	l.
Röntgen unit	r.
†Normal (concentration) . . .	N
†Molar (concentration) . . .	M

* E.g. 'ma.' for 'milliampere'; but 'amp.' is preferred for 'ampere'.
† Separated by a hyphen (and no full stop) from a chemical formula which follows it.

The following prefixes to abbreviations for the names of units should be used to indicate the specified multiples or sub-multiples of these units:

M	mega-	$10^6 \times$
k	kilo-	$10^3 \times$
d	deci-	$10^{-1} \times$
c	centi-	$10^{-2} \times$
m	milli-	$10^{-3} \times$
μ	micro-	$10^{-6} \times$

e.g. MΩ denotes megohm; kw., kilowatt; and μg., microgram. The use of μμ instead of mμ to denote 10^{-7} cm., or of γ to denote microgram is deprecated.

TABLE 11

Collected conversion factors.

Conversion	Factor	log.
N μg. to μg.-atom N	0·07139	$\bar{2}$·8536
NO$_3$ μg. to μg.-atom NO$_3$-N	0·01613	$\bar{2}$·2076
NO$_2$ μg. to μg.-atom NO$_2$-N	0·02174	$\bar{2}$·3373
NH$_3$ μg. to μg.-atom NH$_3$-N	0·05871	$\bar{2}$·7687
P μg. to μg.-atom P	0·03228	$\bar{2}$·5089
PO$_4$ μg. to μg.-atom PO$_4$-P	0·01053	$\bar{2}$·0224
P$_2$O$_5$ μg. to μg.-atom PO$_4$-P	0·01409	$\bar{2}$·1488
Si μg. to μg.-atom Si	0·03560	$\bar{2}$·5515
SiO$_2$ μg. to μg.-atom SiO$_4$-Si	0·01664	$\bar{2}$·2212
SiO$_4$ μg. to μg.-atom SiO$_4$-Si	0·01086	$\bar{2}$·0359

TABLE 12

International atomic weights (1952) and their reciprocals

(From *J. Amer. chem. Soc.*, 1952, **74**, 2447).

Element	Atomic Weight	Reciprocal
Aluminium	26·98	0·03706
Arsenic	74·91	0·01335
Barium	137·36	0·00728
Boron	10·82	0·09242
Bromine	79·916	0·01251
Cadmium	112·41	0·00890
Caesium	132·91	0·00752
Calcium	40·08	0·02495
Carbon	12·010	0·08326
Cerium	140·13	0·00714
Chlorine	35·457	0·02820
Chromium	52·01	0·01923
Cobalt	58·94	0·01697
Copper	63·54	0·01574
Fluorine	19·00	0·05263
Gold	197·2	0·00507
Hydrogen	1·0080	0·99206
Iodine	126·91	0·00788
Iron	55·85	0·01791
Lanthanum	138·92	0·00720
Lead	207·21	0·00483
Lithium	6·940	0·14409
Magnesium	24·32	0·04112
Manganese	54·93	0·01820
Mercury	200·61	0·00498
Molybdenum	95·95	0·01042
Nickel	58·69	0·01704
Nitrogen	14·008	0·07139
Oxygen	16·00000	0·06250
Phosphorus	30·975	0·03228
Potassium	39·100	0·02558
Radium	226·05	0·00442
Rubidium	85·48	0·01170
Scandium	44·96	0·02217
Selenium	78·96	0·01266
Silicon	28·09	0·03560
Silver	107·880	0·00927
Sodium	22·997	0·04348
Strontium	87·63	0·01141
Sulphur	32·066	0·03119
Thorium	232·12	0·00431
Tin	118·70	0·00842
Uranium	238·07	0·00420
Vanadium	50·95	0·01963
Yttrium	88·92	0·01125
Zinc	65·38	0·01530

TABLE 13

Molecular and equivalent weights, common substances

	Formula	Molecular Weight	Equivalent Weight
Acidimetry			
Sodium hydroxide	NaOH	40·005	40·005
Sodium carbonate	Na_2CO_3	106·00	53·00
Potassium hydroxide	KOH	56·10	56·10
Sodium borate	$Na_2B_4O_7.10H_2O$	381·44	190·72
Potassium hydrogen phthalate	$KHC_8H_4O_4$	204·22	204·22
Oxalic acid	$H_2C_2O_4.2H_2O$	126·068	63·034
Oxidimetry			
Potassium permanganate	$KMnO_4$	158·03	31·606
Ferrous ammonium sulphate	$FeSO_4.(NH_4)_2SO_4.6H_2O$	392·14	392·14
Potassium dichromate	$K_2Cr_2O_7$	294·21	49·035
Oxalic acid	$H_2C_2O_4.2H_2O$	126·068	63·034
Sodium oxalate	$Na_2C_2O_4$	134·01	67·005
Potassium tetraoxalate	$KH_3(C_2O_4)_2.2H_2O$	254·19	63·55
Ceric sulphate	$Ce(SO_4)_2$	332·25	332·25
Iodimetry			
Potassium biiodate	$KH(IO_3)_2$	389·94	32·495
Potassium iodate	KIO_3	214·02	35·670
Sodium thiosulphate	$Na_2S_2O_3.5H_2O$	248·192	248·192
Arsenious oxide	As_2O_3	197·82	49·455
Iodine	I_2	253·84	126·92

TABLE 14

Preparation of acids and alkali of approximate strength.

Hydrochloric acid

S.G. 1·178 at 15°C.; 35% HCl

g./l. required	ml. taken to 1 litre
10	24·26
20	48·52
36·46 (=N)	88·45
50	121·29
100	242·58

Sulphuric acid

S.G. 1·835 at 15°C.

g./l. required	ml. taken to 1 litre
5	3
20	11·6
49 (=N)	28·4
100	58·0
150	87·0

Nitric acid

S. G. 1·4146 at 15°C.

g./l. required	ml. taken to 1 litre
5	5·2
20	10·4
63 (=N)	65·5
100	104·0

Ammonia

S.G. 0·09; 27% NH_3 by weight

g./l. required	ml. taken to 1 litre
5	20·6
20	82·3
35 (=N)	61·4
50	205·8
100	411·5

TABLE 15

Transmission data. %. Ilford spectrum filters (standard).

(From Ilford Ltd. Handbook, London.)

Wavelength in mμ	600	601	602	603	604	605	606	607	608	609
350	—	—	—	—	—	—	—	—	—	—
360	—	—	—	—	—	—	—	—	—	—
370	—	—	—	—	—	—	—	—	—	—
380	1·0	1·5	—	—	—	—	—	—	—	—
390	2·1	4·2	—	—	—	—	—	—	—	—
400	3·2	9·1	—	—	—	—	—	—	—	—
410	3·0	12·0	—	—	—	—	—	—	—	—
420	1·5	13·0	—	—	—	—	—	—	—	—
430	1·8	13·0	—	—	—	—	—	—	—	—
440	4·0	13·0	1·9	—	—	—	—	—	—	—
450	0·5	11·0	3·7	—	—	—	—	—	—	—
460	—	6·4	10·0	—	—	—	—	—	—	—
470	—	4·2	11·0	0·6	—	—	—	—	—	—
480	—	0·2	6·9	6·8	—	—	—	—	—	—
490	—	—	1·9	12·0	—	—	—	—	—	—
500	—	—	—	8·5	0·8	—	—	—	—	—
510	—	—	—	3·5	2·1	—	—	—	—	—
520	—	—	—	0·6	7·4	—	—	—	—	—
530	—	—	—	—	7·2	0·2	—	—	—	—
540	—	—	—	—	0·7	5·0	—	—	—	—
550	—	—	—	—	—	6·0	—	—	—	—
560	—	—	—	—	—	3·6	0·6	—	—	—
570	—	—	—	—	—	1·0	5·7	—	—	—
580	—	—	—	—	—	—	6·4	3·1	—	—
590	—	—	—	—	—	—	3·2	16·0	—	—
600	—	—	—	—	—	—	1·3	17·0	—	—
610	—	—	—	—	—	—	0·6	14·0	0·1	—
620	—	—	—	—	—	—	—	11·0	0·7	—
630	—	—	—	—	—	—	—	9·1	3·8	—
640	—	—	—	—	—	—	—	7·6	16·0	0·1
650	—	—	—	—	—	—	—	7·2	39·0	0·6
660	—	—	—	—	—	—	—	7·2	63·0	3·5
670	—	—	—	—	—	—	—	6·9	76·0	17·0
680	—	—	—	—	—	—	—	6·9	79·0	41·0
690	—	—	—	—	—	—	—	6·3	81·0	62·0
700	—	—	—	—	—	—	—	5·3	83·0	72·0
710	—	—	—	—	—	—	—	4·9	83·0	76·0
720	—	—	—	—	—	—	—	4·8	83·0	76·0

TABLE 16

Transmission data. %. Ilford spectrum filters (bright).
Broader band width, higher transmission.

(From Ilford Ltd. Handbook, London.)

Wave-length in mμ	621	622	623	624	625	626
350	8·0	—	—	—	—	—
360	10·0	—	—	—	—	—
370	14·0	—	—	—	—	—
380	17·0	1·2	—	—	—	—
390	25·0	3·5	—	—	—	—
400	29·0	6·8	—	—	—	—
410	35·0	8·5	—	—	—	—
420	35·0	11·0	—	—	—	—
430	39·0	15·0	—	—	—	—
440	47·0	22·0	—	—	—	—
450	47·0	26·0	—	—	—	—
460	43·0	29·0	0·6	—	—	—
470	38·0	34·0	8·5	—	—	—
480	30·0	33·0	27·0	—	—	—
490	17·0	26·0	37·0	0·6	—	—
500	6·6	15·0	35·0	8·5	—	—
510	1·8	6·0	29·0	21·0	0·6	—
520	0·3	1·7	18·0	32·0	12·0	—
530	—	0·3	7·4	28·0	29·0	—
540	—	—	5·2	20·0	33·0	—
550	—	—	0·3	13·0	28·0	2·7
560	—	—	—	5·8	18·0	9·8
570	—	—	—	2·2	9·8	15·0
580	—	—	—	—	3·9	15·0
590	—	—	—	—	1·2	8·9
600	—	—	—	—	—	5·5
610	—	—	—	—	—	2·6
620	—	—	—	—	—	0·8
630	—	—	—	—	—	—
640	—	—	—	—	—	—

TABLE 17

Conversion of transmission (T) to absorption $(A=\log_{10} 1/T)$.

T	A	T	A	T	A	T	A	T	A
1·00	0·00000	·950	0·02227	·900	0·04575	·850	0·07061	·800	0·09691
·999	0·00043	·949	0·02272	·899	0·04622	·849	0·07111	·799	0·09747
·998	0·00087	·948	0·02321	·898	0·04673	·848	0·07158	·798	0·09798
·997	0·00130	·947	0·02366	·897	0·04720	·847	0·07210	·797	0·09854
·996	0·00174	·946	0·02411	·896	0·04770	·846	0·07262	·796	0·09909
·995	0·00218	·945	0·02457	·895	0·04817	·845	0·07313	·795	0·09965
·994	0·00261	·944	0·02502	·894	0·04867	·844	0·07364	·794	0·10017
·993	0·00305	·943	0·02547	·893	0·04914	·843	0·07410	·793	0·10072
·992	0·00350	·942	0·02596	·892	0·04965	·842	0·07467	·792	0·10127
·991	0·00393	·941	0·02641	·891	0·05011	·841	0·07522	·791	0·10182
·990	0·00436	·940	0·02686	·890	0·05061	·840	0·07573	·790	0·10236
·989	0·00479	·939	0·02735	·889	0·05112	·839	0·07623	·789	0·10292
·988	0·00522	·938	0·02780	·888	0·05158	·838	0·07675	·788	0·10346
·987	0·00569	·937	0·02824	·887	0·05208	·837	0·07725	·787	0·10400
·986	0·00612	·936	0·02873	·886	0·05258	·836	0·07780	·786	0·10459
·985	0·00655	·935	0·02918	·885	0·05304	·835	0·07831	·785	0·10514
·984	0·00702	·934	0·02966	·884	0·05354	·834	0·07882	·784	0·10568
·983	0·00745	·933	0·03011	·883	0·05404	·833	0·07936	·783	0·10622
·982	0·00788	·932	0·03060	·882	0·05453	·832	0·07986	·782	0·10680
·981	0·00834	·931	0·03104	·881	0·05504	·831	0·08041	·781	0·10735
·980	0·00877	·930	0·03153	·880	0·05553	·830	0·08092	·780	0·10792
·979	0·00924	·929	0·03197	·879	0·05603	·829	0·08149	·779	0·10847
·978	0·00966	·928	0·03246	·878	0·05652	·828	0·08196	·778	0·10900
·977	0·01009	·927	0·03290	·877	0·05701	·827	0·08250	·777	0·10958
·976	0·01055	·926	0·03338	·876	0·05752	·826	0·08304	·776	0·11016
·975	0·01100	·925	0·03387	·875	0·05801	·825	0·08354	·775	0·11069
·974	0·01145	·924	0·03435	·874	0·05851	·824	0·08407	·774	0·11126
·973	0·01187	·923	0·03479	·873	0·05900	·823	0·08462	·773	0·11184
·972	0·01233	·922	0·03527	·872	0·05948	·822	0·08511	·772	0·11242
·971	0·01280	·921	0·03575	·871	0·05998	·821	0·08565	·771	0·11294
·970	0·01332	·920	0·03623	·870	0·06047	·820	0·08618	·770	0·11351
·969	0·01368	·919	0·03667	·869	0·06096	·819	0·08672	·769	0·11407
·968	0·01414	·918	0·03715	·868	0·06149	·818	0·08725	·768	0·11464
·967	0·01456	·917	0·03763	·867	0·06198	·817	0·08778	·767	0·11521
·966	0·01502	·916	0·03810	·866	0·06247	·816	0·08832	·766	0·11578
·965	0·01549	·915	0·03858	·865	0·06300	·815	0·08884	·765	0·11635
·964	0·01591	·914	0·03906	·864	0·06348	·814	0·08938	·764	0·11691
·963	0·01637	·913	0·03953	·863	0·06397	·813	0·08991	·763	0·11747
·962	0·01683	·912	0·04001	·862	0·06450	·812	0·09043	·762	0·11803
·961	0·01728	·911	0·04049	·861	0·06498	·811	0·09096	·761	0·11863
·960	0·01774	·910	0·04096	·860	0·06551	·810	0·09153	·760	0·11919
·959	0·01821	·909	0·04143	·859	0·06599	·809	0·09206	·759	0·11976
·958	0·01862	·908	0·04191	·858	0·06652	·808	0·09258	·758	0·12034
·957	0·01908	·907	0·04238	·857	0·06703	·807	0·09314	·757	0·12090
·956	0·01953	·906	0·04289	·856	0·06751	·806	0·09366	·756	0·12149
·955	0·01999	·905	0·04336	·855	0·06803	·805	0·09419	·755	0·12205
·954	0·02044	·904	0·04384	·854	0·06856	·804	0·09475	·754	0·12264
·953	0·02090	·903	0·04431	·853	0·06904	·803	0·09527	·753	0·12320
·952	0·02136	·902	0·04478	·852	0·06955	·802	0·09583	·752	0·12378
·951	0·02181	·901	0·04527	·851	0·07009	·801	0·09635	·751	0·12438

TABLE 17—continued

(see also pages 298 and 299)

T	A	T	A	T	A	T	A	T	A
·750	0·12493	·700	0·15491	·650	0·18710	·600	0·22185	·550	0·25964
·749	0·12551	·699	0·15552	·649	0·18775	·599	0·22256	·549	0·26043
·748	0·12610	·698	0·15615	·648	0·18843	·598	0·22329	·548	0·26121
·747	0·12669	·697	0·15676	·647	0·18910	·597	0·22401	·547	0·26203
·746	0·12726	·696	0·15739	·646	0·18977	·596	0·22476	·546	0·26281
·745	0·12785	·695	0·15800	·645	0·19044	·595	0·22549	·545	0·26361
·744	0·12843	·694	0·15863	·644	0·19111	·594	0·22621	·544	0·26440
·743	0·12901	·693	0·15927	·643	0·19179	·593	0·22694	·543	0·26519
·742	0·12960	·692	0·15990	·642	0·19246	·592	0·22768	·542	0·26600
·741	0·13017	·691	0·16053	·641	0·19315	·591	0·22840	·541	0·26679
·740	0·13079	·690	0·16116	·640	0·19382	·590	0·22914	·540	0·26762
·739	0·13136	·689	0·16179	·639	0·19449	·589	0·22989	·539	0·26841
·738	0·13194	·688	0·16242	·638	0·19518	·588	0·23063	·538	0·26921
·737	0·13255	·687	0·16304	·637	0·19587	·587	0·23136	·537	0·27003
·736	0·13312	·686	0·16367	·636	0·19656	·586	0·23211	·536	0·27084
·735	0·13370	·685	0·16433	·635	0·19722	·585	0·23284	·535	0·27166
·734	0·13431	·684	0·16495	·634	0·19791	·584	0·23358	·534	0·27247
·733	0·13491	·683	0·16557	·633	0·19860	·583	0·23434	·533	0·27325
·732	0·13548	·682	0·16622	·632	0·19929	·582	0·23507	·532	0·27409
·731	0·13609	·681	0·16685	·631	0·19998	·581	0·23583	·531	0·27490
·730	0·13669	·680	0·16750	·630	0·20066	·580	0·23657	·530	0·27572
·729	0·13726	·679	0·16815	·629	0·20134	·579	0·23732	·529	0·27655
·728	0·13786	·678	0·16876	·628	0·20205	·578	0·23807	·528	0·27736
·727	0·13846	·677	0·16941	·627	0·20274	·577	0·23882	·527	0·27818
·726	0·13906	·676	0·17006	·626	0·20341	·576	0·23957	·526	0·27900
·725	0·13966	·675	0·17071	·625	0·20412	·575	0·24032	·525	0·27985
·724	0·14025	·674	0·17134	·624	0·20482	·574	0·24110	·524	0·28067
·723	0·14085	·673	0·17199	·623	0·20550	·573	0·24185	·523	0·28149
·722	0·14145	·672	0·17263	·622	0·20621	·572	0·24261	·522	0·28233
·721	0·14208	·671	0·17328	·621	0·20691	·571	0·24336	·521	0·28316
·720	0·14267	·670	0·17392	·620	0·20760	·570	0·24413	·520	0·28400
·719	0·14326	·669	0·17458	·619	0·20830	·569	0·24489	·519	0·28484
·718	0·14389	·668	0·17522	·618	0·20901	·568	0·24566	·518	0·28567
·717	0·14448	·667	0·17589	·617	0·20970	·567	0·24642	·517	0·28650
·716	0·14508	·666	0·17652	·616	0·21043	·566	0·24719	·516	0·28735
·715	0·14570	·665	0·17719	·615	0·21112	·565	0·24795	·515	0·28819
·714	0·14632	·664	0·17782	·614	0·21184	·564	0·34871	·514	0·28903
·713	0·14690	·663	0·17849	·613	0·21253	·563	0·24949	·513	0·28988
·712	0·14752	·662	0·17915	·612	0·21325	·562	0·25028	·512	0·29072
·711	0·14814	·661	0·17981	·611	0·21397	·561	0·25111	·511	0·29157
·710	0·14875	·660	0·18047	·610	0·21465	·560	0·25181	·510	0·29244
·709	0·14934	·659	0·18113	·609	0·21537	·559	0·25259	·509	0·29327
·708	0·14995	·658	0·18179	·608	0·21608	·558	0·25336	·508	0·29414
·707	0·15057	·657	0·18244	·607	0·21680	·557	0·25413	·507	0·29500
·706	0·15118	·656	0·18301	·606	0·21753	·556	0·25494	·506	0·29586
·705	0·15180	·655	0·18375	·605	0·21825	·555	0·25570	·505	0·29671
·704	0·15244	·654	0·18444	·604	0·21896	·554	0·25650	·504	0·29756
·703	0·15305	·653	0·18509	·603	0·21968	·553	0·25727	·503	0·29844
·702	0·15366	·652	0·18574	·602	0·22040	·552	0·25806	·502	0·29929
·701	0·15427	·651	0·18642	·601	0·22112	·551	0·25886	·501	0·30016

TABLE 17—*continued*

T	A	T	A	T	A	T	A	T	A
·500	0·30103	·450	0·34678	·400	0·39794	·350	0·45593	·300	0·52288
·499	0·30190	·449	0·34776	·399	0·39903	·349	0·45717	·299	0·52433
·498	0·30276	·448	0·34871	·398	0·40012	·348	0·45843	·298	0·52578
·497	0·30365	·447	0·34968	·397	0·40122	·347	0·45966	·297	0·52724
·496	0·30451	·446	0·35068	·396	0·40231	·346	0·46093	·296	0·52871
·495	0·30539	·445	0·35164	·395	0·40339	·345	0·46219	·295	0·53017
·494	0·30627	·444	0·35263	·394	0·40451	·344	0·46344	·294	0·53166
·493	0·30716	·443	0·35359	·393	0·40561	·343	0·46471	·293	0·53314
·492	0·30803	·442	0·35457	·392	0·40671	·342	0·46598	·292	0·53462
·491	0·30892	·441	0·35557	·391	0·40781	·341	0·46725	·291	0·53610
·490	0·30980	·440	0·35654	·390	0·40894	·340	0·46852	·290	0·53761
·489	0·31069	·439	0·35763	·389	0·41005	·339	0·46980	·289	0·53911
·488	0·31158	·438	0·35853	·388	0·41116	·338	0·47109	·288	0·54060
·487	0·31247	·437	0·35952	·387	0·41229	·337	0·47238	·287	0·54212
·486	0·31336	·436	0·36051	·386	0·41342	·336	0·47366	·286	0·54363
·485	0·31427	·435	0·36152	·385	0·41454	·335	0·47495	·285	0·54516
·484	0·31515	·434	0·36252	·384	0·41567	·334	0·47625	·284	0·54668
·483	0·31605	·433	0·36351	·383	0·41680	·333	0·47756	·283	0·54821
·482	0·31696	·432	0·36452	·382	0·41794	·332	0·47885	·282	0·54975
·481	0·31785	·431	0·36552	·381	0·41908	·331	0·48016	·281	0·55130
·480	0·31875	·430	0·36653	·380	0·42022	·330	0·48148	·280	0·55284
·479	0·31967	·429	0·36754	·379	0·42135	·329	0·48280	·279	0·55439
·478	0·32058	·428	0·36854	·378	0·42251	·328	0·48412	·278	0·55595
·477	0·32147	·427	0·36957	·377	0·42365	·327	0·48545	·277	0·55752
·476	0·32238	·426	0·37058	·376	0·42482	·326	0·48678	·276	0·55909
475	0·32331	·425	0·37161	·375	0·42597	·325	0·48812	·275	0·56067
·474	0·32422	·424	0·37263	·374	0·42713	·324	0·48946	·274	0·56224
·473	0·32514	·423	0·37367	·373	0·42830	·323	0·49080	·273	0·56384
·472	0·32605	·422	0·37470	·372	0·42946	·322	0·49214	·272	0·56544
·471	0·32697	·421	0·37571	·371	0·43060	·321	0·49350	·271	0·56703
·470	0·32791	·420	0·37676	·370	0·43180	·320	0·49485	·270	0·56863
·469	0·32883	·419	0·37778	·369	0·43297	·319	0·49621	·269	0·57025
·468	0·32976	·418	0·37881	·368	0·43415	·318	0·49758	·268	0·57186
·467	0·33068	·417	0·37987	·367	0·43534	·317	0·49894	·267	0·57348
·466	0·33161	·416	0·38089	·366	0·43653	·316	0·50032	·266	0·57512
·465	0·33254	·415	0·38195	·365	0·43770	·315	0·50169	·265	0·57676
·464	0·33347	·414	0·38301	·364	0·43891	·314	0·50307	·264	0·57840
·463	0·33441	·413	0·38404	·363	0·44009	·313	0·50445	·263	0·58004
·462	0·33536	·412	0·38511	·362	0·44128	·312	0·50584	·262	0·58170
·461	0·33630	·411	0·38616	·361	0·44250	·311	0·50723	·261	0·58336
·460	0·33724	·410	0·38721	·360	0·44371	·310	0·50864	·260	0·58503
·459	0·33818	·409	0·38828	·359	0·44491	·309	0·51004	·259	0·58670
·458	0·33913	·408	0·38934	·358	0·44612	·308	0·51146	·258	0·58838
·457	0·34009	·407	0·39041	·357	0·44733	·307	0·51286	·257	0·59007
·456	0·34104	·406	0·39148	·356	0·44855	·306	0·51428	·256	0·59176
·455	0·34199	·405	0·39254	·355	0·44977	·305	0·51570	·255	0·59347
·454	0·34294	·404	0·39362	·354	0·45100	·304	0·51713	·254	0·59517
·453	0·34391	·403	0·39470	·353	0·45223	·303	0·51855	·253	0·59689
·452	0·34487	·402	0·39578	·352	0·45346	·302	0·52000	·252	0·59860
·451	0·34583	·401	0·39686	·351	0·45469	·301	0·52144	·251	0·60033

TABLE 17—*continued*

T	A	T	A	T	A	T	A	T	A
·250	0·60206	·200	0·69897	·150	0·82391	·100	2·00000	·050	1·30103
·249	0·60380	·199	0·70115	·149	0·82682	·099	1·00436	·049	1·30980
·248	0·60555	·198	0·70333	·148	0·82974	·098	1·00877	·048	1·31875
·247	0·60730	·197	0·70553	·147	0·83268	·097	1·01323	·047	1·32791
·246	0·60906	·196	0·70774	·146	0·83565	·096	1·01774	·046	1·33724
·245	0·61083	·195	0·70997	·145	0·83864	·095	1·02227	·045	1·34678
·244	0·61261	·194	0·71218	·144	0·84163	·094	1·02686	·044	1·35654
·243	0·61439	·193	0·71444	·143	0·84466	·093	1·03153	·043	1·36653
·242	0·61618	·192	0·71669	·142	0·84772	·092	1·03623	·042	1·37676
·241	0·61798	·191	0·71897	·141	0·85078	·091	1·04096	·041	1·38721
·240	0·61979	·190	0·72125	·140	0·85387	·090	1·04575	·040	1·39794
·239	0·62160	·189	0·72354	·139	0·85698	·089	1·05061	·039	1·40894
·238	0·62342	·188	0·72584	·138	0·86012	·088	1·05553	·038	1·42022
·237	0·62525	·187	0·72816	·137	0·86328	·087	1·06047	·037	1·43180
·236	0·62709	·186	0·73048	·136	0·86646	·086	1·06551	·036	1·44371
·235	0·62893	·185	0·73283	·135	0·86966	·085	1·07061	·035	1·45593
·234	0·63078	·184	0·73518	·134	0·87290	·084	1·07573	·034	1·46852
·233	0·63264	·183	0·73755	·133	0·87615	·083	1·08092	·033	1·48148
·232	0·63451	·182	0·73993	·132	0·87943	·082	1·08618	·032	1·49485
·231	0·63639	·181	0·74232	·131	0·88273	·081	1·09153	·031	1·50864
·230	0·63827	·180	0·74473	·130	0·88606	·080	1·09691	·030	1·52288
·229	0·64016	·179	0·74715	·129	0·88941	·079	1·10236	·029	1·53761
·228	0·64207	·178	0·74958	·128	0·89279	·078	1·10792	·028	1·55284
·227	0·64398	·177	0·75202	·127	0·89620	·077	1·11351	·027	1·56863
·226	0·64590	·176	0·75448	·126	0·89963	·076	1·11919	·026	1·58503
·225	0·64781	·175	0·75696	·125	0·90309	·075	1·12493	·025	1·60206
·224	0·64975	·174	0·75945	·124	0·90658	·074	1·13079	·024	1·61979
·223	0·65170	·173	0·76195	·123	0·91010	·073	1·13669	·023	1·63827
·222	0·65365	·172	0·76448	·122	0·91364	·072	1·14267	·022	1·65758
·221	0·65561	·171	0·76701	·121	0·91722	·071	1·14875	·021	1·67778
·220	0·65758	·170	0·76955	·120	0·92082	·070	1·15491	·020	1·69897
·219	0·65956	·169	0·77211	·119	0·92445	·069	1·16116	·019	1·72125
·218	0·66155	·168	0·77469	·118	0·92812	·068	1·16750	·018	1·74473
·217	0·66354	·167	0·77728	·117	0·93181	·067	1·17392	·017	1·76955
·216	0·66555	·166	0·77989	·116	0·93555	·066	1·18047	·016	1·79588
·215	0·66757	·165	0·78251	·115	0·93930	·065	1·18710	·015	1·82391
·214	0·66958	·164	0·78516	·114	0·94309	·064	1·19382	·014	1·85387
·213	0·67161	·163	0·78781	·113	0·94692	·063	1·20066	·013	1·88606
·212	0·67367	·162	0·79049	·112	0·95078	·062	1·20760	·012	1·92082
·211	0·67572	·161	0·79317	·111	0·95468	·061	1·21465	·011	1·95860
·210	0·67778	·160	0·79588	·110	0·95860	·060	1·22185	·010	2·00000
·209	0·67985	·159	0·79861	·109	0·96257	·059	1·22914	·009	2·04575
·208	0·68193	·158	0·80135	·108	0·96657	·058	1·23657	·008	2·09691
·207	0·68403	·157	0·80410	·107	0·97062	·057	1·24413	·007	2·15491
·206	0·68614	·156	0·80688	·106	0·97470	·056	1·25181	·006	2·22185
·205	0·68824	·155	0·80967	·105	0·97881	·055	1·25964	·005	2·30103
·204	0·69037	·154	0·81248	·104	0·98297	·054	1·26762	·004	2·39794
·203	0·69250	·153	0·81531	·103	0·98716	·053	1·27572	·003	2·52288
·202	0·69465	·152	0·81815	·102	0·99140	·052	1·28400	·002	2·69897
·201	0·69680	·151	0·82102	·101	0·99568	·051	1·29244	·001	3·00000

TABLE 18

Mg.-atoms of oxygen contained in 1 litre of sea water of a chlorinity, Cl‰, at temperature $t°$ when in equilibrium with an oxygen atmosphere having a pressure $0 \cdot 209 \times 760$ Torr. Calculated from data of C. J. J. Fox.

(From J. P. Jacobsen, R. J. Robinson, and T. G. Thompson, *Publ. sci. Ass. Océanogr. phys.*, 1950, No. 11, pp. 18 and 19, Table 1.)

$t°C$	0‰	1‰	2‰	3‰	4‰	5‰	6‰	7‰	8‰	9‰	10‰	11‰	12‰	13‰	14‰	15‰	16‰	17‰	18‰	19‰	20‰
−1	·919	·908	·898	·888	·878	·867	·856	·847	·836	·826	·815	·805	·795	·784	·795	·784	·773	·763	·752	·741	·731
0	·895	·884	·874	·865	·855	·844	·834	·824	·815	·805	·794	·784	·774	·764	·773	·764	·753	·743	·732	·722	·712
1	·871	·861	·851	·842	·832	·823	·813	·803	·793	·784	·774	·764	·755	·745	·754	·744	·734	·724	·714	·704	·694
2	·848	·839	·830	·821	·811	·802	·792	·783	·773	·764	·755	·746	·736	·727	·735	·725	·716	·706	·697	·687	·677
3	·827	·818	·809	·799	·790	·781	·773	·764	·755	·746	·736	·727	·718	·709	·717	·708	·698	·689	·680	·671	·661
4	·806	·798	·789	·780	·772	·763	·754	·745	·736	·727	·719	·710	·701	·692	·700	·691	·682	·673	·664	·655	·646
5	·787	·778	·770	·761	·753	·744	·736	·727	·719	·710	·702	·693	·685	·676	·683	·675	·666	·657	·648	·639	·631
6	·768	·759	·751	·743	·735	·727	·718	·710	·702	·694	·686	·678	·670	·661	·668	·660	·651	·643	·634	·626	·617
7	·750	·742	·734	·726	·718	·710	·702	·694	·686	·678	·671	·663	·655	·647	·653	·645	·637	·629	·621	·612	·604
8	·733	·725	·717	·710	·702	·694	·687	·679	·672	·664	·656	·648	·640	·633	·639	·631	·622	·615	·607	·599	·591
9	·716	·709	·701	·694	·687	·679	·672	·664	·657	·649	·642	·634	·627	·620	·625	·617	·610	·602	·595	·587	·579
10	·700	·693	·686	·679	·672	·664	·657	·650	·643	·636	·629	·622	·614	·607	·612	·605	·597	·589	·582	·575	·567
11	·686	·679	·672	·664	·657	·651	·644	·637	·630	·622	·615	·609	·602	·595	·599	·592	·585	·578	·571	·564	·556
12	·672	·664	·657	·651	·644	·638	·631	·623	·617	·610	·604	·597	·590	·583	·588	·581	·574	·568	·560	·553	·546
13	·658	·651	·644	·638	·631	·625	·618	·612	·605	·598	·592	·585	·579	·572	·577	·570	·564	·556	·549	·543	·536
14	·645	·639	·631	·625	·619	·613	·606	·600	·593	·587	·581	·574	·568	·561	·566	·559	·553	·546	·539	·533	·526
15	·632	·626	·620	·614	·607	·601	·595	·589	·582	·576	·570	·564	·557	·551	·556	·548	·542	·536	·530	·523	·517
16	·620	·614	·608	·602	·596	·589	·584	·578	·572	·565	·559	·554	·547	·541	·545	·539	·532	·526	·520	·514	·508
17	·608	·603	·597	·591	·585	·579	·573	·567	·561	·556	·549	·544	·538	·532	·535	·530	·523	·517	·511	·505	·499
18	·597	·592	·586	·581	·575	·569	·563	·557	·551	·546	·540	·534	·529	·523	·526	·521	·514	·508	·503	·497	·490
19	·587	·581	·575	·570	·565	·559	·553	·547	·542	·536	·531	·525	·520	·514	·517	·512	·505	·500	·494	·489	·482
20	·577	·572	·565	·560	·556	·549	·544	·539	·532	·527	·522	·516	·511	·505	·508	·503	·497	·491	·486	·480	·474
21	·567	·562	·556	·551	·546	·539	·534	·529	·523	·518	·514	·507	·502	·497	·499	·494	·489	·483	·478	·472	·466
22	·557	·552	·547	·541	·537	·531	·525	·520	·515	·510	·505	·499	·494	·489	·491	·486	·480	·475	·470	·464	·458
23	·548	·543	·538	·533	·528	·522	·517	·512	·506	·501	·496	·491	·486	·480	·483	·478	·472	·467	·462	·456	·450
24	·539	·535	·529	·524	·519	·514	·508	·504	·498	·493	·488	·483	·478	·472	·475	·470	·464	·459	·455	·449	·442
25	·531	·526	·520	·515	·510	·505	·500	·496	·490	·485	·480	·475	·470	·464	·467	·462	·457	·452	·447	·442	·434
26	·522	·517	·512	·506	·502	·497	·492	·488	·482	·477	·472	·467	·462	·456	·459	·455	·449	·444	·439	·434	·427
27	·514	·508	·504	·498	·494	·489	·484	·480	·474	·469	·464	·459	·454	·448	·452	·447	·441	·437	·431	·427	·420
28	·508	·500	·496	·490	·486	·481	·476	·472	·466	·461	·455	·451	·446	·440	·444	·439	·434	·429	·424	·419	·413
29	·505	·492	·488	·482	·478	·473	·468	·464	·458	·453	·447	·443	·438	·433	·436	·431	·426	·421	·416	·411	·405
30	·497	·485	·480	·474	·470	·465	·460	·456	·450	·445	·439	·435	·430	·425	·428	·423	·418	·414	·409	·404	·398

TABLE 19

Millilitre of oxygen at S.T.P. contained in 1 litre of sea water of a chlorinity, $Cl‰$, at a temperature $t°$ when in equilibrium with an oxygen atmosphere having a pressure $0·209 \times 760$ Torr. From data of C. J. J. Fox.

(From J. P. Jacobsen, R. J. Robinson, and T. G. Thompson, *Publ. sci. Ass. Oceanogr. phys.* 1950, No. 11, pp. 20 and 21, Table 2.)

$t°$C.	0‰	1‰	2‰	3‰	4‰	5‰	6‰	7‰	8‰	9‰	10‰	11‰	12‰	13‰	14‰	15‰	16‰	17‰	18‰	19‰	20‰
0	10·29	10·17	10·09	9·94	9·83	9·71	9·59	9·48	9·36	9·25	9·13	9·01	8·90	8·78	8·66	8·55	8·43	8·32	8·20	8·08	7·97
1	10·02	9·90	9·79	9·68	9·57	9·45	9·34	9·23	9·12	9·01	8·89	8·78	8·67	8·56	8·44	8·33	8·22	8·11	8·00	7·88	7·77
2	9·75	9·64	9·53	9·43	9·32	9·21	9·10	8·99	8·88	8·78	8·67	8·56	8·45	8·34	8·23	8·12	8·02	7·91	7·80	7·69	7·58
3	9·50	9·39	9·29	9·19	9·08	8·98	8·87	8·77	8·66	8·56	8·45	8·35	8·24	8·14	8·03	7·93	7·82	7·72	7·61	7·51	7·40
4	9·26	9·16	9·06	8·95	8·85	8·75	8·65	8·55	8·45	8·35	8·24	8·14	8·04	7·94	7·84	7·74	7·64	7·53	7·43	7·33	7·23
5	9·03	8·93	8·83	8·73	8·64	8·54	8·44	8·34	8·24	8·14	8·05	7·95	7·85	7·75	7·65	7·56	7·46	7·36	7·26	7·16	7·07
6	8·81	8·71	8·62	8·52	8·43	8·33	8·24	8·14	8·05	7·95	7·86	7·76	7·67	7·57	7·48	7·38	7·28	7·20	7·10	7·01	6·91
7	8·60	8·50	8·41	8·32	8·23	8·14	8·04	7·95	7·85	7·77	7·68	7·59	7·50	7·40	7·31	7·22	7·13	7·04	6·95	6·85	6·76
8	8·40	8·31	8·22	8·13	8·04	7·95	7·86	7·77	7·68	7·59	7·51	7·42	7·33	7·24	7·15	7·06	6·97	6·89	6·80	6·71	6·62
9	8·21	8·12	8·03	7·95	7·86	7·77	7·69	7·60	7·52	7·43	7·34	7·26	7·17	7·09	7·00	6·91	6·83	6·74	6·66	6·57	6·48
10	8·02	7·94	7·85	7·77	7·69	7·60	7·52	7·44	7·36	7·27	7·19	7·10	7·02	6·94	6·85	6·77	6·69	6·60	6·52	6·44	6·35
11	7·84	7·76	7·68	7·60	7·52	7·44	7·36	7·28	7·20	7·12	7·04	6·96	6·88	6·80	6·71	6·63	6·55	6·47	6·39	6·31	6·23
12	7·68	7·60	7·52	7·44	7·36	7·29	7·21	7·13	7·05	6·97	6·89	6·82	6·74	6·66	6·58	6·50	6·43	6·35	6·27	6·19	6·11
13	7·52	7·44	7·36	7·29	7·21	7·14	7·06	6·98	6·91	6·83	6·76	6·68	6·61	6·53	6·46	6·38	6·31	6·23	6·15	6·08	6·00
14	7·37	7·30	7·21	7·14	7·07	7·00	6·92	6·85	6·77	6·70	6·63	6·55	6·48	6·41	6·34	6·26	6·19	6·11	6·04	5·97	5·89
15	7·22	7·15	7·07	7·00	6·93	6·86	6·79	6·72	6·64	6·57	6·50	6·43	6·36	6·29	6·22	6·14	6·07	6·00	5·93	5·86	5·79
16	7·08	7·01	6·94	6·87	6·80	6·73	6·66	6·59	6·52	6·45	6·38	6·31	6·24	6·17	6·10	6·03	5·96	5·89	5·82	5·76	5·69
17	6·94	6·88	6·81	6·74	6·67	6·60	6·54	6·47	6·40	6·33	6·26	6·20	6·13	6·06	5·99	5·93	5·86	5·79	5·72	5·66	5·59
18	6·81	6·75	6·68	6·62	6·55	6·48	6·42	6·35	6·28	6·22	6·15	6·09	6·02	5·96	5·89	5·83	5·76	5·69	5·63	5·56	5·49
19	6·69	6·63	6·56	6·50	6·44	6·37	6·30	6·24	6·17	6·11	6·05	5·98	5·92	5·86	5·79	5·73	5·66	5·60	5·53	5·47	5·40
20	6·57	6·51	6·44	6·38	6·33	6·26	6·19	6·13	6·07	6·00	5·95	5·88	5·82	5·76	5·69	5·63	5·56	5·50	5·44	5·38	5·31
21	6·46	6·40	6·33	6·27	6·22	6·15	6·09	6·03	5·96	5·90	5·85	5·78	5·72	5·66	5·59	5·53	5·47	5·41	5·35	5·29	5·22
22	6·35	6·29	6·23	6·17	6·11	6·04	5·98	5·92	5·86	5·80	5·75	5·68	5·62	5·56	5·50	5·44	5·38	5·32	5·26	5·20	5·13
23	6·24	6·18	6·12	6·06	6·01	5·94	5·88	5·82	5·77	5·71	5·65	5·59	5·53	5·47	5·41	5·35	5·29	5·23	5·17	5·11	5·04
24	6·14	6·08	6·02	5·97	5·91	5·84	5·79	5·73	5·67	5·61	5·55	5·50	5·44	5·38	5·32	5·26	5·20	5·14	5·09	5·03	4·95
25	6·04	5·99	5·92	5·87	5·81	5·75	5·69	5·64	5·58	5·52	5·46	5·41	5·35	5·29	5·23	5·17	5·12	5·06	5·00	4·95	4·86
26	5·94	5·89	5·82	5·77	5·71	5·66	5·60	5·55	5·49	5·43	5·37	5·32	5·26	5·20	5·14	5·09	5·03	4·97	4·92	4·86	4·78
27	5·84	5·79	5·73	5·67	5·62	5·57	5·51	5·46	5·40	5·34	5·28	5·23	5·17	5·11	5·06	5·00	4·94	4·89	4·83	4·78	4·70
28	5·75	5·69	5·64	5·58	5·53	5·48	5·42	5·37	5·31	5·25	5·19	5·14	5·08	5·02	4·97	4·91	4·86	4·80	4·75	4·69	4·62
29	5·66	5·60	5·55	5·49	5·44	5·39	5·33	5·28	5·22	5·16	5·10	5·05	4·99	4·93	4·88	4·83	4·77	4·71	4·66	4·60	4·54
30	5·57	5·31	5·46	5·40	5·35	5·30	5·24	5·19	5·13	5·07	5·01	4·96	4·90	4·85	4·79	4·74	4·68	4·63	4·58	4·52	4·46

Handwritten margin note (pointing to the circled value 5·31 at 30 °C, 1‰): 5·51 (Harvey)

TABLE 20*

Mg.-atoms of oxygen contained in 1 litre of sea water of a chlorinity, Cl‰, at temperature, $t°$, when exposed to an atmosphere of wet, CO_2-free air at a pressure of 760 mm.

(From G. A. Truesdale, A. L. Downing, and G. F. Lowden, J. appl. Chem., 1955, 5, calculated from Equation 3 and Table III, pp. 58 and 59.)

$t°C.$	0‰	1‰	2‰	3‰	4‰	5‰	6‰	7‰	8‰	9‰	10‰	11‰	12‰	13‰	14‰	15‰	16‰	17‰	18‰	19‰	20‰
0°	0·885	·875	·866	·856	·847	·837	·828	·818	·809	·799	·790	·780	·771	·761	·752	·743	·733	·724	·714	·705	·695
1°	·860	·851	·842	·833	·824	·814	·805	·796	·787	·778	·769	·759	·750	·741	·732	·723	·713	·704	·695	·686	·677
2°	·837	·828	·820	·811	·802	·793	·784	·775	·766	·757	·748	·739	·730	·721	·712	·703	·695	·686	·677	·668	·659
3°	·815	·807	·798	·789	·781	·772	·764	·755	·746	·738	·729	·720	·712	·703	·694	·686	·677	·668	·660	·651	·642
4°	·794	·785	·777	·768	·760	·752	·743	·735	·726	·718	·710	·701	·693	·684	·676	·668	·659	·651	·643	·634	·626
5°	·773	·765	·757	·749	·740	·732	·724	·716	·708	·700	·692	·683	·675	·667	·659	·651	·643	·635	·626	·618	·610
6°	·754	·746	·738	·730	·722	·714	·706	·698	·690	·683	·675	·667	·659	·651	·643	·635	·627	·619	·611	·604	·596
7°	·735	·727	·720	·712	·704	·696	·689	·681	·674	·666	·658	·650	·643	·635	·627	·620	·612	·604	·597	·589	·581
8°	·717	·709	·702	·694	·687	·680	·672	·665	·657	·650	·642	·635	·627	·620	·613	·605	·598	·590	·583	·575	·568
9°	·699	·692	·685	·678	·670	·663	·656	·649	·641	·634	·627	·620	·613	·605	·598	·591	·584	·576	·569	·562	·555
10°	·682	·675	·668	·661	·654	·647	·640	·633	·626	·619	·612	·605	·598	·591	·584	·577	·570	·563	·556	·549	·542
11°	·666	·660	·653	·646	·640	·633	·626	·619	·612	·605	·599	·592	·585	·578	·571	·564	·558	·551	·544	·537	·530
12°	·652	·645	·639	·632	·625	·619	·612	·605	·599	·592	·586	·579	·572	·566	·559	·552	·546	·539	·533	·526	·519
13°	·637	·631	·625	·618	·612	·605	·599	·592	·586	·579	·573	·567	·560	·554	·547	·541	·534	·528	·521	·515	·509
14°	·624	·617	·611	·605	·599	·592	·586	·580	·574	·567	·561	·555	·549	·542	·536	·530	·524	·517	·511	·505	·499
15°	·610	·604	·598	·592	·586	·579	·573	·567	·561	·555	·549	·543	·537	·531	·525	·519	·512	·506	·500	·494	·488
16°	·597	·591	·586	·580	·574	·568	·562	·556	·550	·544	·538	·532	·526	·520	·514	·508	·502	·497	·491	·485	·479
17°	·586	·580	·574	·568	·562	·557	·551	·545	·539	·533	·528	·522	·516	·510	·505	·499	·493	·487	·481	·476	·470
18°	·574	·568	·562	·557	·551	·545	·540	·534	·528	·523	·517	·511	·506	·500	·495	·489	·483	·478	·472	·466	·461
19°	·563	·558	·552	·546	·541	·535	·530	·525	·519	·513	·508	·502	·497	·491	·486	·480	·475	·469	·464	·458	·453
20°	·552	·547	·542	·536	·531	·525	·520	·513	·509	·504	·498	·493	·488	·482	·477	·472	·466	·461	·455	·450	·445
21°	·542	·537	·532	·527	·521	·516	·511	·506	·500	·495	·490	·484	·479	·474	·469	·463	·458	·453	·448	·442	·437
22°	·533	·528	·523	·518	·512	·507	·502	·497	·492	·487	·481	·476	·471	·466	·461	·456	·450	·445	·440	·435	·430
23°	·524	·519	·514	·508	·503	·498	·493	·488	·483	·478	·473	·468	·463	·458	·453	·448	·443	·438	·432	·427	·422
24°	·516	·511	·506	·501	·496	·491	·486	·481	·476	·471	·466	·461	·456	·451	·446	·441	·436	·431	·426	·421	·416
25°	·507	·502	·497	·492	·487	·482	·477	·473	·468	·463	·458	·453	·448	·443	·438	·433	·428	·424	·419	·414	·409
26°	·499	·494	·490	·485	·480	·475	·470	·466	·461	·456	·451	·446	·441	·437	·432	·427	·422	·417	·413	·408	·403
27°	·491	·486	·482	·477	·472	·467	·463	·458	·453	·448	·444	·439	·434	·429	·425	·420	·415	·410	·406	·401	·396
28°	·484	·480	·475	·470	·466	·461	·456	·451	·447	·442	·437	·433	·428	·423	·419	·414	·409	·405	·400	·395	·390
29°	·477	·473	·468	·463	·459	·454	·450	·445	·440	·436	·431	·426	·422	·417	·412	·408	·403	·398	·394	·389	·384
30°	·471	·466	·461	·457	·452	·447	·443	·438	·434	·429	·424	·420	·415	·411	·406	·401	·397	·392	·387	·383	·378

Millilitre of oxygen at S.T.P. contained in 1 litre of sea water of a chlorinity, Cl‰, at a temperature, $t°$, when exposed to an atmosphere of wet, CO_2-free air at a pressure of 760 mm.

(From G. A. Truesdale, A. L. Downing, and G. F. Lowden, *J. appl. Chem.*, 1955, **5**, calculated from Equation 3 and Table III, pp. 58 and 59).

$t°C$	0‰	1‰	2‰	3‰	4‰	5‰	6‰	7‰	8‰	9‰	10‰	11‰	12‰	13‰	14‰	15‰	16‰	17‰	18‰	19‰	20‰
0°	9·91	9·80	9·70	9·59	9·48	9·38	9·27	9·16	9·06	8·95	8·85	8·74	8·63	8·53	8·42	8·31	8·21	8·10	8·00	7·89	7·78
1°	9·64	9·53	9·43	9·33	9·22	9·12	9·02	8·91	8·81	8·71	8·61	8·50	8·40	8·30	8·19	8·09	7·99	7·89	7·78	7·68	7·58
2°	9·38	9·28	9·18	9·08	8·98	8·88	8·78	8·68	8·58	8·48	8·38	8·28	8·18	8·08	7·98	7·88	7·78	7·68	7·58	7·48	7·38
3°	9·13	9·04	8·94	8·84	8·74	8·65	8·55	8·45	8·36	8·26	8·16	8·07	7·97	7·87	7·78	7·68	7·58	7·48	7·39	7·29	7·19
4°	8·89	8·79	8·70	8·61	8·51	8·42	8·32	8·23	8·14	8·04	7·95	7·85	7·76	7·67	7·57	7·48	7·38	7·29	7·20	7·10	7·01
5°	8·66	8·56	8·47	8·38	8·29	8·20	8·11	8·02	7·93	7·84	7·74	7·65	7·56	7·47	7·38	7·29	7·20	7·11	7·01	6·92	6·83
6°	8·44	8·35	8·26	8·17	8·09	8·00	7·91	7·82	7·73	7·64	7·56	7·47	7·38	7·29	7·20	7·11	7·02	6·94	6·85	6·76	6·67
7°	8·23	8·14	8·06	7·97	7·89	7·80	7·71	7·63	7·54	7·46	7·38	7·28	7·20	7·11	7·03	6·94	6·85	6·77	6·68	6·60	6·51
8°	8·03	7·94	7·86	7·78	7·69	7·61	7·53	7·44	7·36	7·28	7·19	7·11	7·03	6·94	6·86	6·78	6·69	6·61	6·53	6·44	6·36
9°	7·83	7·75	7·67	7·59	7·51	7·43	7·35	7·26	7·18	7·10	7·02	6·94	6·86	6·78	6·70	6·62	6·54	6·46	6·38	6·29	6·21
10°	7·64	7·56	7·48	7·41	7·33	7·25	7·17	7·09	7·01	6·93	6·86	6·78	6·70	6·62	6·54	6·46	6·38	6·31	6·23	6·15	6·07
11°	7·47	7·39	7·31	7·24	7·16	7·09	7·01	6·93	6·86	6·78	6·70	6·63	6·55	6·47	6·40	6·32	6·25	6·17	6·09	6·02	5·94
12°	7·30	7·22	7·15	7·08	7·00	6·93	6·85	6·78	6·71	6·63	6·56	6·48	6·41	6·33	6·26	6·19	6·11	6·04	5·96	5·89	5·82
13°	7·14	7·07	6·99	6·92	6·85	6·78	6·71	6·63	6·56	6·49	6·42	6·34	6·27	6·20	6·13	6·06	5·98	5·91	5·84	5·77	5·70
14°	6·98	6·91	6·84	6·77	6·70	6·63	6·56	6·49	6·42	6·35	6·28	6·21	6·14	6·07	6·00	5·93	5·86	5·79	5·72	5·65	5·58
15°	6·83	6·76	6·69	6·63	6·56	6·49	6·42	6·35	6·28	6·22	6·15	6·08	6·01	5·94	5·87	5·81	5·74	5·67	5·60	5·53	5·47
16°	6·69	6·62	6·56	6·49	6·42	6·36	6·29	6·22	6·16	6·09	6·03	5·96	5·89	5·83	5·76	5·69	5·63	5·56	5·49	5·43	5·36
17°	6·56	6·49	6·43	6·36	6·30	6·23	6·17	6·10	6·04	5·97	5·91	5·84	5·78	5·71	5·65	5·58	5·52	5·46	5·39	5·33	5·26
18°	6·42	6·36	6·30	6·23	6·17	6·11	6·04	5·98	5·92	5·85	5·79	5·73	5·66	5·60	5·54	5·47	5·41	5·35	5·28	5·22	5·16
19°	6·31	6·24	6·18	6·12	6·06	6·00	5·93	5·87	5·81	5·75	5·69	5·63	5·56	5·50	5·44	5·38	5·32	5·25	5·19	5·13	5·07
20°	6·19	6·13	6·07	6·00	5·94	5·88	5·82	5·76	5·70	5·64	5·58	5·52	5·46	5·40	5·34	5·28	5·22	5·16	5·10	5·04	4·98
21°	6·07	6·02	5·96	5·90	5·84	5·78	5·72	5·66	5·60	5·54	5·48	5·43	5·37	5·31	5·25	5·19	5·13	5·07	5·01	4·95	4·89
22°	5·97	5·91	5·85	5·80	5·74	5·68	5·62	5·56	5·51	5·45	5·39	5·33	5·27	5·22	5·16	5·10	5·04	4·99	4·93	4·87	4·81
23°	5·86	5·81	5·75	5·69	5·64	5·58	5·52	5·47	5·41	5·35	5·30	5·24	5·18	5·13	5·07	5·01	4·96	4·90	4·84	4·79	4·73
24°	5·77	5·72	5·66	5·61	5·55	5·49	5·44	5·38	5·33	5·27	5·22	5·16	5·10	5·05	4·99	4·94	4·88	4·83	4·77	4·71	4·66
25°	5·68	5·62	5·57	5·51	5·46	5·40	5·35	5·29	5·24	5·18	5·13	5·07	5·02	4·96	4·91	4·85	4·80	4·74	4·69	4·63	4·58
26°	5·59	5·54	5·48	5·43	5·38	5·32	5·27	5·21	5·16	5·11	5·05	5·00	4·94	4·89	4·84	4·78	4·73	4·67	4·62	4·57	4·51
27°	5·50	5·45	5·39	5·34	5·29	5·23	5·18	5·13	5·07	5·02	4·97	4·92	4·86	4·81	4·76	4·70	4·65	4·60	4·54	4·49	4·44
28°	5·42	5·37	5·32	5·27	5·21	5·16	5·11	5·06	5·00	4·95	4·90	4·85	4·79	4·74	4·69	4·63	4·58	4·53	4·48	4·42	4·37
29°	5·35	5·29	5·24	5·19	5·14	5·09	5·03	4·98	4·93	4·88	4·83	4·77	4·72	4·67	4·62	4·57	4·51	4·46	4·41	4·36	4·31
30°	5·27	5·22	5·17	5·11	5·06	5·01	4·96	4·91	4·86	4·80	4·75	4·70	4·65	4·60	4·55	4·49	4·44	4·39	4·34	4·29	4·24

*As pointed out in Section 14 (p. 185) Truesdale, Downing and Lowden have redetermined the solubility of oxygen in saline (and pure) waters. Tables 20 and 21 have been calculated using the equation

$$Cl' = a - b.S.$$

taking the values of a and b from their tables and the salinities for the chlorinities shown from Knudsen's Tables.

TABLE 22

The depth coefficient of pH, δpH (ξ).

Cl=19.5‰. t=0-5°C

(From K. Buch and S. Gripenberg, J. Cons. int. Explor. Mer, 1932, 7, p. 242, Table 3.)

pH Surface	7·5	7·6	7·7	7·8	7·9	8·0	8·1	8·2	8·3	8·4	8·5
δpH, ξ (per 1000 metres)	0·035	0·031	0·028	0·025	0·023	0·022	0·021	0·020	0·020	0·020	0·020

TABLE 23

The temperature (°C) coefficient (x) of pH and chlorinity.

(From K. Buch and O. Nynäs, Acta Acad. åbo., 1939, 12, p. 26, Table 3.)

	Cl=0·5‰			Cl=2‰			Cl=5‰			Cl=10‰		
pH	0-20°	10-20°	20-30°	0-20°	10-20°	20-30°	0-20°	10-20°	20-30°	0-20°	10-20°	20-30°
6·8	-0·0075	-0·0072	-0·0053	-0·0076	-0·0071	-0·0054	-0·0080	-0·0072	-0·0053	-0·0082	-0·0076	-0·0055
7·0	75	72	53	76	72	54	80	72	54	83	77	57
7·2	75	72	54	76	72	56	80	73	57	84	80	61
7·4	76	73	55	77	73	60	83	75	64	87	84	69
7·6	76	73	58	80	77	67	86	81	75	92	92	79
7·8	77	76	63	84	81	78	89	88	89	100	101	89
8·0	81	79	70	92	89	92	101	96	99	108	109	94
8·2	86	83	86	101	97	100	109	103	104	114	115	98
8·4	94	93	97	110	104	106	114	106	107	117	117	99

	Cl=15‰			Cl=19·5‰			Cl=21‰		
pH	0-20°	10-20°	20-30°	0-20°	10-20°	20-30°	0-20°	10-20°	20-30°
7·4	-0·0088	-0·0087	-0·0076	-0·0089	-0·0087	-0·0081	-0·0092	-0·0089	-0·0079
7·6	95	96	83	95	95	91	97	98	88
7·8	103	105	90	104	104	98	106	108	93
8·0	110	112	94	110	109	102	116	114	96
8·2	115	117	96	114	112	103	116	116	98
8·4	118	118	98	116	114	104	118	119	100

TABLE 24

pHs of N.B.S. standards from 0 to 95°C.

(From R. G. Bates, *Electrometric pH Determinations.* J. Wiley & Sons, Inc. New York, 1954.)

$t°C$	0·05 M K tetroxalate	KH tartrate (satd. at 25°)	0·05 M KH phthalate	0·025 M KH_2PO_4, 0·025 M Na_2HPO_4	0·01 M borax
0	1·67	—	4·01	6·98	9·46
5	1·67	—	4·01	6·95	9·39
10	1·67	—	4·00	6·92	9·33
15	1·67	—	4·00	6·90	9·27
20	1·68	—	4·00	6·88	9·22
25	1·68	3·56	4·01	6·86	9·18
30	1·69	3·55	4·01	6·85	9·14
35	1·69	3·55	4·02	6·84	9·10
40	1·70	3·54	4·03	6·84	9·07
45	1·70	3·55	4·04	6·83	9·04
50	1·71	3·55	4·06	6·83	9·01
55	1·72	3·56	4·08	6·84	8·99
60	1·73	3·57	4·10	6·84	8·96
70	—	3·59	4·12	6·85	8·92
80	—	3·61	4·16	6·86	8·88
90	—	3·64	4·20	6·86	8·85
95	—	3·65	4·22	6·87	8·83

TABLE 25

The first apparent dissociation constant $\times 10^{-6}$ of carbon dioxide in sea water, K_1'.

(From K. Buch, *Merentutkimuslait. Julk.*, 1951, N:o. 151, p. 6, Table 1b.)

Cl‰	°C 0	2	4	6	8	10	12	14	16	18	20	22	24	26	28	30
15	0·58	0·62	0·65	0·68	0·71	0·74	0·77	0·80	0·83	0·86	0·89	0·92	0·95	0·97	0·99	1·01
16	0·59	0·63	0·66	0·69	0·72	0·75	0·78	0·81	0·84	0·87	0·91	0·93	0·96	0·99	1·01	1·03
17	0·60	0·64	0·67	0·70	0·73	0·76	0·79	0·82	0·86	0·89	0·92	0·95	0·98	1·00	1·02	1·05
18	0·61	0·65	0·68	0·71	0·74	0·77	0·81	0·84	0·87	0·90	0·93	0·97	0·99	1·02	1·04	1·06
19	0·62	0·66	0·69	0·72	0·76	0·79	0·82	0·85	0·88	0·92	0·95	0·98	1·01	1·04	1·06	1·08
20	0·63	0·67	0·70	0·73	0·77	0·80	0·83	0·87	0·90	0·93	0·97	1·00	1·03	1·05	1·07	1·10
21	0·64	0·68	0·71	0·75	0·78	0·81	0·84	0·88	0·91	0·95	0·98	1·01	1·04	1·07	1·09	1·12
0	0·26	0·28	0·29	0·31	0·32	0·34	0·35	0·37	0·38	0·39	0·40	0·42	0·43	0·44	0·44	0·45

TABLE 26

The second apparent dissociation constant $\times 10^{-9}$ of carbon dioxide in sea water, K_2'.

(From K. Buch, *Merentutkimuslait. Julk.*, 1951, N:o. 151, p. 8, Table 2b, in part.)

Cl‰	°C 0	2	4	6	8	10	12	14	16	18	20	22	24	26	28	30
15	0·43	0·46	0·49	0·53	0·56	0·60	0·63	0·66	0·69	0·73	0·76	0·79	0·83	0·86	0·90	0·93
16	0·46	0·49	0·53	0·56	0·60	0·63	0·67	0·71	0·74	0·78	0·81	0·85	0·88	0·92	0·96	0·99
17	0·48	0·51	0·55	0·59	0·63	0·67	0·71	0·74	0·78	0·82	0·86	0·90	0·93	0·97	1·01	1·05
18	0·51	0·55	0·59	0·63	0·67	0·71	0·75	0·79	0·83	0·87	0·91	0·95	0·99	1·03	1·07	1·11
19	0·54	0·58	0·62	0·66	0·71	0·75	0·79	0·83	0·88	0·92	0·96	1·01	1·05	1·10	1·14	1·18
20	0·57	0·62	0·66	0·71	0·75	0·80	0·84	0·89	0·93	0·98	1·02	1·07	1·12	1·16	1·21	1·26
21	0·60	0·65	0·69	0·74	0·79	0·84	0·89	0·93	0·98	1·03	1·08	1·13	1·18	1·23	1·28	1·33
0	0·23	0·25	0·27	0·29	0·30	0·32	0·34	0·36	0·38	0·40	0·42	0·44	0·46	0·48	0·50	$0·51 \times 10^{-10}$

TABLE 27

Values of the correction factor γ in equivalent/l. $\times 10^{-5}$. $A' = A - \gamma$.

(From K. Buch, *Merentutkimuslait. Julk.*, 1951, N:o. 151, p. 10, Table 3, in part.)

t°C....	0	2	4	6	8	10	12	14	16	18	20	22	24	26	28	30
pH							*Cl* = 15‰									
7·4	1	1	1	1	1	1	1	1	1	1	1	1	1	1	1	2
7·5	1	1	1	1	1	1	1	1	2	2	2	2	2	2	2	2
7·6	1	1	1	2	2	2	2	2	2	2	2	2	2	2	2	2
7·7	2	2	2	2	2	2	2	2	2	2	2	3	3	3	3	3
7·8	2	2	2	2	3	3	3	3	3	3	3	3	3	3	3	4
7·9	3	3	3	3	3	3	3	3	4	4	4	4	4	4	4	4
8·0	3	3	4	4	4	4	4	4	4	5	5	5	5	5	5	5
8·1	4	4	4	4	5	5	5	5	5	5	6	6	6	6	6	6
8·2	5	5	5	5	6	6	6	6	6	7	7	7	7	7	8	8
8·3	6	6	6	7	7	7	7	7	8	8	8	8	9	9	9	9
8·4	7	7	8	8	8	8	9	9	9	9	10	10	10	10	11	11
8·5	8	9	9	9	10	10	10	10	11	11	11	11	12	12	12	13
							Cl = 17‰									
7·4	1	1	1	1	1	1	1	1	1	2	2	2	2	2	2	2
7·5	1	1	1	2	2	2	2	2	2	2	2	2	2	2	2	2
7·6	2	2	2	2	2	2	2	2	2	2	2	3	3	3	3	3
7·7	2	2	2	2	3	3	3	3	3	3	3	3	3	3	4	4
7·8	3	3	3	3	3	3	3	3	4	4	4	4	4	4	4	4
7·9	3	3	3	4	4	4	4	4	4	4	5	5	5	5	5	5
8·0	4	4	4	4	5	5	5	5	5	6	6	6	6	6	6	6
8·1	5	5	5	5	6	6	6	6	6	7	7	7	7	8	8	8
8·2	6	6	6	6	7	7	7	7	8	8	8	8	9	9	9	9
8·3	7	7	8	8	8	8	9	9	9	9	10	10	10	11	11	11
8·4	8	9	9	9	10	10	10	11	11	11	11	12	12	12	13	13
8·5	10	10	11	11	11	12	12	12	13	13	13	14	14	14	15	15

t°C....	0	2	4	6	8	10	12	14	16	18	20	22	24	26	28	30
pH							*Cl* = 19‰									
7·4	1	1	1	1	2	2	2	2	2	2	2	2	2	2	2	2
7·5	2	2	2	2	2	2	2	2	2	2	2	3	3	3	3	3
7·6	2	2	2	2	2	2	3	3	3	3	3	3	3	3	3	3
7·7	2	3	3	3	3	3	3	3	3	3	4	4	4	4	4	4
7·8	3	3	3	3	4	4	4	4	4	4	5	5	5	5	5	5
7·9	4	4	4	4	4	5	5	5	5	5	5	6	6	6	6	6
8·0	5	5	5	5	5	6	6	6	6	6	7	7	7	7	7	8
8·1	6	6	6	6	7	7	7	7	8	8	8	8	9	9	9	9
8·2	7	7	7	8	8	8	9	9	9	9	10	10	10	10	11	11
8·3	8	9	9	9	10	10	10	10	11	11	11	12	12	12	13	13
8·4	10	10	11	11	11	12	12	12	13	13	13	14	14	14	15	15
8·5	12	12	13	13	13	14	14	14	15	15	16	16	16	17	17	17
							Cl = 21‰									
7·4	1	2	2	2	2	2	2	2	2	3	3	3	3	3	3	3
7·5	2	2	2	2	3	3	3	3	3	3	3	4	4	4	4	4
7·6	2	2	2	3	3	3	3	3	3	3	3	4	4	4	4	4
7·7	3	3	3	3	4	4	4	4	4	4	4	5	5	5	5	5
7·8	4	4	4	4	4	5	5	5	5	5	5	6	6	6	6	6
7·9	4	4	5	5	5	5	6	6	6	6	7	7	7	7	7	7
8·0	5	6	6	6	6	7	7	7	7	7	8	8	8	8	9	9
8·1	7	7	7	7	8	8	8	8	9	9	9	10	10	10	10	11
8·2	8	8	9	9	9	10	10	10	10	11	11	11	12	12	12	13
8·3	10	10	10	11	11	11	12	12	12	13	13	13	14	14	14	15
8·4	11	11	11	12	12	13	13	13	14	14	14	15	15	15	16	16
8·5	14	14	14	15	15	16	16	17	17	17	18	18	19	19	20	20

TABLE 28

Values of the factor P_{CO_2}/A'.

(From K. Buch, *Merentutkimuslait. Julk.*, 1951, N:o. 151, p. 12, Table 4, in part.)

$t°C....$	0	2	4	6	8	10	12	14	16	18	20	22	24	26	28	30
pH								$Cl=15\%$								
7·4	0·88	0·90	0·92	0·94	0·97	0·99	1·01	1·04	1·06	1·08	1·11	1·13	1·16	1·20	1·24	1·28
7·5	0·70	0·71	0·73	0·75	0·76	0·78	0·80	0·82	0·84	0·85	0·87	0·89	0·91	0·94	0·96	1·00
7·6	0·55	0·56	0·57	0·59	0·60	0·61	0·63	0·64	0·66	0·67	0·68	0·70	0·72	0·74	0·76	0·79
7·7	0·43	0·44	0·45	0·46	0·47	0·48	0·49	0·50	0·52	0·53	0·54	0·55	0·56	0·58	0·60	0·61
7·8	0·34	0·35	0·35	0·36	0·37	0·38	0·38	0·39	0·40	0·41	0·42	0·43	0·44	0·45	0·46	0·48
7·9	0·27	0·27	0·28	0·28	0·29	0·29	0·30	0·31	0·31	0·32	0·33	0·33	0·34	0·35	0·36	0·37
8·0	0·21	0·21	0·22	0·22	0·22	0·23	0·23	0·24	0·24	0·25	0·25	0·26	0·26	0·27	0·28	0·28
8·1	0·16	0·16	0·17	0·17	0·17	0·18	0·18	0·18	0·19	0·19	0·19	0·20	0·20	0·20	0·21	0·27
8·2	0·12	0·13	0·13	0·13	0·13	0·14	0·14	0·14	0·14	0·14	0·15	0·15	0·15	0·16	0·16	0·16
8·3	0·09	0·10	0·10	0·10	0·10	0·10	0·10	0·11	0·11	0·11	0·11	0·11	0·11	0·12	0·12	0·12
8·4	0·07	0·07	0·08	0·08	0·08	0·08	0·08	0·08	0·08	0·08	0·08	0·09	0·09	0·09	0·09	0·09
8·5	0·05	0·05	0·06	0·06	0·06	0·06	0·06	0·06	0·06	0·06	0·06	0·06	0·06	0·06	0·06	0·07	0·07
pH								$Cl=17\%$								
7·4	0·85	0·87	0·89	0·92	0·94	0·96	0·98	1·00	1·02	1·05	1·07	1·09	1·12	1·16	1·19	1·23
7·5	0·67	0·69	0·70	0·72	0·74	0·75	0·77	0·79	0·81	0·83	0·84	0·86	0·88	0·91	0·94	0·97
7·6	0·53	0·54	0·56	0·57	0·58	0·60	0·61	0·62	0·63	0·65	0·66	0·67	0·69	0·71	0·74	0·76
7·7	0·41	0·42	0·43	0·45	0·46	0·47	0·48	0·49	0·50	0·51	0·52	0·53	0·54	0·56	0·57	0·59
7·8	0·33	0·33	0·34	0·35	0·35	0·36	0·37	0·38	0·38	0·39	0·40	0·41	0·42	0·43	0·44	0·45
7·9	0·25	0·26	0·27	0·27	0·28	0·28	0·29	0·29	0·30	0·31	0·31	0·33	0·33	0·33	0·34	0·35
8·0	0·20	0·20	0·21	0·21	0·22	0·22	0·22	0·23	0·23	0·24	0·24	0·24	0·25	0·25	0·26	0·27
8·1	0·16	0·16	0·16	0·16	0·17	0·17	0·17	0·17	0·18	0·18	0·18	0·19	0·19	0·20	0·20	0·20
8·2	0·12	0·12	0·12	0·13	0·13	0·13	0·13	0·13	0·13	0·14	0·14	0·14	0·14	0·15	0·15	0·15
8·3	0·09	0·09	0·09	0·10	0·10	0·10	0·10	0·10	0·10	0·10	0·10	0·11	0·11	0·11	0·11	0·11
8·4	0·07	0·07	0·07	0·07	0·07	0·07	0·07	0·07	0·08	0·08	0·08	0·08	0·08	0·08	0·08	0·09
8·5	0·05	0·05	0·05	0·05	0·05	0·05	0·05	0·06	0·06	0·06	0·06	0·06	0·06	0·06	0·06	0·06

$t°C....$	0	2	4	6	8	10	12	14	16	18	20	22	24	26	28	30
pH								$Cl=19\%$								
7·4	0·82	0·84	0·86	0·88	0·90	0·92	0·94	0·96	0·99	1·01	1·03	1·06	1·08	1·11	1·14	1·18
7·5	0·65	0·66	0·68	0·69	0·71	0·72	0·74	0·76	0·77	0·79	0·81	0·83	0·85	0·87	0·90	0·97
7·6	0·51	0·52	0·53	0·55	0·56	0·57	0·58	0·59	0·61	0·62	0·63	0·64	0·66	0·68	0·70	0·72
7·7	0·40	0·41	0·42	0·43	0·44	0·45	0·46	0·47	0·48	0·49	0·50	0·51	0·52	0·53	0·55	0·56
7·8	0·31	0·32	0·33	0·33	0·34	0·35	0·36	0·36	0·37	0·38	0·38	0·39	0·41	0·41	0·42	0·43
7·9	0·24	0·25	0·25	0·26	0·26	0·27	0·28	0·28	0·29	0·29	0·30	0·30	0·31	0·32	0·32	0·33
8·0	0·19	0·20	0·20	0·20	0·20	0·21	0·21	0·22	0·22	0·22	0·23	0·23	0·24	0·24	0·25	0·25
8·1	0·15	0·15	0·15	0·15	0·16	0·16	0·16	0·16	0·17	0·17	0·17	0·17	0·18	0·18	0·18	0·19
8·2	0·11	0·12	0·12	0·12	0·12	0·12	0·12	0·12	0·13	0·13	0·13	0·13	0·13	0·14	0·14	0·15
8·3	0·09	0·09	0·09	0·09	0·09	0·09	0·09	0·10	0·10	0·10	0·10	0·10	0·10	0·10	0·11	0·11
8·4	0·07	0·07	0·07	0·07	0·07	0·07	0·07	0·07	0·07	0·07	0·07	0·07	0·07	0·07	0·08	0·08
8·5	0·05	0·05	0·05	0·05	0·05	0·05	0·05	0·05	0·05	0·05	0·05	0·05	0·05	0·05	0·06	0·06
pH								$Cl=21\%$								
7·4	0·79	0·81	0·83	0·85	0·87	0·89	0·92	0·93	0·95	0·98	1·00	1·02	1·05	1·07	1·11	1·14
7·5	0·63	0·64	0·66	0·67	0·69	0·70	0·72	0·73	0·75	0·77	0·78	0·80	0·82	0·84	0·87	0·89
7·6	0·49	0·50	0·52	0·53	0·54	0·55	0·56	0·57	0·58	0·60	0·61	0·62	0·64	0·65	0·67	0·69
7·7	0·39	0·40	0·40	0·41	0·42	0·43	0·44	0·45	0·46	0·47	0·48	0·49	0·50	0·51	0·52	0·54
7·8	0·30	0·31	0·31	0·32	0·33	0·33	0·34	0·35	0·35	0·36	0·37	0·37	0·38	0·39	0·40	0·42
7·9	0·23	0·24	0·24	0·25	0·25	0·26	0·26	0·27	0·27	0·28	0·28	0·29	0·29	0·30	0·31	0·32
8·0	0·18	0·18	0·19	0·19	0·19	0·20	0·20	0·20	0·21	0·21	0·21	0·22	0·22	0·23	0·24	0·24
8·1	0·14	0·14	0·14	0·15	0·15	0·15	0·15	0·16	0·16	0·16	0·16	0·17	0·17	0·18	0·18	0·18
8·2	0·11	0·11	0·11	0·11	0·11	0·11	0·12	0·12	0·12	0·12	0·12	0·12	0·13	0·13	0·13	0·13
8·3	0·08	0·08	0·08	0·09	0·09	0·09	0·09	0·09	0·09	0·09	0·09	0·09	0·09	0·10	0·10	0·10
8·4	0·06	0·06	0·06	0·06	0·06	0·07	0·07	0·07	0·07	0·07	0·07	0·07	0·07	0·07	0·07	0·07
8·5	0·05	0·05	0·05	0·05	0·05	0·05	0·05	0·05	0·05	0·05	0·05	0·05	0·05	0·05	0·05	0·05

TABLE 29

Values of the factor $\Sigma CO_2/A'$ (g.-mols/l.).

(From K. Buch, *Merentutkimuslait. Julk.*, 1951, N:o. 151, p. 16, Table 6, in part.)

t°C....	0	2	4	6	8	10	12	14	16	18	20	22	24	26	28	30
pH							$Cl=15\%$									
7·4	1·05	1·05	1·04	1·04	1·04	1·03	1·03	1·03	1·03	1·02	1·02	1·02	1·02	1·01	1·01	1·01
7·5	1·03	1·03	1·03	1·02	1·02	1·02	1·02	1·01	1·01	1·01	1·01	1·00	1·00	1·00	1·00	1·00
7·6	1·02	1·02	1·01	1·01	1·01	1·01	1·00	1·00	1·00	1·00	1·00	0·99	0·99	0·99	0·99	0·99
7·7	1·01	1·01	1·00	1·00	1·00	1·00	0·99	0·99	0·99	0·99	0·98	0·98	0·98	0·98	0·97	0·97
7·8	1·00	0·99	0·99	0·99	0·99	0·98	0·98	0·98	0·98	0·97	0·97	0·97	0·97	0·96	0·96	0·96
7·9	0·99	0·98	0·98	0·98	0·97	0·97	0·97	0·97	0·96	0·96	0·96	0·96	0·95	0·95	0·95	0·95
8·0	0·98	0·97	0·97	0·96	0·96	0·96	0·96	0·95	0·95	0·95	0·94	0·94	0·94	0·93	0·93	0·93
8·1	0·96	0·96	0·95	0·95	0·95	0·94	0·94	0·94	0·93	0·93	0·93	0·92	0·92	0·92	0·91	0·91
8·2	0·95	0·95	0·94	0·94	0·93	0·93	0·92	0·92	0·92	0·91	0·91	0·90	0·90	0·90	0·89	0·89
8·3	0·93	0·93	0·92	0·92	0·91	0·91	0·90	0·90	0·90	0·89	0·89	0·88	0·88	0·88	0·87	0·87
8·4	0·92	0·91	0·90	0·90	0·89	0·89	0·88	0·88	0·87	0·87	0·86	0·86	0·86	0·85	0·85	0·84
8·5	0·90	0·89	0·88	0·88	0·87	0·87	0·86	0·86	0·86	0·85	0·85	0·84	0·84	0·83	0·83	0·82
pH							$Cl=\%17$									
7·4	1·04	1·04	1·04	1·03	1·03	1·03	1·03	1·02	1·02	1·02	1·02	1·02	1·01	1·01	1·01	1·01
7·5	1·03	1·03	1·02	1·02	1·02	1·02	1·01	1·01	1·01	1·01	1·00	1·00	1·00	1·00	1·00	0·99
7·6	1·02	1·02	1·01	1·01	1·01	1·01	1·00	1·00	1·00	0·99	0·99	0·99	0·99	0·99	0·98	0·98
7·7	1·01	1·00	1·00	1·00	1·00	0·99	0·99	0·99	0·99	0·98	0·98	0·98	0·98	0·97	0·97	0·97
7·8	1·00	0·99	0·99	0·99	0·98	0·98	0·98	0·98	0·97	0·97	0·97	0·97	0·96	0·96	0·96	0·95
7·9	0·99	0·98	0·98	0·98	0·97	0·97	0·96	0·96	0·96	0·95	0·95	0·95	0·95	0·94	0·94	0·94
8·0	0·97	0·97	0·96	0·96	0·96	0·95	0·95	0·95	0·94	0·94	0·93	0·93	0·93	0·93	0·92	0·92
8·1	0·96	0·95	0·95	0·95	0·94	0·94	0·93	0·93	0·92	0·92	0·92	0·91	0·91	0·91	0·90	0·90
8·2	0·94	0·93	0·93	0·92	0·92	0·91	0·91	0·91	0·91	0·90	0·90	0·90	0·89	0·89	0·88	0·88
8·3	0·93	0·92	0·92	0·91	0·91	0·90	0·89	0·89	0·89	0·88	0·88	0·87	0·87	0·86	0·86	0·85
8·4	0·91	0·90	0·90	0·89	0·88	0·88	0·87	0·87	0·86	0·86	0·85	0·85	0·84	0·84	0·83	0·83
8·5	0·89	0·88	0·87	0·87	0·86	0·85	0·85	0·84	0·84	0·83	0·82	0·82	0·82	0·81	0·81	0·80

t°C....	0	2	4	6	8	10	12	14	16	18	20	22	24	26	28	30
pH							$Cl=19\%$									
7·4	1·04	1·04	1·03	1·03	1·03	1·02	1·02	1·02	1·02	1·01	1·01	1·01	1·01	1·01	1·00	1·00
7·5	1·03	1·02	1·02	1·02	1·01	1·01	1·01	1·01	1·00	1·00	1·00	1·00	0·99	0·99	0·99	0·99
7·6	1·01	1·01	1·01	1·00	1·00	1·00	1·00	0·99	0·99	0·99	0·99	0·98	0·98	0·98	0·98	0·98
7·7	1·00	1·00	1·00	0·99	0·99	0·99	0·98	0·98	0·98	0·98	0·97	0·97	0·97	0·97	0·96	0·96
7·8	0·99	0·99	0·98	0·98	0·98	0·97	0·97	0·97	0·96	0·96	0·96	0·96	0·95	0·95	0·95	0·95
7·9	0·98	0·97	0·97	0·97	0·96	0·96	0·96	0·95	0·95	0·95	0·94	0·94	0·94	0·93	0·93	0·93
8·0	0·96	0·96	0·95	0·95	0·95	0·94	0·94	0·94	0·93	0·93	0·93	0·92	0·92	0·92	0·91	0·91
8·1	0·95	0·94	0·94	0·94	0·93	0·93	0·92	0·92	0·92	0·91	0·91	0·90	0·90	0·90	0·89	0·89
8·2	0·93	0·93	0·92	0·92	0·92	0·91	0·91	0·90	0·90	0·89	0·89	0·88	0·88	0·88	0·87	0·87
8·3	0·92	0·91	0·91	0·90	0·90	0·89	0·88	0·88	0·87	0·87	0·87	0·86	0·86	0·85	0·85	0·84
8·4	0·90	0·89	0·89	0·88	0·87	0·87	0·86	0·86	0·85	0·84	0·84	0·83	0·83	0·82	0·82	0·81
8·5	0·87	0·87	0·86	0·86	0·85	0·84	0·84	0·83	0·83	0·82	0·81	0·81	0·80	0·80	0·79	0·79
pH							$Cl=21\%$									
7·4	1·03	1·03	1·03	1·03	1·02	1·02	1·02	1·02	1·01	1·01	1·01	1·01	1·00	1·00	1·00	1·00
7·5	1·02	1·02	1·02	1·01	1·01	1·01	1·01	1·00	1·00	1·00	1·00	0·99	0·99	0·99	0·99	0·98
7·6	1·01	1·00	1·00	1·00	1·00	0·99	0·99	0·99	0·99	0·98	0·98	0·98	0·98	0·97	0·97	0·97
7·7	0·99	0·99	0·99	0·99	0·98	0·98	0·98	0·97	0·97	0·97	0·97	0·96	0·96	0·96	0·96	0·96
7·8	0·98	0·98	0·98	0·97	0·97	0·97	0·96	0·96	0·96	0·96	0·95	0·95	0·95	0·95	0·94	0·94
7·9	0·97	0·97	0·96	0·96	0·96	0·95	0·95	0·95	0·94	0·94	0·94	0·93	0·93	0·93	0·92	0·92
8·0	0·96	0·95	0·95	0·95	0·94	0·94	0·93	0·93	0·93	0·92	0·92	0·92	0·91	0·91	0·91	0·90
8·1	0·94	0·94	0·94	0·93	0·92	0·92	0·92	0·92	0·91	0·91	0·90	0·90	0·89	0·89	0·89	0·88
8·2	0·93	0·92	0·92	0·91	0·91	0·90	0·90	0·89	0·89	0·88	0·88	0·87	0·87	0·86	0·86	0·85
8·3	0·91	0·90	0·90	0·89	0·89	0·88	0·87	0·87	0·86	0·86	0·85	0·85	0·84	0·84	0·83	0·83
8·4	0·89	0·88	0·87	0·87	0·86	0·86	0·85	0·85	0·84	0·83	0·83	0·82	0·82	0·81	0·81	0·80
8·5	0·86	0·86	0·85	0·84	0·84	0·83	0·82	0·82	0·81	0·81	0·80	0·79	0·79	0·78	0·78	0·77

TABLE 30

Solubility of carbon dioxide in pure water c_o and in
sea waters, c_s, in g.mols/l. $\times 10^{-4}$.

(From K. Buch, *Merentutkimuslait. Julk.*, 1951, N:o 151, p. 14, Table 5.)

$t°C$.... $Cl‰$	0	2	4	6	8	10	12	14	16	18	20	22	24	26	28	30
0	$c_o=$770	712	662	619	576	536	502	472	442	417	394	372	351	332	314	299
15	$c_s=$674	623	578	538	504	472	442	416	393	371	351	331	314	299	284	270
16	$c_s=$667	617	573	533	499	468	438	413	390	368	348	329	312	297	281	268
17	$c_s=$660	611	567	528	495	464	434	410	387	365	346	327	310	294	279	266
18	$c_s=$653	605	562	524	490	460	431	406	384	362	343	324	307	292	277	264
19	$c_s=$646	599	557	519	486	456	428	403	381	359	340	321	304	289	275	262
20	$c_s=$640	593	551	514	482	452	424	400	377	356	337	319	302	287	273	260
21	$c_s=$633	587	546	509	477	448	421	396	374	354	335	317	300	285	271	258

TABLE 31

The activity of water in sea water of varying salinity.

$Cl‰$	a_{H_2O}	$Cl‰$	a_{H_2O}
2	0·998	14	0·986
4	0·996	16	0·984
6	0·994	18	0·983
8	0·992	20	0·981
10	0·990	22	0·979

TABLE 32

Comparison of Dittmar's ratios with present best values and composition of sea water having chlorinity 19·000 ‰.

(From J. Lyman and R. H. Fleming, *J. Mar. Res.*, 1940, 3, p. 137, Table III.)

Ion	Ratio to chlorinity (Dittmar)	Ratio to chlorinity (best value)	Authority	Equivalents per kilogram	Weights per kilogram
Cl	0·99894	0·99894	Dittmar (1884) and Jacobsen and Knudsen (1940)	0·53529	18·9799
Br	0·00340	0·00340	Dittmar (1884)	0·00081	0·0646
SO$_4$	0·1388	0·1394	Thompson, Johnston, and Wirth (1931)	0·05514	2·6486
HCO$_3$	0·00760	0·00735	Revelle (1936)	0·00229	0·1397
F	—	7×10^{-5}	Thompson and Taylor (1933)	0·00007	0·0013
				0·59360	
Ca	0·02163*	0·02106	Kirk and Moberg (1933), and Thompson and Wright (1930)	0·01996	0·4001
Mg	0·06801	0·06695	Thompson and Wright (1930)	0·10460	1·2720
K	0·02029	0·02000	Thompson and Robinson (1932)	0·00972	0·3800
Sr	—	0·000702	Webb (1938)	0·00030	0·0133
				0·13458	
Na	0·5530	0·5556	By difference	0·45902	10·5561
				0·59360	
H$_3$BO$_3$	—	0·00137	Harding and Moberg (1933), and Igelsrud, Thompson and Zwicker (1938)		0·0260
					34·4816

* This ratio of Dittmar's is for calcium plus strontium, determined gravimetrically as oxide. The calcium and strontium best values would be 0·02165 if calculated on this basis.

TABLE 33

Grams per kilogram of sea water for chlorinity 1–23‰ ($S‰ = 1·84$–41·55‰).
Calculated from the best available ratios of ions to chlorinity, and equations in Ref. Table 32.

(From H. Barnes, *J. exp. Biol.*, 1954, **31**, p. 585, Table 1.)

Cl‰	S‰	Cl	Br	SO$_4$	HCO$_3$	Ca	Mg	K	Sr	Na	H$_3$BO$_3$
1	1·84	0·9989	0·0034	0·1452	0·05406	0·03565	0·06884	0·0200	0·000702	0·5556	0·00137
2	3·64	1·9979	0·0068	0·2843	0·05881	0·05590	0·1357	0·0400	0·001404	1·1112	0·00274
3	5·45	2·9968	0·0102	0·4234	0·06357	0·07615	0·2025	0·0600	0·002106	1·6668	0·00411
4	7·25	3·9958	0·0136	0·5625	0·06832	0·09640	0·2694	0·0800	0·002808	2·2224	0·00548
5	9·06	4·9947	0·0170	0·7016	0·07308	0·1167	0·3362	0·1000	0·003510	2·7780	0·00685
6	10·86	5·9936	0·0204	0·8407	0·07783	0·1369	0·4030	0·1200	0·004212	3·3336	0·00822
7	12·67	6·9926	0·0238	0·9798	0·08259	0·1572	0·4699	0·1400	0·004914	3·8892	0·00959
8	14·47	7·9915	0·0272	1·1189	0·08734	0·1774	0·5367	0·1600	0·005616	4·4448	0·01096
9	16·28	8·9905	0·0306	1·2580	0·09210	0·1977	0·6036	0·1800	0·006318	5·0004	0·01233
10	18·08	9·9894	0·0340	1·3971	0·09685	0·2179	0·6704	0·2000	0·007020	5·5560	0·01370
11	19·89	10·9883	0·0374	1·5362	0·1016	0·2382	0·7372	0·2200	0·007722	6·1116	0·01507
12	21·69	11·9873	0·0408	1·6753	0·1064	0·2584	0·8041	0·2400	0·008424	6·6672	0·01644
13	23·50	12·9862	0·0442	1·8144	0·1111	0·2787	0·8709	0·2600	0·009126	7·2228	0·01781
14	25·30	13·9852	0·0476	1·9535	0·1159	0·2989	0·9378	0·2800	0·009828	7·7784	0·01918
15	27·11	14·9841	0·0510	2·0926	0·1206	0·3192	1·0046	0·3000	0·01053	8·3340	0·02055
16	28·91	15·9831	0·0544	2·2317	0·1254	0·3394	1·0714	0·3200	0·01123	8·8896	0·02192
17	30·72	16·9820	0·0578	2·3708	0·1301	0·3597	1·1383	0·3400	0·01193	9·4452	0·02329
18	32·52	17·9809	0·0612	2·5099	0·1349	0·3799	1·2051	0·3600	0·01264	10·0008	0·02466
19	34·33	18·9799	0·0646	2·6490	0·1396	0·4002	1·2720	0·3800	0·01334	10·5564	0·02603
20	36·13	19·9788	0·0680	2·7881	0·1444	0·4204	1·3388	0·4000	0·01404	11·1120	0·02740
21	37·94	20·9777	0·0714	2·9272	0·1492	0·4407	1·4056	0·4200	0·01474	11·6676	0·02877
22	39·74	21·9767	0·0748	3·0663	0·1539	0·4609	1·4725	0·4400	0·01544	12·2232	0·03014
23	41·55	22·9756	0·0782	3·2054	0·1587	0·4812	1·5393	0·4600	0·01615	12·7788	0·03151

TABLE 34

Grams per litre (20° C.) of sea water for chlorinity 1–23‰ ($S‰ = 1.84–41.55‰$).
Calculated from Table 33 and the densities obtained from Knudsen's Tables.

(From H. Barnes, *J. exp. Biol.*, 1954, **31**, p. 585, Table 2.)

Cl‰	S‰	Cl	Br	SO₄	HCO₃	Ca	Mg	K	Sr	Na	H₃BO₃
1	1·84	0·9986	0·003399	0·1452	0·05404	0·03564	0·06882	0·01999	0·0007018	0·5554	0·001370
2	3·64	2·0000	0·006807	0·2846	0·05887	0·05596	0·1358	0·04004	0·001405	1·1124	0·002743
3	5·45	3·0040	0·01022	0·4244	0·06372	0·07633	0·2030	0·06014	0·002111	1·6708	0·004120
4	7·25	4·0108	0·01365	0·5646	0·06858	0·09676	0·2704	0·08030	0·002819	2·2308	0·005501
5	9·06	5·0204	0·01709	0·7052	0·07345	0·1172	0·3379	0·1005	0·003528	2·7923	0·006885
6	10·86	6·0327	0·02053	0·8462	0·07834	0·1378	0·4057	0·1208	0·004239	3·3553	0·008274
7	12·67	7·0476	0·02399	0·9875	0·08323	0·1584	0·4736	0·1411	0·004953	3·9198	0·009665
8	14·47	8·0654	0·02745	1·1292	0·08815	0·1790	0·5417	0·1615	0·005668	4·4859	0·01106
9	16·28	9·0858	0·03092	1·2713	0·09307	0·1997	0·6100	0·1819	0·006385	5·0534	0·01246
10	18·08	10·1089	0·03441	1·4138	0·09801	0·2205	0·6784	0·2024	0·007104	5·6225	0·01386
11	19·89	11·1348	0·03790	1·5567	0·1030	0·2413	0·7471	0·2229	0·007825	6·1930	0·01527
12	21·69	12·1634	0·04140	1·6999	0·1079	0·2622	0·8159	0·2435	0·008548	6·7651	0·01668
13	23·50	13·1947	0·04491	1·8435	0·1129	0·2831	0·8849	0·2642	0·009273	7·3388	0·01810
14	25·30	14·2288	0·04843	1·9875	0·1179	0·3041	0·9541	0·2849	0·009999	7·9139	0·01951
15	27·11	15·2656	0·05196	2·1319	0·1229	0·3251	1·0235	0·3056	0·01073	8·4906	0·02094
16	28·91	16·3051	0·05550	2·2767	0·1279	0·3462	1·0930	0·3264	0·01146	9·0687	0·02236
17	30·72	17·3476	0·05904	2·4218	0·1329	0·3674	1·1628	0·3473	0·01219	9·6485	0·02379
18	32·52	18·3926	0·06260	2·5674	0·1380	0·3886	1·2327	0·3682	0·01293	10·2298	0·02522
19	34·33	19·4404	0·06617	2·7133	0·1430	0·4099	1·3028	0·3892	0·01366	10·8126	0·02666
20	36·13	20·4911	0·06974	2·8596	0·1481	0·4312	1·3731	0·4103	0·01440	11·3970	0·02810
21	37·94	21·5444	0·07333	3·0063	0·1532	0·4526	1·4436	0·4313	0·01514	11·9828	0·02955
22	39·74	22·6007	0·07692	3·1534	0·1583	0·4740	1·5143	0·4525	0·01588	12·5703	0·03100
23	41·55	23·6597	0·08053	3·3008	0·1634	0·4955	1·5852	0·4737	0·01663	13·1593	0·03245

TABLE 35

Millimoles (milligram-ions) per kilogram of sea water for chlorinity 1–23‰ ($S‰ = 1.84–41.55‰$).
Calculated from Table 33 and 1940 values for atomic weights.

(From H. Barnes, *J. exp. Biol.*, 1954, **31**, p. 586, Table 3.)

Cl‰	S‰	Cl	Br	SO4	HCO3	Ca	Mg	K	Sr	Na	H3BO3
1	1·84	28·17	0·04254	1·512	0·8859	0·8895	2·831	0·5116	0·008011	24·16	0·02215
2	3·64	56·35	0·08509	2·960	0·9638	1·395	5·579	1·023	0·01602	48·32	0·04431
3	5·45	84·52	0·1276	4·408	1·042	1·900	8·327	1·535	0·02403	72·48	0·06646
4	7·25	112·7	0·1702	5·856	1·120	2·405	11·08	2·046	0·03204	96·64	0·08861
5	9·06	140·9	0·2127	7·304	1·198	2·910	13·82	2·558	0·04005	120·8	0·1108
6	10·86	169·0	0·2553	8·752	1·276	3·416	16·57	3·069	0·04807	145·0	0·1329
7	12·67	197·2	0·2978	10·20	1·354	3·921	19·32	3·581	0·05608	169·1	0·1551
8	14·47	225·4	0·3404	11·65	1·431	4·426	22·07	4·093	0·06409	193·3	0·1772
9	16·28	253·6	0·3829	13·10	1·509	4·931	24·82	4·604	0·07210	217·4	0·1994
10	18·08	281·7	0·4254	14·54	1·587	5·437	27·57	5·116	0·08011	241·6	0·2215
11	19·89	309·9	0·4680	15·99	1·665	5·942	30·31	5·627	0·08812	265·8	0·2437
12	21·69	338·1	0·5105	17·44	1·743	6·447	33·06	6·139	0·09613	289·9	0·2658
13	23·50	366·3	0·5531	18·89	1·821	6·952	35·81	6·650	0·1041	314·1	0·2880
14	25·30	394·4	0·5956	20·34	1·899	7·458	38·56	7·162	0·1122	338·2	0·3101
15	27·11	422·6	0·6382	21·78	1·977	7·963	41·31	7·673	0·1202	362·4	0·3323
16	28·91	450·8	0·6807	23·23	2·055	8·468	44·06	8·185	0·1282	386·6	0·3544
17	30·72	478·9	0·7233	24·68	2·133	8·973	46·80	8·697	0·1362	410·7	0·3766
18	32·52	507·1	0·7658	26·13	2·211	9·479	49·55	9·208	0·1442	434·9	0·3987
19	34·33	535·3	0·8083	27·58	2·289	9·984	52·30	9·720	0·1522	459·0	0·4209
20	36·13	563·5	0·8509	29·02	2·367	10·49	55·05	10·23	0·1602	483·2	0·4431
21	37·94	591·6	0·8934	30·47	2·444	10·99	57·80	10·74	0·1682	507·4	0·4652
22	39·74	619·8	0·9360	31·92	2·522	11·50	60·55	11·25	0·1762	531·5	0·4874
23	41·55	648·0	0·9785	33·37	2·600	12·00	63·29	11·77	0·1843	555·7	0·5095

TABLE 36

Millimoles (milligram-ions) per litre (20° C.) (of sea watermolarity) for chlorinity 1–23‰ ($S‰ = 1·84$–$41·55‰$).
Calculated from Table 34 and the 1940 values for atomic weights. *Note.*—The milli-equivalents per kilogram or per litre (20° C.) are readily obtained from Tables 35 and 36 by multiplying the values by the valency of the particular ion.

(From H. Barnes, *J. exp. Biol.*, 1954, **31**, p. 586, Table 4.)

Cl‰	S‰	Cl	Br	SO₄	HCO₃	Ca	Mg	K	Sr	Na	H₃BO₃
1	1·84	28·16	0·04253	1·511	0·8856	0·8892	2·830	0·5114	0·008008	24·15	0·02215
2	3·64	56·41	0·08518	2·963	0·9648	1·396	5·585	1·024	0·01604	48·37	0·04435
3	5·45	84·72	0·1279	4·418	1·044	1·905	8·347	1·538	0·02409	72·65	0·06662
4	7·25	113·1	0·1708	5·878	1·124	2·414	11·12	2·054	0·03216	97·00	0·08894
5	9·06	141·6	0·2138	7·341	1·204	2·925	13·90	2·571	0·04026	121·4	0·1113
6	10·86	170·1	0·2569	8·809	1·284	3·438	16·68	3·089	0·04838	145·9	0·1338
7	12·67	198·8	0·3002	10·28	1·364	3·952	19·47	3·609	0·05652	170·4	0·1563
8	14·47	227·5	0·3435	11·76	1·445	4·467	22·27	4·130	0·06468	195·1	0·1789
9	16·28	256·2	0·3870	13·23	1·525	4·984	25·08	4·653	0·07286	219·7	0·2015
10	18·08	285·1	0·4305	14·72	1·606	5·502	27·90	5·177	0·08107	244·5	0·2242
11	19·89	314·0	0·4742	16·21	1·687	6·021	30·72	5·702	0·08929	269·3	0·2469
12	21·69	343·0	0·5180	17·70	1·769	6·542	33·55	6·229	0·09754	294·2	0·2697
13	23·50	372·1	0·5620	19·19	1·850	7·064	36·39	6·757	0·1058	319·1	0·2926
14	25·30	401·3	0·6060	20·69	1·932	7·588	39·23	7·287	0·1141	344·1	0·3155
15	27·11	430·5	0·6502	22·19	2·014	8·112	42·08	7·818	0·1224	369·2	0·3385
16	28·91	459·9	0·6944	23·70	2·096	8·639	44·94	8·350	0·1308	394·3	0·3616
17	30·72	489·3	0·7388	25·21	2·179	9·167	47·81	8·884	0·1391	419·6	0·3847
18	32·52	518·7	0·7833	26·73	2·261	9·696	50·69	9·419	0·1475	444·8	0·4079
19	34·33	548·3	0·8280	28·25	2·344	10·23	53·57	9·956	0·1559	470·2	0·4311
20	36·13	577·9	0·8727	29·77	2·427	10·76	56·46	10·49	0·1643	495·6	0·4544
21	37·94	607·6	0·9176	31·30	2·511	11·29	59·36	11·03	0·1728	521·1	0·4778
22	39·74	637·4	0·9626	32·83	2·594	11·83	62·27	11·57	0·1812	546·6	0·5012
23	41·55	667·3	1·008	34·36	2·678	12·36	65·18	12·12	0·1897	572·2	0·5247

TABLE 37

Grams per kilogram of water for chlorinity 1–23‰ ($S\%_0 = 1\cdot84\text{--}41\cdot55\%_0$).
Calculated from Table 33 and the values of total salt content from equation, $0\cdot073 + 1\cdot8110\ Cl = $ Total salts.

(From H. Barnes, *J. exp. Biol.*, 1954, **31**, p. 587, Table 5.)

Cl‰	S‰	Cl	Br	SO₄	HCO₃	Ca	Mg	K	Sr	Na	H₃BO₃
1	1·84	1·0008	0·003406	0·1455	0·05416	0·03572	0·06897	0·02004	0·0007033	0·5566	0·001373
2	3·64	2·0053	0·006825	0·2854	0·05903	0·05611	0·1362	0·04015	0·001409	1·1153	0·002750
3	5·45	3·0134	0·01026	0·4257	0·06392	0·07657	0·2036	0·06033	0·002118	1·6760	0·004133
4	7·25	4·0252	0·01370	0·5666	0·06882	0·09711	0·2713	0·08059	0·002829	2·2388	0·005520
5	9·06	5·0407	0·01716	0·7081	0·07375	0·1177	0·3393	0·1009	0·003542	2·8036	0·006913
6	10·86	6·0599	0·02063	0·8500	0·07869	0·1384	0·4075	0·1213	0·004259	3·3705	0·008311
7	12·67	7·0829	0·02411	0·9925	0·08365	0·1592	0·4759	0·1418	0·004977	3·9394	0·009714
8	14·47	8·1096	0·02760	1·1354	0·08863	0·1800	0·5447	0·1624	0·005699	4·5105	0·01112
9	16·28	9·1401	0·03111	1·2789	0·09363	0·2009	0·6136	0·1830	0·006423	5·0836	0·01254
10	18·08	10·1744	0·03463	1·4230	0·09864	0·2219	0·6828	0·2037	0·007150	5·6589	0·01395
11	19·89	11·2125	0·03816	1·5675	0·1037	0·2430	0·7523	0·2245	0·007880	6·2363	0·01538
12	21·69	12·2545	0·04171	1·7126	0·1087	0·2642	0·8220	0·2453	0·008612	6·8158	0·01681
13	23·50	13·3003	0·04527	1·8583	0·1138	0·2854	0·8920	0·2663	0·009347	7·3975	0·01824
14	25·30	14·3500	0·04884	2·0045	0·1189	0·3067	0·9622	0·2873	0·01008	7·9813	0·01968
15	27·11	15·4037	0·05243	2·1512	0·1240	0·3281	1·0327	0·3084	0·01082	8·5674	0·02113
16	28·91	16·4612	0·05603	2·2985	0·1291	0·3496	1·1035	0·3296	0·01157	9·1556	0·02258
17	30·72	17·5227	0·05964	2·4463	0·1343	0·3711	1·1745	0·3508	0·01231	9·7460	0·02403
18	32·52	18·5882	0·06327	2·5947	0·1394	0·3927	1·2458	0·3722	0·01306	10·3386	0·02549
19	34·33	19·6577	0·06691	2·7436	0·1446	0·4144	1·3174	0·3936	0·01381	10·9334	0·02696
20	36·13	20·7312	0·07056	2·8931	0·1498	0·4362	1·3892	0·4151	0·01457	11·5305	0·02843
21	37·94	21·8087	0·07423	3·0432	0·1551	0·4581	1·4613	0·4366	0·01533	12·1298	0·02991
22	39·74	22·8903	0·07791	3·1938	0·1603	0·4801	1·5337	0·4583	0·01609	12·7314	0·03139
23	41·55	23·9760	0·08161	3·3450	0·1656	0·5021	1·6063	0·4800	0·01685	13·3352	0·03288

TABLE 38

Millimoles (milligram-ions) per kilogram of water (molality) for chlorinity 1–23‰ (S‰ = 1·84–41·55‰).
Calculated from Table 37 and the 1940 values for atomic weights. *Note.*—Milli-equivalents can be calculated from Table 38 by multiplying the values by the valency of the particular ion.

(From H. Barnes, *J. exp. Biol.*, 1954, **31**, p. 587, Table 6.)

C‰	S‰	Cl	Br	SO₄	HCO₃	Ca	Mg	K	Sr	Na	H₃BO₃
1	1·84	28·23	0·04262	1·514	0·8876	0·8911	2·836	0·5125	0·008026	24·21	0·02219
2	3·64	56·56	0·08540	2·971	0·9674	1·400	5·600	1·027	0·01608	48·50	0·04447
3	5·45	84·99	0·1283	4·432	1·048	1·910	8·373	1·543	0·02417	72·88	0·06683
4	7·25	113·5	0·1714	5·899	1·128	2·423	11·16	2·061	0·03228	97·35	0·08926
5	9·06	142·1	0·2147	7·371	1·209	2·937	13·95	2·581	0·04042	121·9	0·1118
6	10·86	170·9	0·2581	8·849	1·290	3·453	16·76	3·103	0·04860	146·6	0·1344
7	12·67	199·8	0·3017	10·33	1·371	3·972	19·57	3·627	0·05680	171·3	0·1571
8	14·47	228·7	0·3454	11·82	1·453	4·492	22·40	4·153	0·06503	196·1	0·1798
9	16·28	257·8	0·3893	13·31	1·534	5·013	25·23	4·681	0·07330	221·1	0·2027
10	18·08	287·0	0·4333	14·81	1·617	5·537	28·08	5·210	0·08159	246·1	0·2256
11	19·89	316·2	0·4775	16·32	1·699	6·063	30·93	5·742	0·08992	271·2	0·2486
12	21·69	345·6	0·5219	17·83	1·782	6·591	33·80	6·276	0·09827	296·4	0·2718
13	23·50	375·1	0·5665	19·35	1·865	7·121	36·68	6·811	0·1067	321·7	0·2949
14	25·30	404·7	0·6112	20·87	1·948	7·652	39·57	7·349	0·1151	347·1	0·3182
15	27·11	434·4	0·6560	22·39	2·032	8·186	42·46	7·888	0·1235	372·5	0·3416
16	28·91	464·3	0·7011	23·93	2·116	8·721	45·37	8·430	0·1320	398·1	0·3650
17	30·72	494·2	0·7463	25·47	2·201	9·259	48·29	8·973	0·1405	423·8	0·3886
18	32·52	524·2	0·7917	27·01	2·285	9·799	51·23	9·519	0·1491	449·6	0·4122
19	34·33	554·4	0·8372	28·56	2·370	10·34	54·17	10·07	0·1576	475·4	0·4359
20	36·13	584·7	0·8829	30·12	2·456	10·88	57·12	10·62	0·1663	501·4	0·4597
21	37·94	615·1	0·9288	31·68	2·541	11·43	60·09	11·17	0·1749	527·5	0·4836
22	39·74	645·6	0·9749	33·25	2·627	11·98	63·06	11·72	0·1836	553·6	0·5076
23	41·58	676·2	1·021	34·82	2·714	12·53	66·05	12·28	0·1923	579·9	0·5317

TABLE 39

Vapour pressure and osmotic equivalence of sea water at 25°C.

(From A. R. Robinson, *J. Mar. Biol. Ass. U.K.*, 1955, 33, p. 451, Table II.)

$Cl\text{‰}$	R	NaCl	KCl	$CaCl_2$	$MgCl_2$	$MgSO_4$	Na_2SO_4	Sucrose	Urea	v.p. lowering	Osmotic pressure (atm.)
10	0·02861	0·2861	0·2908	0·2039	0·2005	0·5056	0·2374	0·5065	0·5400	0·00946	12·87
11	0·02869	0·3156	0·3211	0·2240	0·2199	0·5597	0·2643	0·5560	0·5965	0·01042	14·19
12	0·02877	0·3452	0·3516	0·2441	0·2393	0·6138	0·2918	0·6053	0·6534	0·01139	15·51
13	0·02885	0·3751	0·3825	0·2642	0·2588	0·6675	0·3196	0·6546	0·7112	0·01237	16·85
14	0·02893	0·4050	0·4134	0·2841	0·2780	0·7206	0·3477	0·7040	0·7695	0·01334	18·19
15	0·02901	0·4352	0·4447	0·3043	0·2975	0·7738	0·3762	0·7534	0·8285	0·01433	19·55
16	0·02908	0·4653	0·4760	0·3243	0·3165	0·8264	0·4051	0·8025	0·8880	0·01532	20·91
17	0·02916	0·4957	0·5077	0·3445	0·3356	0·8786	0·4347	0·8516	0·9482	0·01631	22·28
18	0·02924	0·5263	0·5397	0·3645	0·3546	0·9300	0·4648	0·9008	1·010	0·01732	23·66
19	0·02932	0·5571	0·5719	0·3845	0·3738	0·9803	0·4954	0·9497	1·071	0·01833	25·06
20	0·02940	0·5880	0·6043	0·4044	0·3929	1·028	0·5264	0·9982	1·133	0·01936	26·47
21	0·02948	0·6191	0·6370	0·4243	0·4122	1·076	0·5578	1·047	1·197	0·02039	27·89
22	0·02956	0·6503	0·6698	0·4440	0·4313	1·123	0·5896	1·095	1·260	0·02142	29·33

The column headed v.p. lowering gives the relative pressure lowering $\Delta p/p_0 = (p_0 - p)/p_0$, where p is the vapour pressure of the sea water and p_0 is the vapour pressure of pure water. $p_0 = 23.756$ mm. 25° C. $R = M\text{-NaCl}/\text{‰ Cl}$.

TABLE 40

Absorption spectra of chlorophylls *a* and *c*.

(From F. A. Richards, *J. Mar. Res.*, 1952, **11**, p. 150, Table II.)

Wave-length $m\mu$	Chlorophyll *a* in 90% acetone $\log E\,^{1\ gm.}_{1\ cm.}$	Chlorophyll *c* in 90% acetone. Corrected for chlorophyll *a* content $\log E\,^{Soln.\,1}_{1\ cm.}$	$\log E\,^{Soln.\,2}_{1\ cm.}$	Chlorophyll *c* in Methanol Corrected for chlorophyll *a* content $\log E\,^{Soln.\,1}_{1\ cm.}$	$\log E\,^{Soln.\,2}_{1\ cm.}$
320	1·449	1·449	1·528	—	—
325	1·453	1·448	1·526	—	—
330	1·399	1·362	1·394	—	—
335	1·419	1·305	1·281	—	—
340	1·403	1·283	1·279	—	—
345	—	1·264	1·257	—	—
350	1·464	1·241	1·245	—	—
355	1·499	1·221	1·233	—	—
360	1·552	1·236	1·233	—	—
365	1·599	—	—	—	—
370	1·648	1·262	1·257	—	—
375	1·685	—	—	—	—
380	1·697	1·307	1·302	—	—
385	1·701	—	—	—	—
390	1·701	1·361	1·352	—	—
395	1·714	—	—	—	—
400	1·764	1·378	1·373	1·299	1·271
405	1·829	—	—	—	—
410	1·859	1·441	1·436	1·362	1·331
415	1·854	—	—	—	—
420	1·849	1·572	1·573	1·461	1·434
425	1·894	—	—	—	—
430	1·940	1·730	1·733	1·626	1·605
440	1·696	1·883	1·889	1·748	1·718
445	1·347	1·922	1·922	1·764	1·764
450	0·949	1·895	1·899	1·763	1·751
455	0·625	—	—	—	—
460	0·405	1·677	1·674	1·635	1·622
465	0·313	—	—	—	—
470	0·276	1·216	1·202	1·342	1·317
480	0·278	0·732	0·718	0·929	0·910
490	0·368	0·468	0·441	0·452	0·442
500	0·410	0·368	0·344	0·237	0·216
505	0·414	—	—	—	—
510	0·412	0·329	0·295	0·201	0·113
515	—	0·325	0·286	—	—
520	0·417	0·353	0·320	0·220	0·192
530	—	0·437	0·415	—	0·238
540	0·591	0·519	0·499	0·384	0·352
550	0·567	0·545	0·529	0·442	0·414
560	0·706	0·654	0·645	0·502	0·493
570	0·855	0·763	0·736	0·580	0·539
580	0·942	0·867	0·857	0·703	0·685
585	—	0·843	0·834	0·720	0·693
590	0·915	0·757	0·748	0·684	0·560
600	0·986	0·583	0·560	0·555	0·560
605	—	0·554	0·541	0·492	0·456
610	1·144	0·573	0·563	0·483	0·442
615	1·179	0·646	0·637	0·538	0·539
620	1·172	0·760	0·760	0·638	0·618
625	1·138	0·931	0·914	0·779	0·776
630	1·076	1·015	1·024	0·856	0·846
631	—	1·021	—	—	—
634	—	—	—	0·869	—
635	1·035	0·985	0·983	0·868	0·851

OVER

TABLE 40—*continued*

Chlorophyll a in 90% acetone		Chlorophyll c in 90% acetone. Corrected for chlorophyll a content		Chlorophyll c in Methanol Corrected for chlorophyll a content	
Wave-length mμ	$\log E\,^{1\ gm.}_{1\ cm.}$	$\log E\,^{Soln.\ 1}_{1\ cm.}$	$\log E\,^{Soln.\ 3}_{1\ cm.}$	$\log E\,^{Soln.\ 1}_{1\ cm.}$	$\log E\,^{Soln.\ 1}_{1\ cm.}$
640	1·074	0·841	0·837	0·821	0·794
645	1·215	0·642	0·621	0·720	0·700
650	1·417	0·444	0·441	0·547	0·493
655	1·730	0·268	0·268	—	—
660	1·838	0·036	0·043	−0·383	−0·461
663	1·851	—	—	—	—
665	1·824	0·020	0·043	—	—
670	1·534	—	—	—	—
675	1·378	—	—	—	—
680	0·972	—	—	—	—
685	0·548	—	—	—	—

Concentrations of chlorophyll a solutions computed from specific absorption coefficients reported by Zscheile.

The relative absorption coefficients of the acetone solutions of chlorophyll c at 445 mμ are arbitrarily given the value 1·922 at 430 mμ. Values for chlorophyll a are *specific* absorption coefficients, those for chlorophyll c are relative absorption coefficients.

TABLE 41

Specific absorption coefficients of beta carotene in 90% acetone.

(From F. A. Richards, *J. Mar. Res.*, 1952, **11**, p. 152, Table III.)

Wave-length	Log $E^{1\ gm.}_{1\ cm.}$	Wave-length	Log $E^{1\ gm.}_{1\ cm.}$
320	1·216	455	2·400
322·5	1·163	456	2·400
325	1·181	460	2·385
330	1·205	465	2·351
335	1·227	470	2·332
340	1·248	475	2·339
345	1·238	480	2·349
350	1·248	485	2·337
355	1·227	490	2·285
360	1·253	500	2·042
370	1·377	510	1·658
380	1·554	520	1·181
390	1·725	530	0·771
400	1·906	540	0·570
410	2·033		
420	2·170	
425	2·212	
430	2·251	
440	2·309	
445	2·355	
450	2·388	
452	2·400	
453	2·400	

Concentrations of solutions determined from aliquot samples in hexane, using specific absorption coefficients reported by Zechmeister and Polgar. In 90% acetone the maximum is a little lower (cf. 2·410) and displaced slightly toward the longer wave-lengths (cf. 450 mμ) than in hexane solutions.

Absorption spectra of diatom xanthophylls in ethanol and 90% acetone solution. Values of log $E_{1\,cm}$ given.

(From F. A. Richards, *J. Mar. Res.*, 1952, **11**, p. 153, Table IV.)

Wave-length mμ	Neofucoxanthin A		Neofucoxanthin B		Fucoxanthin		Diadinoxanthin		Diatoxanthin	
	Ethanol	90% Acetone	Ethanol	90% Acetone	Ethanol	90% Acetone	Ethanol	90% Acetone	Ethanol	90% Acetone
350	1·657	1·667	1·581	1·553	1·328	1·312	1·494	1·521	1·808	1·805
355	—	1·675	—	1·568	1·336	1·340	1·464	1·472	1·757	1·765
360	1·688	1·706	1·620	1·608	1·402	1·400	1·494	1·480	1·729	1·734
365					1·465		1·552	1·537	1·731	1·734
370	1·761	1·789	1·714	1·721	1·550	1·567	1·622	1·610	1·771	1·756
375					1·621		1·687		1·808	
380	1·868	1·892	1·833	1·846	1·700	1·726	1·753	1·748	1·879	1·846
390	1·966	1·996	1·950	1·974	1·854	1·885	1·913	1·907	1·957	1·946
400	2·081	2·110	2·070	2·099	1·994	2·027	2·022	2·027	2·070	2·066
410	2·166	2·196	2·178	2·206	2·114	2·148	2·157	2·157	2·171	2·162
420	2·244	2·279	2·251	2·283	2·216	2·252	2·239	2·258	2·266	2·264
430	2·302	2·330	2·316	2·343	2·283	2·316	2·272	2·282	2·297	2·314
440	2·352	2·381	2·359	2·392	2·346	2·377	2·365	2·376	2·354	2·353
444				2·398	2·369	2·394	2·375	2·400	2·371	
445	2·367	2·397	2·373	2·398	2·369	2·398	2·372	2·400	2·373	2·381
446	2·369	2·398	2·374	2·400	2·368	2·400	2·365	2·399	2·373	2·384
448	2·370	2·400	2·375	2·400	2·374	2·400	2·354		2·375	2·392
449	2·374	2·399	2·373	2·395		2·400				
450	2·375	2·397			2·374	2·398	2·336	2·379	2·371	2·396
451	2·374		2·371		2·374					2·400
452	2·373		2·367	2·385	2·375	2·387	2·317		2·363	2·396
455	2·369	2·379	2·358	2·374	2·373	2·373	2·285	2·330	2·343	2·388
460	2·360	2·374		2·361	2·364	2·366	2·258	2·389	2·308	2·360
465		2·366		2·351	2·358	2·362	2·272	2·320	2·288	2·329
470	2·346	2·359	2·336		2·352		2·299	2·320	2·293	2·314
472	—						2·300	2·327	2·317	
475	—				2·337		2·287	2·321	2·318	2·318
476	—								2·317	2·322
478	—									2·324
480	2·304	2·312	2·277	2·278	2·305	2·308	2·201	2·269	2·275	2·322
485	—	2·257	—	2·213	2·259	2·246	2·037	2·139	2·211	2·294
490	2·206	2·184	2·160	2·135	2·201	2·171	1·793	1·933	2·091	2·198
500	2·056	1·998	1·993	1·931	2·043	1·969	1·229	1·362	1·715	1·905
510	1·890	1·792	1·808	1·710	1·866	1·753	0·871	0·953	1·322	1·527
520	1·673	1·583	1·598	1·448	1·645	1·494	0·649	0·706	1·021	1·187
530	1·442	1·306	1·346	1·192	1·409	1·222	0·514	0·417	0·817	0·960
540	1·211	1·049	1·101	0·939	1·152	0·960	0·376	0·379	0·662	0·797
560	0·734	0·634	0·592	0·448	0·637	0·358	0·251	0·254	0·516	0·659

Values of log $E_{1\,cm}$ computed by arbitrarily assigning the value 2·375 to the maxima of ethanol solutions and 2·400 in 90% acetone. The former value is close to the value found by Strain for eight-leaf xanthophylls in ethanol; the latter is an average observed for aliquot samples in acetone solution.

TABLE 43

Absorbancies of solutions containing one specified pigment unit per litre of 90% acetone at wave-length of absorption maximum.

(From F. A. Richards, with T. G. Thompson, *J. Mar. Res.*, 1952, **11**, p. 162. Table I.)

Compound	Wave-length of absorption maximum, $m\mu$	Specified absorbency $(E_{1\,cm.}^{s.p.u.})$ of a 1-cm. layer
Chlorophyll c	445	83·5
Neofucoxanthin A	447–8	251
Neofucoxanthin B	446–8	251
Fucoxanthin	448–9	251
Diatoxanthin	451	251
Diadinoxanthin	444–5	251
Astacin-type pigment	475	251

TABLE 44

Specific and specified absorption coefficients of some plankton pigments in 90% acetone solution.*

(From F. A. Richards, with T. G. Thompson, *J. Mar. Res.*, 1952, **11**, p. 163, Table II.)

Wave-length mμ	Chlorophyll a E 1 gm. 1 cm.	Chlorophyll b E 1 gm. 1 cm.	Chlorophyll c E s.p.u. 1 cm.	Beta Carotene E 1 gm. 1 cm.	Neofucoxanthin A E s.p.u. 1 cm.	Neofucoxanthin B E s.p.u. 1 cm.	Fucoxanthin E s.p.u. 1 cm.	Diadinoxanthin E s.p.u. 1 cm.	Diatoxanthin E s.p.u. 1 cm.	Astacin-type pigment E s.p.u. 1 cm.	Nonastacin type Carotenoids in average mixture E s.p.u. 1 cm.
665	66·7	6·5	1·1	0	0	0	0	0	0	0	0
645	16·4	45·6	4·4	0	0	0	0	0	0	0	0
630	11·9	12·7	10·4	0	0	0	0	0	0	169	0
510	2·6	3·5†	2·1	45·5	62·0	51·3	56·6	9·0	33·7	249	45
480	1·9	13·6	5·4	223	205	190	203	186	210	221	203
450	8·9	54·0	78·5	244	249	248	249	239	250	147	246
420	70·7	26·8	37·3	148	190	192	169	181	184		171

* Values from Richards, except chlorophyll b values, which are from Zscheile, Comar, and Mackinney.
† Estimated.

TABLE 45

Relative absorption spectrum of a 90% acetone solution of
astacin-type pigment extracted from crustaceans, corrected
for chlorophyll *a* absorption.

(From F. A. Richards, with T. G. Thompson, *J. Mar. Res.*, 1952, **11**, p. 165, Table III.)

Wave-length $m\mu$	E_1 cm.	Wave-length $m\mu$	E_1 cm.	Wave-length $m\mu$	E_1 cm.	Wave-length $m\mu$	E_1 cm.
350	47·2	400	84·3	450	220·9	500	204·2
355	48·9	405	92·7	455	236·0	510	168·7
360	47·2	410	106·2	460	236·0	520	126·5
365	50·6	415	121·3	465	246·0	530	86·1
370	52·2	420	134·9	470	251·2	540	50·5
380	59·0	425	146·9	475	251·2	550	28·6
390	69·0	430	161·8	480	249·5	560	16·9
—	—	435	177·0	490	227·5	—	—
—	—	440	195·4	—	—	—	—
—	—	445	208·9	—	—	—	—

SUBJECT INDEX

Absorbance, 20

Absorbance index, 21

Absorbancy, 21, 27, 29, 81–2

Absorbancy index, 21, 27, 81–2

Absorbancy index, molar, 21, 27, 31

Absorbancy index, spectrophotometer, 52

Absorbancy/wave-length curves for potassium permanganate, 28, 29

Absorptiometer, definition, 15

Absorptiometers, 45–8

Absorptiometers, calculation of results, 81–3

Absorptiometers, in oceanography, 54–5

Absorptiometers, Spekker, 46

Accuracy, 31–2

Acid addition, pH method for alkalinity, 202–4

Activity, 99, 100

Adjustments, pH meter, 107

After-drainage, burettes, 71–2

Agitation of solution, chlorinity, 88, 94, 96

Agla syringe burette (pipette), 191

Air-displacement correction, constant glass error, 74–5

Albuminoid nitrogen, 146

Alkali-hypochlorite method, oxygen in polluted waters, 188–9

Alkalinity (Section 15), 200

Alkalinity, acid addition, pH method, 202–4

Alkalinity, carbonate, equation for, 207

Alkalinity, titration methods, 204

Alsterberg azide method, oxygen in polluted waters, 188

Ammonia estimation (Section 8), 129

Ammonia, freshwater, Nessler, 137

Ammonia, micro-distillation, Krogh, 131–5

Ammonia, micro-distillation, Riley, 135–7

Ammonia, phenyl-hypochlorite method, procedure, 137, 139, 140

Ammonia, phenyl-hypochlorite method, reagents, 138, 140

Ammonia, Wattenberg method, 131

Ammonia, Witting-Buch, 129–30

Ammonia-free water, 131

Amperometric titration, 184, 185

Amplification, photo-voltaic cells, 45

Arny 'permanent' standards, 36–7

Ashing for cations, 209–10

Atterberg grade scales, 250–1, 252, 257

Automatic chlorinity titrator (ACT), 97

Balancing methods, colour comparators, 33

Balancing-type instruments, 38–9

Barrier layer cells, 33, 41–2

Beckman D.U. spectrophotometer, 54, 55

Beer's Law, 21

Beer's Law, deviations from, 22, 23, 24, 25

Bicarbonate ion, equation for, 207, 208

Block comparator, 37–8

Bouguer-Lambert Law, 19–21

von Brand's method for organic nitrogen, 144–5

British E.S.A. sieve series, 255

British I.M.M. sieve series, 254–5

Buffer solutions, N.B. standards, 104–5

Burettes, 70–4

Burettes, after-drainage time, 71–2
Burettes, delivery error, 70–1
Burettes, end-point emergence, 72
Burettes, Knudsen, 86–7, 93
Burettes, manipulation error, 72–3

Calcium carbonate, sediments, 264–6
Calcium, micro-method for, 213–15
Calculation of results (Section 3), 78
Calculation of results, absorptiometer, 81–3
Calculation of results, chlorinity, 92–3
Calculation of results, chlorinity, slide rules for, 95
Calculation of results, spectrophotometers, 81–3
Calculation of results, visual comparators, 78–80
Calibration curves (Section 3), 78
Calibration curves, effect of temperature on, 82
Calibration curves, for iron-phenanthroline complex, 24
Calibration curves, types of, 26
Calomel reference electrode, 105, 106
Campbell-Hurley comparator, 39
Candela, definition of, 19
Carbonate alkalinity, equation for, 207
Carbonate ion, equation for, 207, 208
Carbon dioxide, dissolved, equation for, 207, 208
Carbon dioxide, partial pressure, equation for, 207
Carbon dioxide, system in sea water (Section 16), 206
Carbon dioxide, total, equation for, 207
Cations, ashing for, 209–10
Cavett flasks, 139
Ceric sulphate, standard solution, 212, 213, 214, 215

Chemical errors, 67
Chloride estimation, micro-methods for, 217–19
Chloride estimation, removal of protein, 219
Chloride estimation, silver iodate method, 217–18
Chlorinity (Section 14), 84
Chlorinity, agitation of solution, 88, 94, 96
Chlorinity, calculation of results, 92–3
Chlorinity, calculation of results, slide rules for, 95
Chlorinity, definition of, 84
Chlorinity, potentiometric method, 96–7
Chlorinity, preparation of instruments, 89
Chlorinity, reagents, 88–9
Chlorinity, semi-micro titration method, 97
Chlorinity, storage of sea-water samples, 94–5
Chlorinity, titration method, 85–93
Chlorinity, titration, procedure, 89–92
Chlorinity, titration method, simplified technique, 95–6
Chlorinity, titration, vessel, 87–8
Chloroform, recovery from dithizone extracts, 236
Choice of working regions, spectrophotometers, 52–3
Coefficient of variation, 67
Collection of water samples, oxygen, 179
Colorimeter, definition, 15
Colorimeter, Duboscq, 33
Colorimeter, Pulfrich, 33
Colour comparators (Section 1), 15
Colour comparators, desiderata for, 34–5
Colour comparators, errors, 35–6
Colour comparators, methods, 32
Colour comparators, methods, advantages, 36

Colour comparators, methods of comparison, 33–4

Colour comparators, standards, 36–7

Colour comparators, types of, 37–9

Colour systems, desiderata for, 15–17

Comparison of variances, 62–3

Compensating circuit, photovoltaic cells, 47–8

Conservative elements, micromethods (Section 17), 209

Constant error, 67

Constant glass error, 74–7

Constant glass error, air-displacement correction 74–5

Constant glass error, density correction, 74

Constant glass error, expansion of glass correction, 75

Constant glass error, temperature effect on wall-fluid correction, 75–6

Conventional (paH) scale, 102

Conventional (pH$_s$) scale, 102, 103

Copper, 228–30

Copper, 2:2' diquinolyl method, 230

Copper, sodium diethyldithiocarbamate method, 229–30

Copper sulphate, catalyst for nitrate, 119

Definitions, pH, 99–100

Delivery error, burettes, 70–1

Delivery time, pipettes, 70

Density correction, constant glass error, 74

Difference between means, significance of, 64–6

Differences, variance of, 63–4

Dilution, colour comparators, 33

Diphenylbenzidine method, nitrates, 117–18

2:2' diquinolyl method for copper, 230

Dispersion of sediments, 259

Distillation (micro-), ammonia, Krogh, 131–5

Distillation (micro-), ammonia, Riley, 135–7

Dithizone absorbent, separation of trace metals, 233–4

Dithizone, as an analytical reagent, 234–7

Dithizone, preparation and storage of solutions, 235–6

Dithizone, procedure for estimations, 236–7

Dithizone, recovery of chloroform from extracts, 236

Duboscq colorimeter, 33, 39, 78

Duplication method, colour comparators, 33

Effect of temperature on calibration curves, 82

Efficiency of sieving, 256

Emery's settling tube for sands, 262–4

End-point emergence, burette, 72

Equipment errors, colour comparators, 35

Equivalent circuit, photo-emissive cell, 43

Equivalent circuit, photo-voltaic cell, 41

Errors and precision (Section 2), 60

Errors, chemical, 67

Errors, constant, 67

Errors, contributing to overall precision of analysis, 66–8

Errors, manipulation, 67

Errors, pH meter, 107

Errors, spectrophotometry, 51–2

Estimation of blank, 78–80

Extinction, 27

Extinction coefficient, 20, 27

Extinction coefficient, molar, 21, 27

Extraction, plankton pigments, 33–40, 242

Eye, relative sensitivity curve for, 34

Feed-back, photo-emissive cells, 44
Filters, membrane, 247, 248
Filters, molecular, 247, 248
Filtration (Section 20), 247
Filtration, separation of plankton by, 247–8
Fiske-Subbarow reagent, 159, 160, 161
Foot-candle, definition of, 19
Foot-lambert, definition of, 19
Free energy, 99, 100
Frequency, 28, 31
Freshwater, ammonia estimation, 137

Gasometric (micro-), method for oxygen, 193–8
Glass electrode, 105–6
Glass electrode, pH estimation, 105–12
Glass errors, constant, 74–7
Glassware, standardization of, 76–7
Grade scales, 250–2
Grade scales, Atterberg, 250–1, 252, 257
Grade scales, phi and zeta, 251–2
Grade scales, Udden-Wentworth, 251, 252, 262

Harvey unit, plankton pigments, 241
Harvey's method for nitrates, 27, 33
Harvey's method for organic phosphorus, 158, 159
Harvey's method for plankton pigments, 33, 241
Hehner cylinders, 32, 33, 38, 39
Heyrovský micro-polarograph, 123
Hutchinson and MacLennan's method for carbonates in sediments, 264, 265
Hydrazine-copper reducing agent (nitrate), 119

Inorganic nitrogen (total), sea water, 138–40
Inorganic phosphorus: phosphate (Section 10), 151
Inorganic phosphorus: phosphate, procedure, 153–4
Inorganic phosphorus: phosphate, reagents, 153
Inorganic phosphorus: phosphate, small quantities, 155
Inorganic silicon: silicate (Section 12), 163
Instruments for chlorinity, preparation of, 89
Iodine difference method, oxygen in polluted waters, 186–7
Iron, 224–8
Iron, particulate, 227
Iron, 'reducible', 225–6
Iron, soluble, 228
Iron, total, 226
Iron-phenanthroline complex, calibration and transmittancy curves, 23, 24

Kay's method for organic carbon, 171–7
Kjeldahl, organic nitrogen, 145–6, 146–50
Knudsen burette, 86–7, 93
Knudsen pipette, 86–7
Knudsen's tables, 84, 86, 93, 95
Krogh and Keys' method for organic carbon, 168–71
Krogh and Keys' method for organic nitrogen, 142–4

Laboratoire Hydrographique, Denmark, 85, 88
Leitz filter photometer, 40–1
Leptopel, 247
Light measurements, terminology, 18–19
Location of difficulties, pH meter, 108–9

Log - absorbancy / wave - length curves, potassium permanganate, 30
Lovibond comparator, *opp.* 38
Lumen, definition of, 19
Luminance, 19
Luminous flux, 19
Luminous intensity, 19
Lux, definition of, 19

Magnesium, micro-method for, 215–17
Manganese, 231–3
Manganese, estimation after co-precipitation with alkali, 231–3
Manganese, estimation by tetrabase method, 231
Manipulative errors, 67
Manipulative errors, burette, 72–3
Marten's photometer, 32
Mean deviation, 60
Mean, sample, 62
Mean, technique, 61
Mechanical analysis of sediments, 252, 257–62
Membrane filters, 247, 248
Methods and instruments, classification of, 32
Methods of delivery, pipettes, 68–9
Molar absorbancy index, 21, 27, 31
Molar extinction coefficient, 21, 27
Molecular filters, 247, 248
Molybdenum blue method for silicate, 165–6
Molybdenum blue reactions, conditions affecting, 151–3
Molybdenum blue transmittancy curve, 52
Muds, organic nitrogen, 146–50
Muds, organic phosphorus, 159–61
Multi-component systems, spectrophotometer, 53

(1 Naphthyl) ethylenediamine hydrochloride (nitrite), 126

α–Naphthylamine reagent, 119, 126
N.B. standards, buffer solutions, 104–5
Nessler reagent (ammonia), for freshwater, 137
Nessler reagent (ammonia), Treadwell, 130
Nessler reagent (ammonia), Wattenberg, 131
Nitrate (Section 6), 113
Nitrate estimation, diphenylbenzidine method, 117–18
Nitrate estimation, freshwater, 120
Nitrate estimation, polarographically, 123–4
Nitrate estimation, reduced strychnine method, 114–17
Nitrate estimation, reduction to nitrate, 118–22
Nitrate, salt-error correction, 122
Nitrite (Section 7), 126
Nitrogen, albuminoid, 146
Normal deviate, 61
Normal distribution, 61
Normal water, 84, 85, 94, 95
Normal water, sub-standards, 93, 95

Optical density, 20, 27
Organic carbon (Section 13), 168
Organic carbon, method of Kay, 171–7
Organic carbon, method of Krogh and Keys, 168–71
Organic carbon, oxidation mixtures for, 168–9, 175
Organic content of sediments, 266–7
Organic nitrogen, in plankton (Section 9), 142
Organic nitrogen, in plankton, von Brand's method, 144
Organic nitrogen, in sea water (Section 9), 142
Organic nitrogen, in sea water, Kjeldahl, 145-6, 146–50

Organic nitrogen, in sea water, method of Krogh and Keys, 142–4

Organic nitrogen, semi-micro, muds, 146–50

Organic nitrogen, semi-micro, plankton, 146–50

Organic nitrogen, semi-micro, tissues, 146–50

Organic phosphorus, Harvey's method, 158–9

Organic phosphorus, in muds, 159–61

Organic phosphorus, in plankton (Section 11), 157

Organic phosphorus, in sea water (Section 11), 157

Organic phosphorus, in tissues, 159–61

Organic phosphorus, wet ashing, 159–61

Overall precision of analysis, 66–8

Overall precision, pipettes, 68–70

Oxidation mixture for organic carbon, 168–9, 175

Oxygen (Section 14), 178

Oxygen bottles, calibration of, 179–83

Oxygen, collection of water samples, 179

Oxygen, gasometric micro-method, 193–8

Oxygen, standard Winkler method (macro-) officially recommended, 178–85

Oxygen, Winkler (micro-), 189–93

Oxygen in polluted waters, 185–9

Oxygen in polluted waters, alkali-hypochlorite method, 188–9

Oxygen in polluted waters, Alsterberg azide method, 188

Oxygen in polluted waters, iodine difference method, 186–7

Partial pressure of carbon dioxide, equation for, 207

'Particulate' iron, 227

pH (Section 5), 99

pH, definitions, 99–100

pH, estimation by glass electrode, 105–12

pH, pressure corrections, 111–12

pH, scales (paH, pH$_s$, psH), definitions, 100–3

pH, standards, 103–4

pH, temperature corrections, 111–12

pH meter, 106–9

pH meter, adjustments, 107

pH meter, errors, 107

pH meter, location of difficulties, 108–9

pH meter, procedure, 111–12

pH meter, repairs, 107

pH meter, standardization of, 110–11

Phenol-hypochlorite reaction for ammonia, 137, 138, 139, 140

Phenol-sodium phenate buffer (nitrate), 119

Phi grade scales, 251–2

Phosphate analysis, storage of sea water for, 155

Phosphate (inorganic), small quantities, 155

Phosphorus (inorganic), phosphate (Section 10), 151

Phosphorus: organic in sea water and plankton (Section 11), 157

Photoelectric filter photometer, 45–8

Photoelectric methods, 33

Photo-emissive cells, 42–5

Photo-emissive cells, amplification, 44

Photo-emissive cells, equivalent circuit, 43

Photo-emissive cells, feed-back, 44

Photometer, definition of, 15

Photometer, Marten's, 32

Photometric analysis (Section 1), 15

Photo-voltaic cells, 33, 41–2

Photo-voltaic cells, amplification, 45

Photo-voltaic cells, compensating circuit, 47–8

Photo-voltaic cells, equivalent circuit, 41

Pigment unit, Harvey, 241

Pigment unit, specified, 244

Pigments, plankton (Section 19), 240

Pipette, Knudsen, 86–7

Pipettes, 68–70

Pipettes, delivery time, 70

Pipettes, method of delivery, 68–9

Pipettes, overall precision, 68–70

Pipettes, wall-fluid, 69–70

Plankton, organic carbon (Section 13), 168

Plankton, organic nitrogen (semi-micro), 146–50

Plankton, pigments, (Section 19), 240

Plankton pigments, extraction, 240–2

Plankton pigments, Harvey unit, 241

Plankton pigments, multiple transmittancy measurements, 242–4

Plankton pigments, single transmittancy measurements, 240–2

Plankton, separation by filtration, 247–8

Plankton, separation for analysis, 144, 145

Polarographic method for estimation of nitrates, 123–4

Polluted waters, oxygen estimation, 185–9

Polythene bottles, 95, 97, 122, 123, 155, 165

Pooling of variances, 63

Potassium, micro-method for estimation, 211–13

Potassium permanganate, absorbancy/wave-length curves, 28, 29, 30

Potassium permanganate, transmittancy/wave-length curves, 26, 27

Potentiometric methods for chlorinity estimation, 96–7

Precision (Section 2), 60

Pressure correction, pH, 111–12

Protein, removal before chloride analysis, 219

Pulfrich's colorimeter, 33

Raney nickel, 138, 139

Range, 31–2

Reagents, desiderata for, 17

Reduced strychnine, preparation of, 114–15

Reduced strychnine method (nitrate), 114–17

'Reducible' iron, 225–6

Relative sensitivity curve for the eye, 34

Repairs, pH meter, 107

Resolution, spectrophotometer, 52

Reversible hydrogen electrode, 99

Reversion procedure for dithizone estimations, 236–7

Salinity, definition, 84

Salt-error correction (nitrate), 122

Salt-error estimation, absorptiometers, 83

Salt-error estimation, spectrophotometers, 83

Salt-error estimation, visual comparators, 80

Sample mean, 62

Sample, standard deviation, 62

Sands, Emery's settling tube, 262–4

Sea water carbon dioxide system (Section 16), 206

Sea water, storage for phosphate analysis, 155

Sediments, calcium carbonate estimation, 264–6

Sediments, dispersion of, 259

Sediments, loss on acid treatment, 256–7

Sediments, mechanical analysis, 252, 257–62

Sediments, organic content, 266–7

Sediments, physical and chemical examination (Section 21), 250

Sensitivity, definition, 31–2

Sensitivity, factors determining, 31–2

Separation of plankton for analysis, 144–5

Settling tube for sands (Emery), 262–4

Settling velocities, 260, 262

Sieves, 252–6

Sieves, B.E.S.A. sieve series, 255

Sieves, B.I.M.M. sieve series, 254–5

Sieves, Tyler sieve series, 253

Sieves, U.S. sieve series, 254

Sieving efficiency, 256

Significance of difference between means, 64–6

Silico-molybdic acid method for silicon, 163–5

Silicon (inorganic), silicate (Section 12), 163

Silicon, molybdenum blue method, 165–6

Silicon, silico-molybdic acid method, 163–5

Silver iodate method for chloride, 217–18

Slide rules for calculation of salinity, 95

Slit width, 49, 51, 52

Sodium acetate buffer (nitrite), 126

Sodium, micro-method for, 210–11

Sodium diethyldithiocarbamate method (copper), 229–30

Sodium fluoresceinate indicator for chlorinity titration, 96, 97

Sodium thiosulphate, standardization, 180–1, 183, 192

Soluble iron, 228

Solution effects, spectrophotometers, 52

Somogyi's reagents, 219

Sørensen pH unit (psH), 101, 102

Specific absorbancy concentration (Wernimont), 31

Specified pigment unit (S.P.U.), 244

Spectrophotometers, 48–54

Spectrophotometers, absorbance index, 52

Spectrophotometers, Beckman D.U., 54, 55

Spectrophotometers, calculation of results, 81–3

Spectrophotometers, choice of working region, 52–3

Spectrophotometers, multi-component systems, 53

Spectrophotometers, oceanography, 54–5

Spectrophotometers, resolution, 52

Spectrophotometers, solution effects, 52

Spectrophotometers, transmittance, 32

Spectrophotometers, transmittancy errors, 52

Spectrophotometers, Uvispek, 49–51

Spectrophotometers, wave-length errors, 52

Spectrophotometric data, method of representation, 26–31

Spectrophotometry, errors, 51–2

Spekker absorptiometer, 46

Standard deviation, normal distribution, 61, 62

Standard deviation, rectangular distribution, 68

Standard deviation, sample, 62

Standard deviation, technique, 61

Standard potential, 101

Standard series, colour comparators, 33

Standard series, instruments, 37–8

Standardization of glassware, 76–7

Standardization of pH meters, 110–11

Standards, colour comparators, 36–7

Storage of dithizone solutions, 235–6
Storage of sea-water samples (chlorinity), 94–5
Strychnidine, preparation of, 115–16
Strychnine method for nitrates, 33, 113–17
Sulphanilic acid reagent, 119, 126
Sulphate, micro-method, 219–21
Sums, variance of, 63–4
Suspended matter, separation by absorption, 248
Suspended matter, separation by filtration, 247–8
Syringe burette (Agla), 191
Syringe pipette, 190–1
Systematic error, 67
Systematic errors, colour comparators, 35

Technique, mean, 61
Technique, standard deviation, 61
Temperature corrections, pH, 111–12
Teorell's hypobromite method, 131, 132, 134, 135
Tetra-base method for manganese, 231
Thallous sulphate for removal of chloride, 168
Tissues, organic nitrogen, 145–50
Tissues, organic phosphorus, 159–61
Titration method for alkalinity, 204
Titration method for chlorinity, 85–93
Titration method for chlorinity, simplified technique, 95–6
Titration, total variable glass error, 73–4
Titration vessel for chlorinity, 87–8
'Total' iron, 226
Total variable glass error, titration, 73–4
Trace analysis, general precautions, 17–18

Trace metals (Section 18), 224
Trace metals, separation of an dithizone absorbent, 233–4
Transformation, logarithmic for grade scales, 251–2
Transmission curves, 26–31
Transmission instruments, 39–54
Transmittance, 20, 27
Transmittancy, 21, 26, 27, 29, 32
Transmittancy curves, iron-phenanthroline complex, 23
Transmittancy curves, potassium permanganate, 25, 26, 27
Transmittancy errors, spectrophotometers, 52
Transmittancy measurements, plankton pigments, 240–4
Tyler sieve series, 253

Udden-Wentworth grade scales, 251, 252, 262
U.S. sieve series, 254
Uvispek spectrophotometer, 49–51

Vacuum phototube, 33, 41–5
Variance, 61
Variances, comparison of, 62–3
Variances of differences, 63–4
Variances, pooling of, 63
Variances, sums of, 63–4
Visual comparators, calculation of results, 78–80
Visual filter photometer, 40–1
Velocities, settling, 260, 262

Wall-fluid, pipettes, 69–70
Water, ammonia-free, 130, 131
Wattenberg method, ammonia, 131
Wave-length, 28
Wave-length errors, spectrophotometer, 52
Wave-number, 28
Wet ashing, organic phosphorus, 159–61
Will-Warrentrapp method, 142

Winkler method (macro-) oxygen, 178–85
Winkler method (micro-) oxygen, 189–93
Witting-Buch method, ammonia, 129, 130

Working errors, colour comparators, 35

Zeta grade scales, 251–2
Zinc uranyl acetate reagent, 210

AUTHOR INDEX

Arons, A. B., *see* Wilson, K. G., 271

Aleem, A. A., 242, 244

Allen, E. C., *see* Greenberg, D. M., 205

Allen, J. A., 270

Allison, L. E., 268

Allport, N. L., 238

Alsterberg, G., 186, 188, 198

Anderson, D. H. 202, 203, 204
see also Thompson, T. G., 205

Anderson, L., *see* Thompson, T. G., 222

Andrew, G., *see* Irving, H. M. N. H., 238

Anselm, C. D., 223

Armstrong, F. A. J., 56, 154, 156, 161, 163, 165, 167, 249, 271

Arny, H. V., 36, 56

Atkins, W. R. G., 56, 113, 118, 124, 125, 156, 167, 228, 237, 241, 244
see also Armstrong, F. A. J., 249

Atterberg, A., 250, 251, 252, 257, 267

Baker, M., *see* Goldberg, E. D., 249

Barnes, H., 56, 128, 159, 221, 235, 236, 237, 238, 312, 313, 314, 315, 316, 317
see also Rothschild, Lord, 221

Barnett, G. R., 199

Bates, R. G., 99, 107, 112, 305

Bather, J. M., 95, 97, 222, 271

Baumann, E. R., *see* Oulman, C. S., 271

Belcher, R., 150, 177

Berenblum, I., 155, 156

Beveridge, J. S., 223

Black, I. A., 267, 268

Black, W. A. P., 118, 125

Block, R. J., 239

Bourne, E. J., *see* Peat, S., 199

Bowen, H. J. M., 271

Braarud, T., 140

Bradstreet, R. B., 150

Brady, J. H., *see* Buchoff, L. S., 270

von Brand, T., 142, 143, 144, 150, 177

Bray, R. H., 125

Bremner, R. W., 225
see also Thompson, T. G., 237

Brew, W., 16, 57

Brice, B. A., 57

Brown, R. H. J., *see* Ramsay, J. A., 221

Bruneau, L., 111, 112, 203, 204

Buch, K., 112, 129, 140, 156, 205, 206, 208, 226, 237, 238, 304, 306, 307, 308, 309, 310

Buchoff, L. S., 270

Buljan, M., 135, 140

Carlisle, D. B., 271

Carpenter, J. H., 271

Carritt, D. E., 55, 233, 234, 238
see also Snodgrass, J. M., 58

Chain, E., 155
see also Berenblum, I., 156

Chow, D. T.-W., 123, 125, 167

Chow, T. G., 222, 228, 237

Christie, A. A., 269

Claff, C. L., *see* Scholander, D. L., 199

Clark, W. M., 57

Comar, C. L., *see* Zscheile, F. P. (jr.), 246

Connor, R. M., 272

Conway, E. J., 67, 77, 204, 284, 285

Cooke, S. J. H., *see* Irving, H. M. N. H., 238

Cooper, L. H. N., 57, 125, 129, 140, 156, 161, 224, 225, 226, 237

Corwin, N., 157
see also Ketchum, B. H., 162
Cox, R. A., 54, 55, 57, 95, 97
Creitz, G. I., 242, 243, 272
Crisp, D. J., 193
see also Thorpe, H. W., 199
Crowther, A. B., 139, 140
Csányi, L., see Szabó, Z. G., 222

van Dam, L., 193, 199
see also Scholander, D. L., 199
Dewer, E. T., *see* Black, W. A. P., 125
Dittmar, W., 84, 98, 311
Downing, A. L., 273, 302, 303
see also Truesdale, G. A., 199
Duboscq, J., 15, 32, 33, 35, 39
Duxbury, A. C., 272

Emery, K. O., 250, 261, 262, 263, 267
Evans, R. M., 57

Falloon, S. W. H. W., *see* Ramsay, J. A., 221
Ferry, J. D., 249
Fisher, R. A., 77, 278, 279
Fiske, C. H., 159, 161
Fleming, R. H., 245, 311
see also Lyman, J., 221
see also Sverdrup, H. U., 221
Folkard, A. R., *see* Barnes, H., 128
Ford, W. L., 55, 56, 57
Fox, C. J. J., 184, 185, 199, 300, 301
Fox, D. L., 159, 242, 245, 248, 249
see also Gorgy, S., 161
see also Goldberg, E. D., 249
Fox, H. M., 189, 190, 193, 199
Føyn, B., *see* Braarud, T., 140
Føyn, E., 125, 129, 140, 270
Freier, R., 270
Fukai, R., 125, 156, 269, 270

Gameson, A. L. H., 270
see also Truesdale, G. A., 271

Gardiner, A. C., 245
Gel'man, N. E., *see* Kurshun, M. A., 270
Gilcreas, F. W., *see* Morgan, G. B., 269
Gillbricht, M., 242, 245
Giral, J., 94, 98
Godbert, A. L., *see* Belcher, R., 150, 177
Goetz, A., 249
Goldberg, E. D., 225, 227, 228, 249
see also Lewis, G. E., 237
Goldschmidt, V. M., 221
Goodwin, T. W., 245
Gorgy, S., 159, 167
Gorschkova, T., 242, 245
Gould, H. R., *see* Emery, K. O., 267
Grady, J. R., see Orr, W. L., 272
Graham, H. W., 245
Greenberg, D. M., 205
Greenfield, L. J., 156
Gripenberg, S., 112, 222, 226, 268, 304
see also Buch, K., 112

Hansen, A. L., 161
Hardin, G., *see* Strain, H. H., 245
Harding, M. W., 223, 311
Hardy, A. C., 57
Harris, W. E., *see* Kolthoff, I. M., 123, 125
Harvey, H. W., 16, 27, 33, 54, 57, 95, 98, 113, 114, 115, 116, 117, 125, 150, 156, 157, 159, 161, 208, 231, 238, 241, 245
see also Armstrong, F. A. J., 161
Haslewanter, F., 71
see also Lindner, J., 77
Hermann, F., 95, 98
Hitchcox, G. I., 112
Honma, M., 269
Hummerstone, L. G., *see* Carlisle, D. B., 271
Hunter, G. I., *see* Beveridge, J. S,, 223

Hurwitz, E., *see* Barnett, G. R., 199

Ibañez, O. G., 155
Igelsrud, I., 222, 311
Ilkovic, D., 125
Ingber, N. M., Buchoff, L. S., 270
Ingols, R. S., *see* Weil, B. H., 239
Inman, D. L., 251, 267
Irving, H. M. N. H., 235, 236, 238
Isaeva, A. B., 269
Ishibashi, M., 239, 270, 271

Jacobsen, J. P., 85, 95, 98, 199, 300, 301, 311
Jenkins, E. N., 230, 237
Jenkins, P. G., *see* Atkins, W. R. G., 244
Jentoft, R. E., 271
Jerlov, N. G., 111, 203, 249
 see also Bruneau, L., 112, 204
Johnson, M. W., *see* Sverdrup, H. U., 221
Johnston, W. R., 311
 see also Thompson, T. G., 222
Jones, L. A., 57

Kalber, F. A., *see* Greenfield, L. G., 156
Kalle, K., 40, 57, 95, 97, 98, 156, 161, 245, 269
Kanamori, S., *see* Tamaka, M., 270
Kanwisher, J. W., *see* Scholander, D. L., 199
Kasline, C. T., 57
Kay, H., 168, 171, 172, 174, 177
Keen, D. J., 157
 see also Ketchum, B. H., 162
Keilin, B., 125
Kendall, M. G., *see* Yule, G. U., 77
Kershaw, F. G., *see* Strafford, N., 239
Ketchum, B. H., 55, 135, 157, 159, 162
 see also Redfield, A. C., 162

Keys, A., 142, 143, 168, 169, 170, 171
 see also Krogh, A., 150, 177
King, J., 85, 87, 89, 90, 91, 92, 93, 98
Kirk, P. L., 222, 311
Kitson, R. E., 53, 57
Kitteridge, J. S., *see* Fox, D. L., 249
Knapman, F. W., *see* Robinson, R. J., 221
Knowles, G., 184, 189
Knudsen, M., 84, 85, 86, 93, 95, 96, 97, 98, 311
 see also Jacobsen, J. P., 98
Koczy, F. F., 96, 111, 203, 266, 268
 see also Bruneau, L., 112, 204
Kolthoff, I. M., 123, 125, 222
Koroleff, F., 231, 238
Korpi, E., *see* Thompson, T. G., 222
Körtum, G., 22, 57, 58
Koyama, T., *see* Sugawara, K., 223
Kreps, E., 162
Krey, J., 242, 245
Krogh, A., 131, 133, 135, 140, 142, 143, 150, 168, 169, 170, 171, 177
Krumbein, W. C., 251, 267
Kuney, J. H., 157, 162
Kurshun, M. A., 270

Lachey, J. B., *see* Morgan, G. B., 269
Laitinen, H. A., *see* Lingane, J. J., 125
Lang, J. W., *see* Thompson, T. G., 222
Lange, B., 41, 52
Large, R. S., 139
 see also Crowther, A. B., 140
Lutz, F., *see* Rakestraw, N. W., 162
Lewis, G. E., 225, 227, 228, 237
Lindner, J., 71, 77

Lingane, J. J., 123, 125
  see also Kolthoff, I. M., 125
Lowden, G. F., 184, 273, 302, 303
  see also Knowles, G., 199
  see also Truesdale, G. A., 199
Lyman, J., 221, 311

Machin, K. E., see Ramsay, J. A., 221
Mackinney, G., see Zscheile, F. P. (jr.), 246
MacNulty, A. B., see Beveridge, J. S., 223
Manning, W. M., see Strain, H. H., 245
Mapper, D., see Smales, A. A., 271
Marvin, K. T., 117, 125, 269
Matida, Y., 115, 117, 125, 128, 162, 204, 205, 222, 223
Matsue, Y., 156
Matsuyama, G., 123
  see also Kolthoff, I. M., 125
McGary, J. W., 95, 98
McNamee, P. D., see Theriault, E. J., 199
Mellon, M. G., 20, 23, 24, 25, 26, 27, 28, 29, 30, 34, 47, 51, 52, 53, 58, 239
  see also Kasline, C. T., 57
  see also Kitson, R. E., 57
  see also Moss, M. L., 237
  see also Rider, B. F., 128
  see also Swank, H. W., 167
Middleton, G., 239
Miller, E. E., see Miller, G. L., 150
Miller, G. L., 150
Mitchell, P. H., 205
Miyake, Y., 97, 98, 221, 222, 223
Moberg, E. G., 311
  see also Greenberg, D., 205
  see also Harding, M. W., 223
  see also Kirk, P. L., 222
Morgan, G. B., 269
Moss, M. L., 237
Mott, N. F., 41, 58

Mullin, J. B., 113, 118, 120, 121, 125, 163, 165, 166, 167, 236, 238, 271
Murphy, J., 155, 270
Murray, P. E., see Weil, B. H., 239

Nakagawa, Y., see Ishibashi, M., 271
Newman, O. F., see Christie, A. A., 97, 269
Nynäs, O., 112, 304
  see also Buch, K., 112

Odum, H. T., 271
Ohle, W., 186, 187, 199
Oppenheimer, C. H., see Fox, D. L., 249
Orr, W. L., 272
Osadich, M., see Kreps, E., 162
Otvos, J. W., see Keilin, B., 125
Oulman, C. S., 271
Oxner, M. 89, 96, 98

Parke, M., 241
  see also Atkins, W. R. G., 244
Pate, B. D., see Smales, A. A., 162
Peat, S., 199
Pettijohn, F. J., see Krumbein, W. C., 267
Piper, C. S., 257, 260, 267
Placak, O. R., 199
Polgar, A., see Zscheile, F. P., (jr.), 246
Potter, E. C., 271
Proctor, C. M., 156, 269

Rakestraw, N. W., 142, 143, 153, 154, 159, 162, 180, 200, 205
  see also von Brand, T., 150
  see also Gorgy, S., 169
  see also Mitchell, P. H., 205
  see also Wooster, W. S., 156
Ramberg, E. G., see Zworykin, V. K., 59

Ramsey, J. A., 209, 221
Rao, S. V., 270
Redfield, A. C., 162
Reed, G. W., *see* Weil, B. H., 239
Resch, G., *see* Freier, R., 270
Revelle, R., 311
Rhodes, D. N., 270
Richards, F. A., 54, 58, 242, 243, 245, 319, 320, 321, 322, 323, 324
see also Creitz, G. I., 272
Riddell, W. A., 125
Rider, B. F., 128
del Riego, A. F., 272
Riley, G. A., 245
Riley, J. P.. 89, 95, 113, 118, 120, 121, 135, 136, 138, 139, 141, 153, 154, 155, 158, 163, 164, 165, 166, 226, 228, 230, 236, 269
see also Bather, J. M., 97, 222, 271
see also Mullin, J. B., 125, 167, 238, 271
see also Murphy, J., 270
see also el Wakeel, S. K., 270
Risdon, E. J., *see* Irving, H. M. N. H., 238
Rittenhouse, G., 267
Rittner, E. S., 44, 45, 58
Roberts, C. H., 54, 55, 58
Robertson, J. D., 209, 213, 217, 219, 220, 221
Robertson, K. G., *see* Gameson, A. L. H., 270
Robinson, A. R., 318
Robinson, G. W., 251, 268
Robinson, R. J., 27, 95, 113, 114, 117, 123, 128, 129, 141, 150, 156, 167, 202, 203, 204, 221, 300, 301, 311
see also Anderson, D. H., 204
see also Anselm, C. D., 223
see also Chow, D. T.-W., 125, 167
see also Hansen, A. L., 161
see also Jacobsen, J. P., 199
see also Jentoff, R. E., 271
see also Thompson, T. G., 199, 221

see also West, L. E., 98, 205
see also Wirth, H. E., 141
see also Zwicker, B. M. G., 59, 125
Rochford, D., 114, 125
Rothschild, Lord, 221
Ruchhoft, R. C., *see* Placak, O. R., 199

Saiki, A., 155, 156
Sandell, E. B., 31, 58, 239
Saruhashi, K., 97, 98, 204, 205
Scholander, D. L., 194, 199
Schottky, W., 41, 58
Scott, M. V., 16
see also Brew, W., 57
Seiler, M., 22
see also Körtum, G., 58
Sendroy, J., 217, 220
Sherman, I., 268
Sherzer, W. H., 268
Shigematsu, T., *see* Ishibashi, M., 271
Sinhaseni, P., *see* Riley, J. P., 269
Smales, A. A., 162, 222, 271
Smith, H. P., *see* Redfield, A. C., 162
Snedecor, G. W., 77, 280, 282
Snell, C. T., *see* Snell, F. D., 58, 239
Snell, F. D., 58, 239
Snodgrass, J. M., 55, 58
Sporek, K. F., 271
Steele, C. C., 245
Stevenson, R. E., *see* Emery, K.O., 267
Stiles, W., 239
Strafford, N., 239
Strain, H. H., 245
Stuckey, R. E., *see* Middleton, G., 239
Subbarow, Y., *see* Fiske, C. H., 161
Sugawara, K., 223
Sund, O., 95, 98
Sverdrup, H. U., 221
Swan, E. F., 271

Swank, H. W., 167
Szabó, Z. G., 222

Tabushi, M., see Ishibashi, M., 270
Takedo, I., 270
Tamaka, M., 270
Taylor, H. J., 311
    see also Thompson, T. G., 223
Tchillingarian, G., 268
Terada, K., see Sugawara, K., 223
Theriault, E. J., 199
Thompson, T. G., 54, 199, 205,
    221, 222, 223, 225, 228, 231, 237,
    238, 242, 300, 301, 311, 322, 323
    see also Chow, T. G., 222
    see also Igelsrud, I., 222
    see also Jacobsen, J. P., 199
    see also Richards, F. A., 58, 245
    see also Robinson, R. J., 128,
    156, 167
Thomsen, H., 85, 89, 90, 91, 94, 96,
    98
Thomson, E. F., 94, 98
Thorpe, W. H., 193, 199
Thrower, R. D., see Peat, S., 199
Tischer, J., 156
Titze, H., 265
    see also Koczy, F. F., 268
Truesdale, G. A., 199, 271, 273,
    302, 303
Tsuneishi, N., see Goetz, A., 249
Tucker, A., 245
Turiekian, K. K., 272

Ungar, J., 269
Urbach, C., 58

Van Landingham, J. W., 269
Vatova, A., 270
Vinograd, A. P., 239

el Wakeel, S. K., 270
Waksman, S. A., 226
Walkley, A., 267, 268
Wattenberg, H., 129, 141
Webb, D. A., 209, 213, 217, 219,
    221, 222, 311
    see also Robertson, J. D., 221

Webster, R. K., see Smales, A. A.,
    271
Weil, B. H., 239
Wentworth, C. K., 268
Wernimont, G., 31, 58
West, L. E., 95, 98, 204, 205
White, J. F., see Potter, E. C.,
    271
Whitford, L. A., 246
Whitney, R. J., 199
Williams, R. J. P., see Irving,
    H. M. N. H., 238
Williams, T. I., 239
Wilson, K. G., 271
Wilson, T. L., 231
    see also Thompson, T. G., 238
Wingfield, C. A., 189, 190, 193
    see also Fox, H. M., 199
Wirth, H. E., 129, 141, 311
    see also Robinson, R. J., 141,
    150, 156
    see also Thompson, T. G., 222
Witting, R., 129
Wood, A. J., see Smales, A. A.,
    271
Wood, D. W., see Proctor, C. M.,
    156
Woodger, S. C., see Irving,
    H. M. N. H., 238
Wooster, W. S., 55, 154, 156
    see also Snodgrass, J. M., 58
Wright, C. C., 311
    see also Thompson, T. G., 221,
    222
Wright, C. H., 267
Wüst, G., 94, 98
Wyatt, P. F., see Strafford, N.,
    239

Yamagata, N., 272
Yamauchi, N., see Matida, Y., 222
Yates, F., see Fisher, R. A., 278,
    279
Yentsch, C. S., see Duxbury, A. C.,
    272
Yoe, J. H., 35, 58
Youden, W. J., 77

Young, R. S., 272
Yule, G. U., 77
Yutzy, H., *see* Kolthoff, I. M., 222

Zobell, C. E., 55

Zscheile, F. P., (jr.), 246
Zwicker, B. M. G., 27, 59, 113, 114, 117, 125, 311
  see also Igelsrud, I., 222
Zworykin, V. K., 59

GEORGE ALLEN & UNWIN LTD
London: 40 Museum Street, W.C.1

Auckland: 24 Wyndham Street
Bombay: 15 Graham Road, Ballard Estate, Bombay 1
Calcutta: 17 Chittaranjan Avenue, Calcutta 13
Cape Town: 109 Long Street
Karachi: Metherson's Estate, Wood Street, Karachi 2
New Delhi: 13–14 Ajmeri Gate Extension, New Delhi 1
São Paulo: Avenida 9 de Julho 1138–Ap. 51
Singapore, South East Asia and Far East, 36c, Prinsep Street
Sydney, N.S.W.: Bradbury House, 55 York Street
Toronto: 91 Wellington Street West

OCEANOGRAPHY AND MARINE BIOLOGY

A BOOK OF TECHNIQUES

H. BARNES

The sea covers some seven-tenths of the earth's surface. It is not therefore surprising that practically every science, zoology, chemistry, geology, physics, etc. contributes to its study and yet many of the problems of technique are peculiar to oceanography. Dr Barnes describes comprehensively the ingenious instruments and the careful methods by which we obtain our knowledge of the sea. First, he deals with our methods of sampling the living organisms—the free living plants and animals and those inhabiting the sea bed. Methods of taking bottom cores and of using nets, pumps, trawls, dredges and grabs are all carefully set out. Then follows a section on the properties of the water itself—temperature, salinity and current. The older standard instruments are described and particular attention is given to new techniques—the bathythermograph, for instance.

The early explorers of the seas noticed underwater noise in 1807—but only recently has the noise originating from marine animals been investigated. Both this and its converse—the use of sound waves—are dealt with, the latter including an account of the construction and working of modern echo sounders and their use in biological problems.

The most spectacular of modern developments—underwater photography and television—he has left for the last section. These techniques which allow observations to be made on the natural conditions will certainly prove of increasing importance. Aerial photography has a growing contribution to make to oceanography and is included here.

There is no book of similar scope and every effort has been made to include modern methods. It is profusely illustrated with diagrams and plates many of which have been specially prepared. The general reader and science student will find the book of greatest interest, while the research workers in the marine sections will be glad to have full accounts of their techniques gathered together.

Illustrated. Demy 8vo. About 35s. net

OCEANOGRAPHY FOR METEOROLOGISTS

H. U. SVERDRUP

Hitherto no adequate book has existed from which a meteorologist could readily obtain information as to findings in physical oceanography that have bearing upon problems of the atmosphere. This book by Professor Sverdrup fills the gap. Besides describing the methods used in physical oceanography, the author summarizes our present knowledge of the current systems of the oceans and of the processes that maintain the currents. Since the processes of the sea surface are of the most direct meteorological significance, the temperature, the salinity, the currents of the upper layers of the oceans, and the factors that control the existing conditions are the features which have been emphasized.

Second Impression. Illustrated. Demy 8vo. 21s. net

THE LAWS OF NATURE

R. E. PEIERLS

How big is an atom and why does it not collapse? How do we know that neutrons spin? The development of Physics, from Newton's laws to relativity and quantum theory, the structure of atoms and nuclei and the recent discoveries of new particles are explained without technical jargon and without mathematics. This is the contemporary physicist's world expounded in lucid English. It is a book which can be read by an engineer, by a general practitioner or by a philosopher.

Popular books in this field are not uncommon, but this treatment is different in its unity and its stress on the essential. Moreover its author is one of the most senior of the British team which worked on the atomic project in the U.S.A. during the war. Professor Peierls was amongst the first scientists in England to see the possibilities of atomic energy and he worked on this undertaking from 1940 until the end of the war, after 1943 in the United States. He is a Vice-President and past President of the Atomic Scientists' Association, which he helped to found. He also has experience of lecturing to audiences ranging from mathematics professors to housewives, an experience which has stood him in good stead in writing this book.

'This is on any reckoning a remarkable book . . . beautifully and lucidly written.' *Times Educational Supplement.*

Third Impression. Demy 8vo. 21s. net

A HISTORY OF WESTERN TECHNOLOGY

FRIEDRICH KLEMM

This is a history of technology in the form of contemporary writings, revealing the influences to which technical progress was due in each epoch, whether internal or originating in other spheres. The author brings out the circumstances which at different times led technical development in one direction rather than another and how the intellectual forces of a period affected and were in turn modified by technical progress.

The texts which are selected begin with classical antiquity and continue through the Renaissance, the Baroque and the Age of Rationalism to the Industrial Era and right up to the new industrial revolution of our own time. They are illustrated by contemporary pictures and drawings. The range of sources from which they have been drawn is also very wide: alongside the writing of technicians in the narrower sense is also that of philosophers, scientists, economists and poets, demonstrating the multiplicity of forces which have contributed to the triumph of modern technology.

Demy 8vo. About 32s. net

GEORGE ALLEN & UNWIN LTD